ANIM
CRACKERS

OPEN WIDE, WILBUR!

ROSE IMPEY ★ SHOO RAYNER

ORCHARD BOOKS

ORCHARD BOOKS
338 Euston Road, London NW1 3BH
Orchard Books Australia
Hachette Children's Books
Level 17/207 Kent Street, Sydney NSW 2000

First published by Orchard Books in 1997
This edition published in 2009

A CIP catalogue record for this book is available from the British Library.

ISBN 978 1 40830 299 6

1 3 5 7 9 10 8 6 4 2
Printed in China

Orchard Books is a division of Hachette Children's Books,
an Hachette Livre UK company.
www.hachettelivre.co.uk

Open Wide Wilbur

Wilbur was a whopper of a whale.
His head was huge.
His mouth was massive.
And his stomach was *stupendous!*
In fact, it was so big
it could hold a complete world inside.

All day long Wilbur swam in the sea
with his mouth wide open,
looking for food.
But all the fishes knew that it was
safe to swim right in.
Wilbur was their friend;
he wouldn't hurt them.
He was the most welcoming whale
in the world.

"Wipe your fins and come on in,"
he said, with a nice wide grin.

Wilbur liked helping his friends.
He was happy to give them a ride.
When Willy Whiting was late for work
he often hitched a lift with Wilbur.

When Hattie Haddock wanted
a holiday, Wilbur took her
all the way to Disney World.
And brought her home again.

And when old Tom Tuna was too tired to visit his family and friends, Wilbur brought *them* to see *him*.

Wilbur was so big and so strong,
a few more fish didn't worry him.
He just swam harder.
"It's always good to help," he said,
with a nod of his huge, kind head.

Wilbur's friends came
in all shapes and sizes:
conger eel, cod and crab,

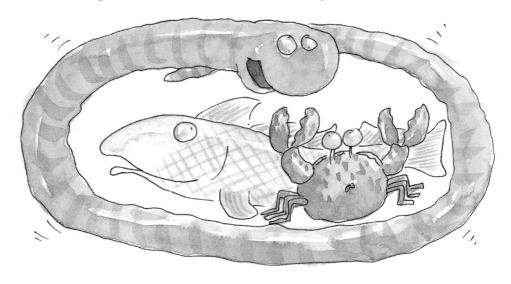

baby dolphins, dogfish and dab.

Perch and plaice and pole,

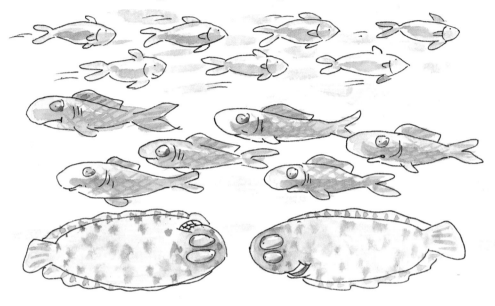

swordfish, stingray and sole.

They all knew that *Wilbur's Place*
was the very best place to be
if you wanted to
meet your friends,
or hear the latest gossip,
or find out the fishing news.

Sometimes there were so many fish
riding in Wilbur's stomach,
he felt weighed down.
But Wilbur didn't complain.
He just swam harder.
"What else are friends for?"
he said with a smile.
"It's only for a little while."

But Wilbur was too kind
and too welcoming
for his own good.
Some of his visitors decided
to stay and set up home.
They moved in their families
and friends
and all their furniture.
It was like a little fish world,
right there in Wilbur's stomach.

The fish had everything they needed.
There was even a school
for the baby fishes,
with teachers and nursemaids
to look after them.

Wilbur couldn't turn anyone away.
He didn't like to say,
"Sorry, no room. Full to the tail.
You'll have to catch the next whale."

But when Wilbur was full up
the fish who were living inside him
began to complain.

They sent the Fighting Fishes
to stand guard in Wilbur's mouth
and frighten the new fish away.

The fish had no need to go out.
Wilbur caught enough food
for everyone.
As it passed through his stomach,
they just helped themselves.
They soon grew fat and lazy,
floating around all day,
doing nothing.

Even when there wasn't much food
left for him,
Wilbur didn't complain.
But the fish inside Wilbur complained.
They complained all the time.

The fish even complained
about each other.
The herrings were very hoity-toity;
they looked down on the dogfish.

The skate were stuck up
and wouldn't speak to the squid.

The flounders were always
falling out with the other flatfish.

And when all the baby brill
started crying, it gave Grandma
Hake one of her headaches.

Sometimes the arguments upset Wilbur.
He felt tired and sad.
"You try to do your best," he said,
"but it's never enough."

And he shook his head.

As time went on, Wilbur had to
travel further and further,
and
dive
deeper
and
deeper,
to
find
enough
food
for
everyone.

Then, one day, disaster struck.
Wilbur was swimming
close to the surface.
He swam close to a huge boat.
It was a fishing boat.
The fishermen spotted Wilbur.
They started to chase him.

Wilbur swam as fast as he could,
but he was tired and heavy.
He couldn't swim fast enough
to escape.

The boat was coming closer
and closer.
Wilbur's heart was beating fast
and his brain was trying to
think what to do.
But it was hard to think
with everyone inside him
complaining.

But Wilbur couldn't even
save himself.
There was only one thing to do.

Wilbur lifted his huge head
and opened his massive mouth
as wide as it would go.
He blew out a *stupendous*
stream of water
and out came all the fish
and all their families.

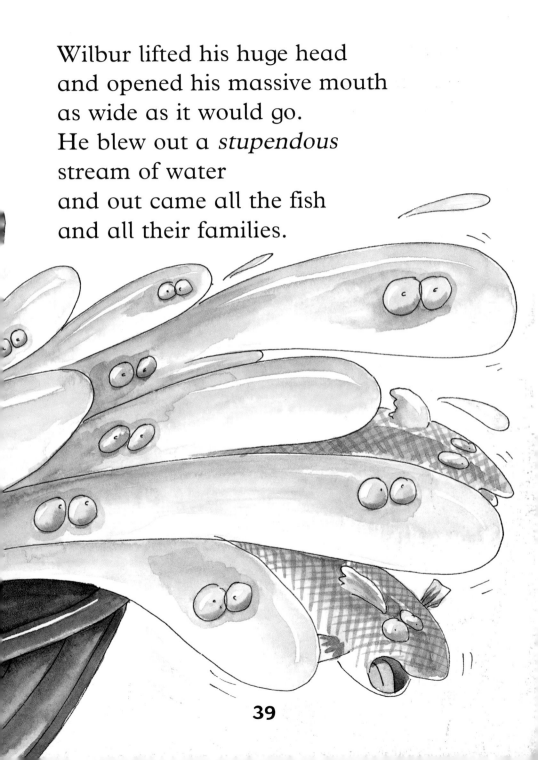

They flew up in the air
and landed in the water.
There were flying fishes
everywhere.

The fishermen could easily
have caught them,
but they only wanted Wilbur.
They kept on chasing him.

But now, Wilbur was so light
and so fast,
he swam away across the ocean.
He led the boat away from his friends
who swam to safety.

Wilbur travelled a very long way
before he escaped;
hundreds of miles away
from all his friends.

For a while he felt a little lonely.
But it wasn't long before
Wilbur made new friends.
Lots and lots and lots of friends.

Because, after all, he was
the most welcoming whale
in the world.

Crack-A-Joke

What zooms along the sea bed on three wheels? **A motorpike and sidecarp!**

What sleeps at the bottom of the sea? **A kipper!**

Why are fish so easy to weigh? **Because they've got their own scales!**

What's the difference between a fish and a piano? **You can't tuna fish!**

Why did the sea roar? **Because it had crabs on its bottom!**

Having a whale of a time!

What did the mummy sardine say
when a submarine passed by?
Don't worry. It's only a tin of people!

What does the ocean say
when it sees the shore?
Nothing. . . it just waves!

Where would you weigh a whale?

At a whale-weigh station!

ANIMAL
CRACKERS

COLLECT ALL THE
ANIMAL CRACKERS BOOKS!

A Birthday for Bluebell	978 1 40830 293 4	£4.99
Too Many Babies	978 1 40830 294 1	£4.99
Hot Dog Harris	978 1 40830 295 8	£4.99
Sleepy Sammy	978 1 40830 296 5	£4.99
Precious Potter	978 1 40830 297 2	£4.99
Phew Sidney	978 1 40830 298 9	£4.99
Open Wide Wilbur	978 1 40830 299 6	£4.99
We Want William	978 1 40830 300 9	£4.99

All priced at £4.99

Orchard Colour Crunchies are available from all good bookshops, or can be
ordered direct from the publisher:
Orchard Books, PO BOX 29, Douglas IM99 1BQ
Credit card orders please telephone 01624 836000
or fax 01624 837033 or visit our internet site: www.orchardbooks.co.uk
or e-mail: bookshop@enterprise.net for details.
To order please quote title, author and ISBN
and your full name and address.
Cheques and postal orders should be made payable to 'Bookpost plc.'
Postage and packing is FREE within the UK
(overseas customers should add £2.00 per book).
Prices and availability are subject to change.

ANIMAL CRACKERS

All the fish in the ocean love **WILBUR** – he's such a welcoming whale. But disaster strikes when Wilbur's friends take him for a ride – and then refuse to go home . . .

INCLUDES COOL **CRACK-A-JOKE** PAGES!

READ MORE ANIMAL CRACKERS!

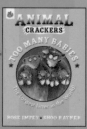

ANIMAL CRACKERS
TOO MANY BABIES
The Largest Litter in the World!
ROSE IMPEY · SHOO RAYNER

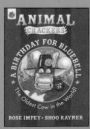

ANIMAL CRACKERS
A BIRTHDAY FOR BLUEBELL
The Oldest Cow in the World!
ROSE IMPEY · SHOO RAYNER

ANIMAL CRACKERS
HOT DOG HARRIS
The Smallest Dog in the World!
ROSE IMPEY · SHOO RAYNER

ANIMAL CRACKERS
PRECIOUS POTTER
The Heaviest Cat in the World!
ROSE IMPEY · SHOO RAYNER

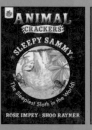

ANIMAL CRACKERS
SLEEPY SAMMY
The Sleepiest Sloth in the World!
ROSE IMPEY · SHOO RAYNER

ANIMAL CRACKERS
PHEW, SIDNEY!
The Sweetest-smelling Skunk in the World!
ROSE IMPEY · SHOO RAYNER

ANIMAL CRACKERS
OPEN WIDE, WILBUR
The Most Welcoming Whale in the World!
ROSE IMPEY · SHOO RAYNER

ANIMAL CRACKERS
WE WANT WILLIAM!
The Wisest Worm in the World!
ROSE IMPEY · SHOO RAYNER

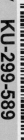

KU-299-589

Introduction

This textbook has been written to meet the needs of A2 students following the new AQA law specification. For Unit 3, you need to study *either* Section A (criminal law) *or* Section B (contract law), and for Unit 4 you again study *either* Section A (criminal law) *or* Section B (law of tort). Section C (concepts of law) is compulsory.

Although this book is comprehensive in its coverage, you should undertake further independent reading, as the law is continually developing, through both statute and cases. Additional resources include *A-Level Law Review* magazine, the *New Law Journal*, the *Times Law Supplement* and the e-lawstudent website (www.e-lawstudent.com).

The aim of this textbook is to make the specification content as accessible as possible. In order to achieve this, a brief overview is provided at the beginning of each topic area, and then the topic is examined under clear subheadings.

In order to achieve high grades, you must understand the importance of examination technique — especially at A2, as the exams test much more than factual recall. They measure how well you *understand* the topics and can *apply* relevant rules on offences and defences to answer problem-solving questions. In Unit 3, a further skill is that of *evaluating* both offences and defences. Unit 4 requires knowledge of the more philosophical aspects of law — morality, justice and fault-based liability — combined with the ability to incorporate relevant legal rules and cases into longer essay answers. Sample exam questions are provided throughout this book. AQA examination questions are reproduced by permission of the Assessment and Qualifications Alliance.

Studying law

Using legal authorities effectively

This textbook aims to build on the knowledge and skills you learned during the AS course. For example, many of the cases you encounter here will be familiar from AS. However, it is important to understand the need for a 'step-change' in your level of knowledge of case facts and the legal rules created by that case. At A2 your answers should feature a greater dependence on case authorities and you should select the most relevant cases to answer problem-solving questions.

At this level of study — which is not far below university level — you have to learn case law effectively. This book provides you with the factual details of important cases, together with the legal rule(s) created by each case. You should get into the habit of summarising the facts and rules of these cases and develop the skill of using them to show legal understanding.

Read-and-précis method of learning

This method requires you to read a chapter ahead of a lesson and then summarise the key points, issues and cases. This will enable you to acquire better understanding of that topic from the lesson, and encourage you to ask questions to clarify more difficult issues or to develop and improve examination technique.

This learning method also strengthens your knowledge of basic facts about a topic and provides a summary that can form the basis of revision notes.

Assessment

The assessment objectives (AOs) for A2 are the same as for AS:

❖ AO1: demonstrate knowledge and understanding of legal rules and principles by selecting and explaining relevant information and illustrating with examples and citation
❖ AO2: analyse legal material, issues and situations and evaluate and apply the appropriate legal rules and principles
❖ AO3: present a logical and coherent argument and communicate relevant material in a clear and effective manner, using appropriate legal terminology

Although the objectives are the same as for AS, the weighting given to them is markedly different.

Weightings given to the assessment objectives at AS and A2

	AS weighting	A2 weighting
AO1	45–55%	35–45%
AO2	30–40%	45–55%
AO3	5–15%	5–15%

AO2 — the ability to analyse, evaluate and apply — has a much greater weighting at A2 than at AS. This needs to become a clear focus of your studies. Thus factual knowledge is more a means to this end, not an end in itself. You only really know the material of each topic if you can use it effectively either to answer a problem-solving question or to provide a well-argued evaluative answer.

Mark scheme descriptors

You should be familiar with the following mark scheme descriptors, which form the basis of examination marks.

Mark scheme descriptors for problem-solving questions

Level	Explanation	Application
'Some'	The answer correctly identifies and accurately explains a limited part of the relevant rules. Explanations are limited, with poor use made of relevant cases. There are significant omissions in terms of offences and/or defences. Overall, the impression is that the explanation is superficial.	The application fails to identify some specific issues raised by the question, e.g. causation or immediacy in assault. The answer tends to make simple assertions about the way in which rules apply to the facts. Cases are rarely used to integrate explanation with application, so no coherent solution is provided.
'Clear'	The answer correctly identifies and accurately explains significant parts of the rules in the main parts of the potential content, though there are some omissions or errors. In the higher part of this level, case/statutory authorities and illustration are used, but there may be some confusion or error in selection and/or explanation, or the explanation may be limited.	The answer selects and emphasises some of the relevant facts and makes reference to them when explaining how the rules (including supporting case/statutory authorities) apply to afford a solution. The application may fail to consider alternative solutions, or there may be error or confusion in the application to the facts. There is often a failure to deal effectively with a key issue in the question.
'Sound'	The answer identifies and accurately explains the key relevant rules in the potential content. Explanations are well supported by relevant case/statutory authorities, which are adequately developed to explain the *ratio* and/or assist in the application to the facts. Any omissions or errors are minor and do not weaken the overall level of explanation.	All the key elements of the question are addressed. Effective use is made of case and statutory authorities to provide strong arguments, which lead to a coherent solution. Alternative explanations are considered. Overall, the candidate demonstrates a sound understanding of the question content.

Planning your revision

At this level of study, you must learn factual information thoroughly. Do this as each unit is being taught. Do not leave it to the revision stage, otherwise you will find that there is too much detailed knowledge to absorb.

The word 'revise' is defined in the *Concise Oxford Dictionary* as 'to read again (work learned or done) to improve one's knowledge'. Skimming over some notes is *not* revision if you have not already learned the material.

The first stage of revision requires organisation of all your work. Ensure that:

❖ your class notes are up to date
❖ you have used the material in this book effectively
❖ you have made accurate notes on any wider reading, especially of case studies

Summarise

Summarising is probably the most important stage in revision. Going over your notes and reducing them to manageable proportions is an effective learning exercise. Organise both explanatory content and case/statutory authorities under the headings and subheadings of each unit.

Summarising makes it easier to recall the material and should reduce the chance of forgetting parts of it in the examination. Most exam marks are lost not through a failure to understand the material, but simply through omitting key elements of potential content.

Use past papers

Study past examination papers (available from www.aqa.org.uk) and attempt to answer the problem-solving questions. Use the IDEA mnemonic (explained on p. xxi) to formulate an effective answer plan. It should match the potential content on the mark scheme, which can also be downloaded from the AQA website.

You should also look at examination reports, which contain details of the common problems encountered by candidates in tackling each question. Once you have looked at a number of such reports, you will recognise that the same problems and weaknesses tend to occur in each examination:

❖ failure to read the scenario effectively
❖ omission of key potential content materials
❖ inadequate use of cases
❖ weak application

Being aware of these common problems should help you to avoid making the same mistakes in your own answers.

Examination advice

Plan your answers effectively

For problem-solving questions especially, make sure you have read the scenario carefully. It is a good idea to underline or highlight relevant words and phrases. For example, 'Fred had been drinking heavily' suggests the possibility of explaining intoxication as a possible defence; 'Mary received a serious cut to her arm' could indicate a possible s.20 or s.18 offence of wounding; or 'Hassan was insulted' could suggest the defence of provocation if it is a murder question.

Make sure you allow yourself enough time to prepare a detailed answer plan. This will help you to avoid omitting key potential content on the one hand and including irrelevant material on the other.

Below is an example of what a plan should look like. Let's assume the question involves serious injuries, with the possibility of using the defences of intoxication and self-defence.

PLAN

Injury — broken collar bone — GBH — s.20, and broken nose — possible s.20 wounding, or under Joint Charging Standard — s.47 ABH.

No weapon used, therefore more likely to be s.20 than s.18.

s.20 — GBH — Actus reus — inflicting GBH = serious harm (*Saunders*); no causation issues. *Mens rea* — intention or reckless as to causing some harm (*Mowatt*).

s.20 — wounding — definition — *Eisenhower* — both layers of skin severed. *Mens rea* as above.

s.47 — ABH — battery causing ABH — definition — *Miller* — any hurt or injury…;

Mens rea — same as for battery (*Savage* or *Roberts*).

Defences:

Intoxication — voluntary therefore not effective for basic intent offence (*Majewski*).

Self-defence — issues necessary and reasonable use of force — level of initial attack by victim, possible mistaken belief by defendant — *Williams* — honestly held mistake.

Structure your answer effectively

To improve the structure of your answer, use the **IDEA** mnemonic:

❖ **I**dentify the relevant offence(s) *and* defences. Also consider what specific issues arise from the scenario, such as causation, transferred malice, immediate loss of self-control (in provocation) and source of diminished responsibility.

❖ **D**efine the *actus reus* and *mens rea* of each offence, and the basic rules of **d**efences.

❖ **E**xplain these rules in greater detail.

❖ **A**pply these rules to the facts of the scenario and ensure that case and statutory **a**uthorities are used effectively.

Correct use of cases

In A2 problem-solving questions, cases are even more crucial than at AS. You must be able to decide which cases are relevant. For example, if in an assault case it is the defendant's actions, not words, that may have caused the victim to fear the immediate infliction of unlawful personal violence, citation of *R* v *Constanza* or *R* v *Ireland* is futile.

It is also important to learn both the facts of the case and the legal rules derived from it. Keeping a card index of leading cases recording both the salient facts and the *ratio decidendi* is a worthwhile discipline.

Plan your time effectively

The Unit 3 examination lasts 1 hour 30 minutes and requires candidates to answer three 25-mark questions: two problem-solving and one evaluative. With time spent in planning your answers, this means writing time of about 25 minutes per question. Accurate timekeeping is essential; many candidates find themselves running out of time for their last question, which then yields only 7–10 marks out of 25.

The new Unit 4 examination — which includes two problem-solving questions on a substantive law topic and one extended essay on concepts of law — lasts 2 hours. Most of 1 hour's planning and writing should be dedicated to the concepts essay, leaving around 30 minutes for each substantive question.

Online resources

The online resources accompanying this textbook contain extension exercises relevant to the subjects covered in this textbook. They offer you a useful way of testing your understanding and they can be accessed by visiting www.hodderplus.co.uk/philipallan.

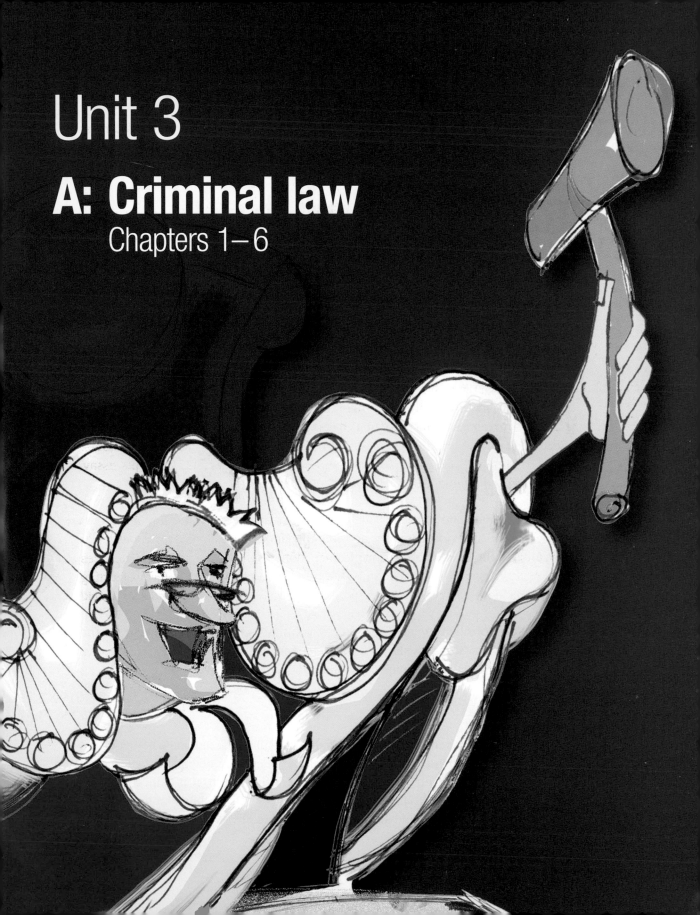

Unit 3

A: Criminal law
Chapters 1–6

Chapter 1

Introduction to criminal liability

You will be familiar with this topic, as it forms a compulsory part of AS Unit 2. Rather than simply restating the rules of *actus reus* and *mens rea*, this chapter considers how best to use these rules in the specific context of A2 problem-solving questions.

Actus reus

For Unit 3 (fatal and non-fatal offences against the person), the key *actus reus* elements are those of voluntary act and causation. Omissions are of particular relevance to the offence of gross negligence manslaughter.

Voluntary act

Criminal responsibility generally requires voluntary conduct on the part of the defendant. If the act is involuntary, the defendant is able to plead the defence of automatism, explained in detail in Chapter 5.

Causation

Students should examine the problem scenario carefully to determine whether or not there are causation issues. In many questions where the defendant has used a weapon to cause grievous bodily harm or to kill the victim, it is unnecessary to explain any causation rules at all; quite often, it is possible to state that there are no causation issues raised in the scenario. Even if there are such issues, it is unlikely

that the factual 'but-for' rule requires explanation. Any causation will deal with legal rules, such as:

❖ negligent medical treatment following the initial attack
❖ escape cases
❖ *novus actus interveniens*
❖ the 'thin skull' rule

Medical treatment

What is the legal position where the defendant has inflicted serious injuries on the victim, but the victim later dies in circumstances where it can be proved that the medical treatment received was poor? If the victim had been promptly and correctly treated, would he or she have made a full recovery?

In *R* v *Smith* (1959), a fight between two soldiers resulted in the victim receiving a bayonet wound requiring medical treatment. While being carried to the medical reception station, the victim was dropped twice. The doctor failed to diagnose a punctured lung and gave treatment later described as 'thoroughly bad'. Smith was convicted of murder and his appeal failed. Lord Parker CJ stated that:

> ...if at the time of death the original wound is still an operating cause and a substantial cause, then the death can properly be said to be the result of the wound, albeit that some other cause of death is also operating. Only if it can be said that the original wounding is merely the setting in which another cause operates can it be said that the death does not result from the wound. Putting it another way, only if the second cause is so overwhelming as to make the original wound merely part of the history can it be said that the death does not flow from the wound.

This situation occurred in *R* v *Jordan* (1956), where the victim of a serious injury made a good recovery in hospital but while recuperating received an injection of a drug to which he was allergic. The doctors confirmed that the death was not caused by the original wound, which was mainly healed at the time of death, but by the injection (and the intravenous introduction of large quantities of liquid).

R v *McKechnie* (1992) also serves to confirm the rule that the courts will hold the defendant responsible for the victim's death even though the injuries inflicted may not be the immediate or medical cause of death. In that case, the defendant, with others, entered the victim's home and caused damage. One man hit the victim over the head with a chair and the defendant then further attacked him, causing severe head injuries. When the victim was admitted to hospital, doctors found they were unable to operate on his duodenal ulcer because the head injuries exacerbated the risk of death from anaesthesia. The victim then died when the ulcer burst. It was held that the doctor's decision not to operate was reasonable and that the head injuries were the significant cause of death. The defendant was rightly convicted of manslaughter.

The best example of an 'escape' case is *R* v *Roberts* (1971): did the victim act reasonably?

Escape cases

When a victim has suffered injury or has been killed while trying to escape from a serious attack, this is known as an escape case. In such cases, the defendant is liable if the victim's conduct in running away was within the range of foreseeable responses to the defendant's behaviour.

The best example of such an 'escape case' is *R* v *Roberts* (1971), the facts of which are described concisely in an article by Giles Bayliss in *A-Level Law Review*, Vol. 2, No. 3:

The defendant, Roberts, met a girl at a party and persuaded her to travel with him in his car to what he said was another party later that night. During the course of the journey, Roberts made unwanted sexual advances towards the girl and told her to undress. He said that he had previously beaten up other girls and then he physically attempted to remove some of her clothing. The alarmed victim opened the car door and jumped out, while the vehicle was still travelling at an estimated 20 to 40 miles per hour. She suffered concussion and grazing and was kept in hospital for 3 days. Roberts was charged with, and convicted of, assault occasioning actual bodily harm under s.47 of the Offences against the Person Act 1861. He appealed [on the basis that he did not intend such injuries to occur, and that the victim had caused these injuries by her own actions]. The appeal focused on whether the victim had broken the chain of causation in behaving the way she did, or whether Roberts was responsible for her injuries. The Court of Appeal ruled that the correct test to apply was to ask whether the reaction of the victim was reasonably foreseeable, rather than to ask whether the victim acted reasonably. Stevenson LJ explained the test in this way:

> *Was it the natural result of what the alleged assailant said and did, in the sense that it was something that could reasonably have been foreseen as the consequences of what he was saying or doing? As it was put in one of the old cases, it had got to be shown to be his act, and if of course the victim does something so daft...or so unexpected...that no reasonable man could be expected to foresee it, then it is only in a very remote and unreal sense a consequence of the assault, it is really occasioned by a voluntary act on the part of the victim.*

He continued by saying that if this were the case, the defendant would not be liable. The injury would be caused:

...by a voluntary act on the part of the victim which could not reasonably be foreseen and which breaks the chain of causation between the assault and the harm or injury.

Compare the decision in *Roberts* with that in *R v Williams and Davis* (1992), where the victim was a hitchhiker who was given a lift in a car by Williams, and Davis was a passenger. The victim jumped from the car when it was moving at about 30 miles per hour and sustained fatal head injuries. Although the defendants were convicted of manslaughter on the basis that they had planned to rob the victim, their conviction was quashed by the Court of Appeal. The court ruled that the jury should have been asked whether the victim's reaction in jumping from a moving vehicle in response to a threat, not actual violence, was 'within the range of responses' that might be expected from a victim placed in such a situation.

Novus actus interveniens

Another causation rule addresses the question of what constitutes a new intervening act (*novus actus interveniens*). This requires something that cannot be foreseen, and it must be so overwhelming as to invalidate the original *actus reus*. For example, A shoots at B and causes B serious internal injuries that could be treated successfully if immediate and specialised medical treatment were provided, but the ambulance takes 10 minutes to arrive and as a result B dies. This is a foreseeable result and A is guilty of murder. However, if C knocks D down and leaves him unconscious in a building that collapses in a sudden earthquake, and D dies as a result, then C would not be liable for D's death. Generally, it seems to be accepted that an 'act of God' (such as an earthquake or a tidal wave), which by definition could not reasonably be foreseen, will break the causal chain.

In *R v Rafferty* (2007), the defendant and two co-defendants attacked the victim on a beach, knocking him unconscious. The defendant's role had been to pin the victim down so that the other defendants could punch and kick him. They then robbed him. The defendant took the victim's credit card to a cash machine; when he returned to the beach, the co-defendants had disappeared. In his absence, they had inflicted further serious injuries on the victim, dragged him 100 metres across the beach and then taken him some distance out to sea, where he drowned. At the defendant's appeal against conviction for the victim's manslaughter, the Court of Appeal accepted the argument that 'the free deliberate and informed intervention of a second person who intends to exploit the situation created by the first, but is not acting on concert with him, is normally held to relieve the first actor of criminal responsibility'. In quashing the defendant's conviction, the court ruled that no jury could properly conclude that the drowning of the victim by the co-defendants was other than a new and intervening act in the chain of events.

The 'thin skull' rule

The 'thin skull' rule, also known as 'take your victim as you find him', refers to the situation where the intervening cause is a pre-existing weakness of the victim, for instance an abnormally thin skull. If, because of this, a blow inflicted on the victim causes serious injury or even death, when in a 'normal' person it would usually only cause a bruise, the attacker is liable for the more serious injury or the death.

This rule covers not only physical but also mental conditions, and even the victim's beliefs or values, as in *R* v *Blaue* (1975). Here, the victim of a stabbing was a Jehovah's Witness, who refused on religious grounds to accept a blood transfusion that would have saved her life. The defendant was convicted of her manslaughter and the Court of Appeal rejected his appeal, holding that the victim's refusal to accept the transfusion did not break the causal chain.

Sample exam question

Petra's best friend, Kerry, has secretly been carrying on a relationship with Petra's boyfriend, Ricky. Petra discovers this a few minutes before she and Kerry are due to meet, and she immediately sends a text message to Kerry's mobile phone which reads: 'Leave Ricky alone or I'll knock your teeth out.' Kerry becomes very agitated when she reads the message and avoids Petra for the next few weeks. However, Petra and Kerry happen to be in the same bar one night when Petra has drunk a large amount of alcohol. Petra has just clumsily broken a glass when Kerry walks by. Petra sticks out her foot and pushes Kerry's face into the floor. The broken glass is underneath Kerry and she suffers extensive and deep cuts to her face. Two days later, Kerry's brother, Simon, goes to Petra's house in the middle of the night and sets fire to it in revenge for Petra's attack on Kerry. He then telephones a warning to the fire service, which, in turn, phones the house. Only Petra's friend, Tracey, is in the house and, despite advice from the fire service about what to do until firefighters arrive, she panics and becomes trapped by the fire in a bedroom upstairs. She then slips and falls to her death while trying to climb onto the roof.

Adapted from AQA Unit 4 paper, January 2007

Considering Tracey's reaction to the advice from the fire service, discuss whether Simon's action in setting fire to Petra's house was the legal cause of her death.

Omissions

Most jurisdictions, including that of England and Wales, have not adopted a general principle of liability for failing to act. However, the law has defined certain factual situations in which persons are under a duty to act, and failure to do so results in

criminal liability. The two most common examples of omissions in A2 exam questions are:

❖ where a relative or other responsible adult assumes responsibility for the care of a child or vulnerable adult
❖ where the defendant has created a dangerous situation by his or her own acts and has thus put himself or herself under a duty of care to do something about it (*R v Miller*, 1983)

These examples are particularly important within the context of gross negligence manslaughter, where they can be used to argue that the defendant owes a duty of care to the victim.

Mens rea

A2 students must be able to explain accurately and then apply the correct *mens rea* element for every offence.

Intention

The meaning of intention is not found in any statute, but in judicial decisions. It is clear that a person intends a result when it is his or her aim, objective or purpose to bring it about. In *R v Mohan* (1976), James LJ stated:

> *...an 'intention'... connotes a state of affairs which... [the party] decides so far as in him lies to bring about and which, in point of possibility, he has a reasonable prospect of being able to bring about by his own act.*

This might be termed 'dictionary intention'.

In exam questions, especially those involving Unit 3 offences against the person, consider whether there is clear evidence of this direct intent; has a weapon been used, or is there any evidence of the attack having been pre-meditated? If so, there is no point speculating about oblique intent.

However, the concept of intention is open to ambiguity. In *R v Hancock and Shankland* (1986), at the heart of the case was how the law should deal with the defendant who has created an unlawful result where it is clear that the outcome was probable, and the defendant may well have foreseen this outcome. The defendants in this case were Welsh coal miners on strike. When one of their fellow miners wanted to return to work, they tried to stop him. The 'strike-breaker' was being driven in a taxi to another coal mine, and the route was via a motorway. The defendants knew that the taxi would pass under a particular bridge, and when the taxi drove under it they pushed concrete blocks onto the road below. One of the blocks smashed through the windscreen of the taxi and killed the driver. The defendants claimed that their only intention was to block the road and prevent the strike-breaker from reaching the coal mine, not to kill the taxi driver. Although they were convicted of murder at their trial, the Court of Appeal and the House of Lords both quashed that conviction and substituted a manslaughter conviction, holding that the issue of intention had not been established. Lord Scarman indicated that, in cases like these, juries needed to be told by the judge that 'the greater the probability of a consequence occurring, the more likely it was so foreseen and, if so, the more likely it was intended'. This emphasised the point that foresight of the degree of probability was the only evidence from which intention could be inferred.

In the cases of *R* v *Nedrick* (1986) and *R* v *Woollin* (1998) (see below), a tighter rule was laid down for such cases of oblique intent. This now requires juries to return a verdict of murder only where they find that 'the defendant foresaw death or serious injury as a virtually certain consequence of his or her voluntary actions'. It is worth pointing out that in both these cases, the original murder conviction was changed on appeal to a manslaughter conviction.

R v *Woollin* (1998)

This case resulted from the death of a 3-month-old baby. Although initially the defendant gave a number of different explanations, he finally admitted that he had 'lost his cool' when his baby started to choke. He had shaken the baby and then, in a fit of rage or frustration, had thrown him in the direction of his pram, which was standing against the wall some 3 or 4 feet away. He knew that the baby's head had hit something hard but denied intending to throw him against the wall or wanting him to die or to suffer serious injury. The trial judge directed the members of jury that they might infer intention if they were satisfied that, when he threw the baby, the defendant appreciated there was a 'substantial risk' of causing serious harm. In the Court of Appeal, the defendant argued that the judge should have used the words 'virtual certainty', as 'substantial risk' was merely a test of recklessness. The Court of Appeal, although critical of the trial judge, dismissed the appeal, and certified questions for the House of Lords. The House of Lords quashed the defendant's conviction for murder and substituted a conviction for manslaughter.

Lord Steyn gave the main speech, saying that 'a result foreseen as virtually certain is an intended result'. Thus the phrase 'substantial risk' used by the trial judge blurred the distinction between intention and recklessness, and was too serious a misdirection for the conviction to stand. In *R* v *Matthews and Alleyne* (2003), the vexed issue of whether foresight of virtual consequences did in fact equal intent or was merely evidence of intention was resolved in favour of it being evidential. This means, at least in theory, that a jury could decide that the defendant in a murder case had foreseen death or serious injury as virtually certain but still return a verdict of 'not guilty' to murder.

Recklessness

A standard dictionary definition of recklessness is 'unjustified risk-taking'. Following the case of *R v G and Others* (2003), English law now recognises only subjective (Cunningham) recklessness. Here, the prosecution must prove that the defendant appreciated that his or her action created an unjustified risk and then went ahead with the action anyway. In *R v Cunningham* (1957), the defendant ripped a gas meter from a wall to steal the money it contained, causing gas to escape. The gas seeped into a neighbouring building, where it overcame a woman. Cunningham was convicted of a s.23 offence — administering a noxious substance — but appealed successfully on the ground that the prosecution had failed to prove that he recognised the risk of the gas escape. The question was quite simply whether the defendant *had* foreseen that his act might injure someone, not whether he *ought* to have foreseen this risk.

Gross negligence

This covers situations where the defendant did not foresee causing any harm, but should have realised the risks involved, for example *R v Adomako* (1995). This topic is cover in detail in Chapter 4.

Coincidence of *actus reus* and *mens rea*

Mens rea must coincide in point of time with the *actus reus* for an offence to occur. This is important to consider in problem-solving questions, and should not be difficult to identify. If relevant, deal with this topic by using either *Thabo Meli v R* (1954) or *R v Le Brun* (1992). In both these cases, the same rule was affirmed that where there is a series of actions that can be regarded as a linked transaction or continuing act, provided that at some point during the transaction the required *mens rea* is present, the coincidence rule is satisfied.

Transferred malice

Under the rule of transferred malice, if A fires a gun at B, intending to kill B, but misses and in fact kills C, A is guilty of murdering C. The intention (malice) is transferred from B to C. The leading case is *R v Latimer* (1886).

However, this rule is limited to situations where the *actus reus* and the *mens rea* of the same crime coincide. In *R v Pembliton* (1874), the defendant threw a stone at the victim, intending to harm him, but missed and broke a window. The defendant was not guilty of malicious damage, as he lacked the *mens rea* for that offence.

Chapter **2**

Non-fatal offences

Having looked closely at *actus reus* and *mens rea* in Chapter 1, this chapter discusses how they apply to the five non-fatal offences:

❖ assault
❖ battery
❖ assault occasioning actual bodily harm (ABH)
❖ malicious wounding or inflicting grievous bodily harm (GBH)
❖ wounding or inflicting grievous bodily harm with intent (to cause GBH)

Although these offences were included in AS Unit 2, you must be able to examine them in greater detail for Unit 3. Problem-solving questions on these offences will be more complex. For example, with assault, you must be able to state whether the victim apprehended unlawful violence or whether the violence could be considered 'immediate'.

Make sure you write out 'actual bodily harm' and 'grievous bodily harm' in full the first time you use them. You can then use the abbreviations ABH and GBH.

Assault and battery were two distinct crimes at common law. Their separate existence is recognised by s.39 of the **Criminal Justice Act 1988** and confirmed in *DPP* v *Little* (1992), where a single charge alleging that the defendant 'did unlawfully assault and batter' the victim was held to be two offences and therefore unsatisfactory, since different offences have to be charged separately.

The other three more serious offences are defined in the **Offences Against the Person Act 1861** (OAPA).

Assault

Assault is any act by which the defendant, intentionally or recklessly, causes the victim to apprehend immediate and unlawful personal violence. No force need actually be applied, and it is sufficient if the victim believes that unlawful force is about to be used against him or her. Accordingly, if any harm is caused, a more

serious offence than assault has been committed, although the defendant may also have committed an assault. An example would be if the defendant shouts at the victim 'I am going to punch you' and then proceeds to do just that.

Actus reus of assault

In a typical case of assault (as opposed to battery), the defendant, by some physical movement, causes the victim to believe that he or she is about to be struck. There may even be an assault where the defendant has no intention of committing battery but only to cause the victim to apprehend one. The word 'apprehend' does not require that the victim is actually afraid, merely that he or she is aware that something violent is about to happen.

In fact, it does not matter if the victim was not actually in any danger. For example, in *Logdon* v *DPP* (1976), the defendant showed the victim a gun in his desk drawer and said it was loaded, and that he would take her hostage. Although the gun was in fact a fake, this was not obvious from its appearance and the victim was afraid. The defendant was convicted of assault and this was upheld on appeal. However, there cannot be an assault if it was obvious that the defendant could not carry out his or her threat — for example, shouting and gesticulating at passengers on a moving train.

According to *R* v *Ireland* (1998), assault may be committed by silent phonecalls

Consider *R* v *Lamb* (1967) (which is discussed again in Chapter 4, pages 37–38). The defendant who pointed a gun at the victim in jest and then shot him accidentally did *not* commit an assault because he did not cause the victim to apprehend immediate violence. As the victim was party to the joke and did not feel threatened, there was no assault and therefore no unlawful act.

Immediacy

There is a tendency to enlarge the concept of assault by taking a generous view of 'immediacy' to include threats in which the impending impact is more remote. In *Smith* v *Superintendent of Woking Police* (1983), the defendant committed an assault by looking at the victim in her night-clothes through a window, intending to frighten her. Kerr LJ stated it was sufficient that the defendant had instilled in the victim an apprehension of what he might do next. As she was in the house and he was in the garden, he could not have attacked her that very second, but nevertheless the victim had thought that 'whatever he might be going to do next, and sufficiently immediately for the purposes of the offence, was something of a violent nature'.

It was made clear in *R* v *Ireland* (1998) that an assault may be committed by words alone or even, as in that case, by silent telephone calls where the caller 'intends by his silence to cause fear and he is so understood'. In this case, Lord Steyn stated:

> *...there is no reason why something said should be incapable of causing an apprehension of immediate personal violence, for example a man accosting a woman in a dark alley saying, 'come with me or I will stab you'.*

In *R* v *Constanza* (1997), where the facts were similar to *Ireland*, the Court of Appeal expanded the immediacy test slightly. Schiemann LJ held it was sufficient for the Crown to have proved an apprehension of violence 'at some time, not excluding the immediate future'. However, the Court of Appeal did note that the victim knew the defendant lived nearby and that 'she thought that something could happen at any time'.

Constanza ruled that the words need not necessarily be verbal. Here, the Court of Appeal held that words in letters could amount to an assault. Schiemann LJ pointed out that what was important was that the victim apprehended violence; the means by which that apprehension arose was 'wholly irrelevant'.

Note, however, that there may be circumstances where the words used by the defendant could negate the possibility of an assault, as illustrated in the historical case of *Turberville* v *Savage* (1669). In this case, the defendant laid his hand on his sword, saying 'If it were not assize time [when High Court judges were present to try serious cases], I would not take such language'. If the defendant had said nothing, the court would have held the act of gripping his sword as evidence of assault.

Mens rea of assault

It is settled law that the defendant must have either intention or subjective recklessness as to causing the victim to apprehend immediate and unlawful violence (*R* v *Venna*, 1975). Therefore, if the defendant causes the victim to apprehend such violence but does not intend to do so or does not foresee this reaction, there is no assault.

Sample exam question

Early one morning, Alan is standing on a stepladder, washing the windows of his house with a powerful detergent solution. Bob and Chris come walking noisily up the street, having spent all night out, drinking alcohol. Bob shouts something and suddenly veers across the street in Alan's direction, followed by Chris, who is trying to take hold of his arm. Alan is convinced that Bob is coming to knock him off the ladder… In fact, though very drunk, Bob merely wants to have a friendly talk to Alan.

Adapted from AQA Unit 4 paper, January 2008

Discuss the criminal liability of Bob for the offence of assault arising out of the incident in the street.

Battery

Battery is defined as 'any act by which the defendant, intentionally or recklessly, inflicts unlawful personal violence'. Most batteries involve an assault, although this is not a requirement — a blow to the back of the head, completely taking the victim by surprise, constitutes battery. Further examples of battery include a push, a kiss, or throwing a projectile or water that lands on another's body.

In *Faulkner* v *Talbot* (1981), Lord Lane CJ said that a battery 'need not necessarily be hostile, rude or aggressive'. However, in *Wilson* v *Pringle* (1987), Croom-Johnson LJ stated that a touching had to be hostile to amount to battery, and in *Brown and Others* (1993), the House of Lords approved that ruling when Lord Jauncey described hostility as 'a necessary ingredient'.

Many unwanted touchings are 'technical' batteries. In *Collins* v *Wilcock* (1984), it was considered that a battery had been inflicted when a policewoman took hold of the arm of a defendant whom she believed to be soliciting in order to detain her but without an intention to arrest. In this case, Goff LJ said:

> It has long been established that any touching of another person, however slight, may amount to a battery... Generally speaking, consent is a defence to battery; and most of the physical contacts of ordinary life are not actionable because they are impliedly consented to by all who move in society and so expose themselves to the risk of bodily contact. So nobody can complain of the jostling which is inevitable from his presence in, for example, a supermarket, an underground station or a busy street; nor can a person who attends a party complain if his hand is seized in friendship...

Actus reus of battery

The *actus reus* of battery is the infliction of unlawful personal violence by the defendant. The use of the term 'violence' here is misleading — all that is required for a battery is that the defendant touches the victim without consent or other lawful excuse. However, under the **Joint Charging Standards**, a prosecution is unlikely in practice, unless some injury has been caused.

Although it is generally held that the defendant must have carried out an act, mere obstruction can also constitute battery in certain circumstances. There may also be a battery when the defendant inadvertently applies force to the victim and then wrongfully refuses to withdraw it. In *Fagan* v *Metropolitan Police Commissioner*

(1969), for example, where the defendant accidentally drove his car onto a police officer's foot and then intentionally left it there, the court held that there was a continuing act, not a mere omission.

It is also settled law that there can be a battery where there has been no direct contact with the victim's body — touching his or her clothing may be enough to constitute this offence, as in *R v Thomas* (1985), where it was stated that touching the woman's skirt was equivalent to touching the woman herself.

Further, the battery may be indirect, as in *Haystead v DPP* (2000), where the defendant punched a woman who was holding a small child in her arms. As a result of the blows, she dropped the child on the ground, and the defendant was then convicted of battery against the child, even though no physical contact had occurred between the defendant and the child.

Mens rea of battery

The law is settled that either intention or recklessness as to the infliction of unlawful personal violence is sufficient. After a brief period of uncertainty, it is now clear that subjective recklessness — 'the conscious taking of an unjustified risk' — is the relevant test (see the cases of *R v Venna*, 1976, *R v Savage*, 1991, and *R v Parmenter*, 1991). The defendant must foresee the risk of causing the application of violence.

Assault occasioning actual bodily harm

Section 47 of the Offences Against the Person Act 1861

Assault occasioning actual bodily harm (ABH) is triable either way and carries a maximum sentence of 5 years' imprisonment, in comparison with the maximum sentence of 6 months for common assault.

Actus reus of s.47

In this offence, the word 'assault' can mean either assault *or* battery, but most often it refers to battery — the infliction of some unlawful violence rather than a threat of violence. The *actus reus* is therefore assault or battery that causes 'actual bodily harm'.

This means that the offence has two components, since the prosecution must first be able to prove that an assault or battery took place, and then that that assault/battery went on to cause injuries consistent with actual bodily harm. This has been given the wide definition of 'any hurt or injury calculated to interfere with the health or comfort of the victim', provided it is not 'merely transient or trifling' (see, for example, *R v Miller*, 1954). In *R v Chan-Fook* (1994), the Court of Appeal stated that the injury 'should not be so trivial as to be wholly insignificant'.

One consequence of this definition is that it has been held to cover psychological harm — where the defendant causes the victim to become hysterical or to suffer substantial fear. For instance in *Chan-Fook*, the defendant, suspecting the victim of theft, manhandled him, dragged him upstairs and locked him in a room. The trial judge directed the jury that it sufficed for ABH that the assault had caused 'a nervous, maybe hysterical, condition'. However, this conviction was quashed on appeal — the court ruled that while the phrase 'actual bodily harm' is capable of including psychiatric injury:

> ...it does not include mere emotions such as fear or distress or panic nor does it include states of mind that are not themselves evidence of some identifiable clinical condition.

A similar conclusion was reached in *R* v *Morris* (1997), where the Court of Appeal held that evidence from the victim's doctor that she suffered from anxiety, fear, tearfulness, sleeplessness and physical tension was insufficient to establish ABH.

Mens rea of s.47

The *mens rea* required for ABH is the same as for battery — intention or recklessness as to the application of some unlawful force to another. This important rule was established in the separate cases of *Savage* and *Parmenter,* where it was held by the House of Lords that the prosecution is not obliged for an s.47 offence to prove that the defendant intended to cause some actual bodily harm or was reckless as to whether such harm would be caused.

In *R* v *Savage* (1991), the defendant admitted throwing the contents of her beer glass over the victim during a bar brawl. The glass slipped out of her hand and broke, and a piece of glass cut the victim's wrist. Although the defendant denied intending to cause the injury suffered by the victim, intending only to throw beer over her, she was convicted of s.47 ABH. This means that a guilty verdict may be returned upon proof of an assault together with proof of the fact that actual bodily harm was occasioned by the assault.

The rule established in *Savage* and *Parmenter* is a key legal point that examiners are looking for. Few marks, if any, are awarded for simply referring to the *mens rea* of s.47 ABH as intention or recklessness, unless there is a clear reference to this issue and these cases. Note too that exam answers should first explain the assault/battery in terms of *actus reus* and *mens rea*, before considering ABH.

The case of *R* v *Roberts* (1971) also confirms that the *mens rea* of s.47 ABH is the same as for assault or battery. As explained in Chapter 1, the defendant gave a lift in his car to a young woman, who jumped out of the moving vehicle, injuring herself, because she was frightened that he was going to rape her. It was held that the defendant had committed the *actus reus* of s.47 by touching her clothes — sufficient for battery — and this act had caused her to suffer actual bodily harm. The defendant argued that he lacked the *mens rea* of the offence, because he had neither intended to cause her actual bodily harm nor seen any risk of her suffering it as a result of his advances. This argument was rejected: the court held that the *mens rea* of battery was sufficient in itself, and there was no need for any extra *mens rea* regarding the actual bodily harm.

Malicious wounding or inflicting grievous bodily harm

Section 20 of the Offences Against the Person Act 1861

Actus reus of s.20

Section 20 created the offence of unlawfully and maliciously wounding or inflicting grievous bodily harm (GBH). The conduct element here is the same as for the more serious offence under s.18 (see below).

Blackout Concepts/Alamy

A burst blood vessel in the eye would not amount to a wound

A **wound** is defined as an injury that breaks both the outer and inner skin. A bruise or a burst blood vessel in the eye would not amount to a wound. In *C (a minor)* v *Eisenhower* (1984), the defendant fired an air rifle at the victim and hit her in the eye. However, this only caused an internal rupturing of blood vessels and not a break in the skin, therefore there was no wound. A scratch that does not break the inner layer of skin is not a wound, nor will there be a wound if a bone is broken but the skin remains intact. Students should note that under the Joint Charging Standards, minor cuts would usually be charged as s.47 ABH, or even as battery.

Grievous bodily harm is simply defined as 'really serious harm' — see *DPP* v *Smith* (1961), where the House of Lords said there was no reason to give these words any meaning other than that understood from their 'ordinary and natural meaning'. In *R* v *Saunders* (1985), the Court of Appeal ruled that there was no difference between 'serious' and 'really serious'.

To qualify as grievous bodily harm, the injury normally requires some immediate hospital treatment, but it does not have to be life-threatening. Examples of injuries that would be regarded as GBH are broken limbs, a dislocated shoulder, a fractured skull, permanent scarring and paralysis of a limb. The case of *R* v *Burstow* (1997) confirmed that GBH could also include serious psychiatric injury, where the defendant was a stalker who had sent his victim hate mail and made malicious phonecalls to her.

Following *R* v *Bollom* (2004), the court can consider the impact of the injury on a particular individual. In that case, the court took into consideration the fact that the victim was a 17-month-old baby who was more likely to be badly affected by extensive bruising than an adult.

Do not get confused about 'wounding' and 'grievous bodily harm'. For both s.20 and s.18 offences, these are alternative *actus reus* elements. Only if bleeding has taken place should wounding be charged (provided both the inner and outer layers of the skin have been breached). Of course, there could be circumstances where *both* wounding and GBH could be charged, for example where a major artery has been severed (because it has caused serious harm).

Inflict

At one time, it was held that the word 'inflict' required there to be some sort of actual and direct battery by the defendant upon the victim. However, in *R* v *Wilson* (1984), the House of Lords decided that this is not the case. Here, the defendant, while driving, nearly ran down the victim. He then got out of his car and punched the victim in the face. This view was confirmed in the later cases of *R* v *Ireland* and *R* v *Burstow* (1997), which made it clear that there is no real distinction to be drawn between 'inflicting GBH' (s.20) and 'causing GBH' (s.18).

Biological GBH

This was established by the 2004 case of *R* v *Dica*, where the defendant was convicted of s.20 'biological' GBH after infecting two women with HIV. The Court of Appeal, having quashed his conviction and ordered a retrial, confirmed that injury by reckless infection *does* constitute a s.20 offence, and upheld the conviction — and so confirmed that the nineteenth-century case of *R* v *Clarence* (1888) was overruled.

The more significant part of the *Dica* judgement appears to relate to the **defence of consent**, as the court ruled that if the other party knew or suspected that his or her partner was infected, no criminal liability would arise.

This apparently widened the scope of the defence of consent in such cases, distinguishing the case of *R* v *Brown* (1993), where this defence was expressly disallowed by the House of Lords. In *Dica*, the court ruled that 'there is a vital difference between consenting to the *deliberate* infliction of harm, and consenting to an activity that you know involves a *risk* of it'. This ruling means that criminal liability does not arise where the other party knows, or suspects, and is prepared to take the risk.

Mens rea of s.20

Section 20 requires either intention or recklessness to inflict *some harm*, not to cause GBH. This fault element is the main difference between this offence and s.18. It was confirmed in the cases of *R* v *Mowatt* (1968) and *R* v *Grimshaw* (1984), which held that there is no need to prove recklessness as to wounding or grievous bodily harm, so long as the court is satisfied that the defendant was reckless as to *some physical harm* to some person, albeit of a minor character. As in all non-fatal offences where the *mens rea* includes recklessness, this is *Cunningham* or subjective recklessness — the prosecution must prove that the defendant did foresee that some physical harm might be done.

If a scenario indicates that the victim suffered an injury that could be characterised as GBH and/or wounding, the most appropriate offence will usually be s.20. It is only in circumstances where a weapon such as a knife has been used to inflict the injury that s.18 would be more appropriate. Even then, consideration should be given to the possibility of s.20 if the necessary level of intent for s.18 is not proved.

Wounding or causing grievous bodily harm with intent

Section 18 of the Offences Against the Person Act 1861

This serious offence carries a maximum sentence of life imprisonment (in comparison with s.20, which has a maximum of 5 years).

There are two forms of intent, the more common being **'intent to cause grievous bodily harm'**. This requires proof that the defendant intended to cause a serious injury — 'specific intent'. This can be either **direct intent**, where the defendant's aim or objective was to cause grievous bodily harm, or **oblique intent**, where the jury is satisfied that the defendant foresaw serious injury as virtually certain — as in *R* v *Nedrick* (1986) and *R* v *Woollin* (1998).

In most cases of s.18 GBH, the defendant will have used some form of weapon to inflict injuries on the victim, which makes it easier for the prosecution to prove the necessary intent. Where the prosecution fails to establish intention, the offence will be reduced to the lower s.20 offence, so long as recklessness is proved.

Note that there is no offence of wounding with intent to cause wounding. If the defendant were to grab hold of the victim's hand and deliberately stick a pin into a finger through both layers of skin, this could only be charged under s.20. Although there is wounding and intent, there was no intent to cause GBH.

The second form of intent available for s.18 relates to circumstances where a lawful arrest is being attempted and the intent is **'to prevent the lawful apprehension of any person'**. The policy behind this element is that attacks on persons engaged in law enforcement are regarded as more serious. Under this, the defendant can be convicted if he or she pushes a police officer to prevent an arrest, and the officer falls and suffers a serious injury. There is no requirement that such serious results should have been foreseen or even foreseeable. It is, however, a requirement in such cases that the prosecution proves the defendant intended some harm, or was reckless as to whether harm was caused. This was confirmed by the Court of Appeal in *R* v *Morrison* (1989).

Consent

The defence of consent, if successfully pleaded, negates the *actus reus* element of unlawfulness in any assault. However, this defence, like intoxication, has restricted and controlled applications.

Indeed, the general rule as far as its application to non-fatal crimes is concerned is that it is *not* a defence. The Court of Appeal in *Attorney General's Reference No. 6 (1980)* declared that where two persons fight, the blows inflicted can amount to battery, and that the unlawfulness cannot be denied by pleading that the other party consented to the fight. Lord Lane CJ stated:

> *It is not in the public interest that people should try to cause each other bodily harm for no good reason. Minor struggles are another matter. So, in our judgement, it is immaterial whether the act occurs in private or in public; it is an assault if actual bodily harm is intended and/or caused.*

This means that consent is not a defence to s.47, s.20 or s.18, unless it falls within any of the exceptions explained below.

Genuineness of consent

Consent must be genuine. In *R v Richardson* (1999), for example, the defendant was a registered dentist who had been suspended from practice by the General Dental Council. While suspended, she carried out dentistry on a number of patients, one of whom complained to the police. A prosecution was brought for ABH and she was convicted. On appeal she argued that she had the defence of consent, as the complainant had consented to the treatment. The appeal was allowed.

However, a potentially broader interpretation of this question of genuine consent was taken in *R v Tabassum* (2000). The defendant was convicted of indecent assault for persuading women to allow him to measure their breasts under the pretext of preparing a medical dossier in connection with breast cancer. The women all consented because they thought he was medically qualified. His appeal against conviction on the grounds of consent was dismissed on the grounds that the consent given by the women had been as to the nature of the act but not its quality. Rose LJ stated:

> *On the evidence, if the jury accepted it, consent was given because they mistakenly believed that the defendant was medically qualified…and that, in consequence, the touching was for a medical purpose. As this was not so, there was no true consent. They were consenting to touching for medical purposes not to indecent behaviour, that is, there was consent to the nature of the act but not its quality.*

Consent as a plea to serious crimes

Consent may only be pleaded to the crimes of assault and battery, and not to any more serious crime, unless the circumstances fall under one of the following headings.

Consent in sports

A person can consent to the risk of accidental injury occurring within a properly conducted contact sport, such as football, hockey or rugby. As regards boxing, a person is deemed to have consented to the deliberate infliction of harm by his or her

opponent, provided the fight takes place under the rules of the governing body. The same applies for martial arts contests.

Until *R* v *Barnes* (2004), it seemed clear that if the injury was caused by a foul committed during the course of play, this could result in a conviction — consent being restricted to accidental injuries received in the course of 'fair play'. In *Barnes*, Lord Woolf CJ ruled that:

A person can consent to the risk of accidental injury within a properly conducted contact sport such as football

> ...*in highly competitive sports, where conduct outside the rules could be expected to occur in the heat of the moment, such conduct might not reach the threshold level required for it to be criminal. That level was an objective one which would be determined by the type of sport, the level at which it was played...the degree of force used, the extent of the risk of injury and the state of mind of the accused.*

This judgement created a higher threshold for sporting injuries to be prosecuted.

Rough horseplay

A person can give consent to the risk of harm being caused during rough horseplay, provided there is no intention to harm. In *R* v *Jones and Others* (1986), a gang of schoolboys threw the victim up to 10 feet into the air, with the result that on hitting the floor he suffered a ruptured spleen and broke his arm. The defence was allowed on the basis that there was no intention to cause injury, and on appeal convictions for GBH were quashed.

Another case to illustrate this exception is *R* v *Richardson and Irwin* (1999). The defendants, victim and others were university students who had been out drinking. On returning to their accommodation, they indulged in horseplay as on previous occasions. This culminated in the victim being lifted over the edge of a balcony and falling about 10 feet. He suffered serious injuries and both defendants were charged with and convicted of a s.20 offence. The Court of Appeal quashed their convictions because the trial judge had confused subjective and objective recklessness in his direction to the jury. More importantly, the court held that a mistaken belief by the defendants that the victim was consenting to run the risk of personal injury would enable the defendants to avoid liability, even if that mistake was induced by intoxication.

Surgery, including tattooing and body piercing

In *R* v *Wilson* (1996), the defendant had, at his wife's request, used a hot knife to brand his initials onto her bottom. The scars were found during a medical examination and he was subsequently charged with s.47 ABH.

At his trial, it was argued that his wife had consented to his conduct, but the judge ruled (following *R* v *Brown*, 1993) that this defence was not available on these facts. However, the Appeal Court allowed his appeal on the basis that it fell within the exception recognised by *Brown* of tattooing, and also distinguished this case from *Brown* on the grounds that the defendant's wife had not only consented to the branding but had also instigated it, and there was clearly no aggressive intent on the part of the husband.

The court finally ruled per Russell LJ that:

> *…consensual activity between husband and wife, in the privacy of the matrimonial home, is not, in our judgement, normally a proper matter for criminal investigation, let alone criminal prosecution.*

In a comment on this decision, Professor J. C. Smith said the only real distinction between *Wilson* and *Brown* was that Mr Wilson derived no sexual pleasure from the branding. Otherwise, the judgement simply agreed with the minority view in *Brown* that there was no public interest in criminalising the activity.

In contrast, in *R* v *Emmett* (unreported case: the *Independent* 19 July 1999), as part of consensual heterosexual activity, a woman agreed to having a plastic bag tied over her head, causing her to lose consciousness, and on another occasion to lighter fuel being poured over her breasts and set alight, causing burns that became infected. Her partner was convicted of s.47 ABH and appealed. Here, the Court of Appeal ruled that consent was no defence, on the basis that the masochistic activity went far beyond that which was evident in *Wilson* — in other words, the activity was *prima facie* unlawful and contrary to the public interest.

Joint Charging Standards

Table 2.1 summarises the Joint Charging Standards for non-fatal offences. These were produced by the police and the Crown Prosecution Service to clarify the offences that would normally be charged following different levels of injuries. However, it is important that you can also identify other potential offences that could be charged; for example, a minor cut or graze could potentially be charged as wounding.

Table 2.1 Joint Charging Standards for non-fatal offences

Section 39 of the Criminal Justice Act: common assault (battery)	Section 47: assault occasioning ABH	Section 18 or Section 20: GBH or wounding
Grazes or scratches	Loss or breaking of a tooth	Injury causing permanent disability or disfigurement
Abrasions	Temporary loss of consciousness	Broken limbs or bones
Minor bruising	Extensive or multiple bruising	Dislocated joints
Swellings	Displaced broken nose	Injuries causing substantial loss of blood
Reddening of the skin	Minor fractures	Injuries resulting in lengthy treatment
Superficial cuts	Minor cuts requiring stitches	
A black eye	Psychiatric injury — more than fear, distress or panic	Severe psychiatric injury — more than fear, distress or panic, and requiring specialist treatment

Note that this table is a *guide only*, and if you refer to these standards you must also use the definitions provided above for each offence. Writing that 'under the Joint Charging Standards, a broken finger will be charged under s.47 ABH' is not sufficient. You would also need to note that the *actus reus* of s.47 ABH requires that the defendant committed an assault or battery which then caused ABH, defined in *R* v *Miller* (1954) as 'any hurt or injury calculated to interfere with the health or comfort of the victim'.

Non-fatal offences have been summarised in Table 2.2.

Table 2.2 Summary of non-fatal offences

Crime	Actus reus	Mens rea	Cases	Joint Charging Standards injuries
Assault	Causing the victim to apprehend immediate, unlawful personal violence	Intention or subjective recklessness to causing *actus reus*	*Logdon, Ireland, Constanza*	None
Battery	Infliction of unlawful personal violence	Intention or subjective recklessness as to inflicting unlawful personal injury	*Fagan, Thomas*	Black eye, graze, scratch
Section 47 ABH	Assault or battery causing actual bodily harm	Intention or recklessness as to the assault or battery: no need to prove intention/recklessness as to ABH	*Miller, Chan-Fook, Savage, Parmenter, Roberts*	Minor fractures, minor cuts requiring stitches, broken nose, loss of tooth
Section 20 GBH/ wounding	Wounding: all layers of skin must be broken; GBH: serious injury	Intention or recklessness as to *some* harm	*Eisenhower, Smith, Mowatt, Grimshaw*	Broken limbs, dislocated joints, substantial bleeding
Section 18 GBH with intent	Wounding or GBH as in s.20	Specific intent to cause GBH, or intent to resist lawful arrest	*Nedrick, Woollin*	Broken limbs, dislocated joints, substantial bleeding

Further reading

Ashworth, A. (1999) *Principles of Criminal Law* (3rd edn), Oxford University Press.

Elliott, C. and Quinn, F. (2006) *Criminal Law* (6th edn), Pearson Longman.

Loveless, J. (2008) *Complete Criminal Law*, Oxford University Press.

McAlhone, C. and Huxley-Binns, R. (2007) *Criminal Law: The Fundamentals*, Sweet & Maxwell.

Storey, T. and Lidbury, A. (2007) *Criminal Law*, Willan.

Yule, I. (2008) 'Criminal law decoded: non-fatal offences against the person', *A-Level Law Review*, Vol. 4, No. 1, pp. 30–32.

Chapter **3**

Murder and voluntary manslaughter

Murder

Murder is the most serious crime against the person, and the offender, if convicted, will receive a mandatory life sentence. Unlike most crimes, murder is still a common-law offence, and as such there is no statute that defines the conduct required. As the author states:

> Sir Edward Coke's 1797 definition is both overlong and generally unhelpful; the actus reus *of murder is simply* **unlawful killing**. *There is no need to examine issues such as 'any reasonable creature in rerum natura' or 'under the queen's peace', nor to deal with brain-stem death, as they are not usually relevant to the scenario.*

I. Yule, 'Criminal law decoded: homicide', *A-Level Law Review*, Vol. 4, No. 2, January 2009

Photofusion Picture Library/Alamy

The *actus reus* of murder is simply unlawful killing

Proving the *actus reus* often involves examining various rules of causation, in order to establish whether the defendant caused or brought about the death of the victim.

However, this must not be allowed to complicate the issue unnecessarily in answering examination questions:

> *Another common mistake is that of explaining in almost exhaustive detail all the rules on causation — even where the scenario raises no causation issues. If the victim has been shot or stabbed and has died immediately of his or her wounds, such explanations are a waste of time.*

Idem.

The key issue in murder cases is usually the *mens rea* — an **intention to kill or commit grievous bodily harm** (GBH). A fatal offence question might ask you to consider whether a killing should be dealt with as murder or involuntary manslaughter. Your answer will depend on whether or not the defendant killed with intent — both direct and oblique intent can be considered here. Involuntary manslaughter only requires the *mens rea* for the unlawful and dangerous act or gross negligence.

Before going any further, revise the rules in Chapter 1 on causation and *mens rea* (pages 2-6 and 7-9).

Constructive liability

It is crucial to remember that the *mens rea* for murder includes intention to commit GBH. This constructive liability rule was established in *R v Vickers* (1957), where a burglar struck the owner of the shop, and the victim eventually died from shock due to general injuries. The rule was confirmed in *R v Cunningham* (1981), where the defendant repeatedly hit his victim with a chair, resulting in the victim's death.

In *Vickers*, Lord Goddard CJ held that malice aforethought consists of either an intention to kill or an intention to cause GBH, even in the absence of knowledge or belief that life would be endangered. The argument is that an attacker bent on causing GBH cannot guarantee that death will not follow.

Voluntary manslaughter

Voluntary manslaughter covers the situation where the defendant has committed the *actus reus* of murder (unlawful killing) with the required *mens rea* (specific intention to kill or commit GBH) but there are extenuating circumstances that reduce the defendant's liability. These circumstances operate as partial defences, and are defined as provocation or diminished responsibility. Uniquely, the defendant is not charged with the offence of voluntary manslaughter but with murder, to which he or she will plead the relevant defence. If successful, he or she will then be convicted of manslaughter.

The justification for this offence is the problem caused by the mandatory life sentence for murder. The basis of all serious criminal liability — liability to be prosecuted and, if convicted, to be punished — rests on the principle of fault. In the case of the two partial defences (which can *only* be pleaded to a murder charge), the law is recognising that in some way the defendant's fault has been reduced and therefore he or she is entitled to receive a lower punishment than life imprisonment. These partial defences, while important today, were even more important before 1963, when the mandatory penalty for murder was hanging. In a sense, these defences operated as 'gallows savers'.

Diminished responsibility

Diminished responsibility is defined in s.2 of the **Homicide Act 1957**:

> *Where a person kills or is a party to the killing of another, he shall not be convicted of murder if he was suffering from such abnormality of mind (whether arising from a condition of arrested or retarded development of mind or any inherent causes or induced by disease or injury) as substantially impaired his mental responsibility for his acts and omissions in doing or being a party to the killing.*

Do not refer to the defence of diminished responsibility except in murder cases, where the possibility of insanity could also be considered. For any offence other than murder, if there is any issue concerning any 'abnormality of mind', this can only be dealt with under insanity.

Burden of proof

A curious and much-criticised feature of this partial defence is that the burden is on the defendant to prove, on the balance of probabilities (the lower, civil law standard), that he or she was suffering from diminished responsibility at the time of the killing. Psychiatric reports testifying to a relevant abnormality of mind must also be presented to the court by the defence in order to substantiate any such claim. The ordinary rule regarding the burden of proof is that the defendant needs only to produce some evidence for a defence, which the prosecution must disprove beyond all reasonable doubt.

A further curiosity is that, when faced with this partial defence, it is open to the prosecution to make a case that the defendant is in fact insane, which, if successfully argued, will lead to the defendant being acquitted by the special verdict of 'not guilty by reason of insanity' (but then being sent to a mental hospital).

Elements

Abnormality of mind

The partial defence of diminished responsibility was introduced into English law from Scots law, where in *HM Advocate* v *Braithwaite* (1945), Lord President Cooper

defined it as 'bordering on but not amounting to insanity'. In *Galbraith* v *Lord Advocate (No. 2)* (2001), it was redefined as an abnormality of mind that substantially impaired the defendant's ability to determine or control conduct, for which the defendant would otherwise be convicted of murder.

The leading English case is that of *R* v *Byrne* (1957), where the defendant strangled his victim and then mutilated her body. He claimed he suffered from perverted sexual desires that created impulses he found impossible to control. Here, Lord Parker CJ stated that 'an abnormality of mind is a state of mind so different from that of ordinary human beings that the reasonable man would term it abnormal'. He went on to stress that once the jury was satisfied that the defendant was suffering from an abnormality of mind, it must then be satisfied that this abnormality was 'significant enough to substantially impair his mental responsibility for his acts'.

Arising from a cause specified in the Act

The definition in s.2 of the Act specifies that the abnormality of mind must arise from a condition of arrested or retarded development of mind or any inherent cause or be induced by disease or injury. In applying the rules of diminished responsibility to the facts of the scenario in a problem-solving question, it is important to be able to state the source of the abnormality of mind.

In 1997, the Court of Appeal accepted that 'battered woman syndrome' was a mental disease and could thus cause an abnormality of mind

The term 'inherent causes' can include recognised psychiatric illnesses, such as schizophrenia, psychosis and any organic brain disorder. It has also been held to cover severe shock or depression, especially in cases of mercy killing. In 1997, the Court of Appeal accepted that 'battered woman syndrome' was a mental disease and could thus cause an abnormality of mind.

Substantial impairment of mental responsibility

In order to satisfy s.2 and for the defence to succeed, the abnormality of mind must have substantially impaired the defendant's mental responsibility. This is a matter of fact for the jury to decide, rather than a psychiatric issue for the expert to consider, and is a moral as opposed to a medical concern.

The impairment of control need not be complete, but it must be considerable. In *Byrne*, there was evidence that the impulses from which the defendant suffered were not absolutely irresistible, but were extremely difficult to control. In that case, this was considered sufficient; but this will always be a matter for the jury to decide. In *R* v *Lloyd* (1967), it was held that for it to be substantial, 'the impairment need not be total but it must be more than trivial or minimal'.

Intoxication and diminished responsibility

A defendant might be able to rely on the defence of diminished responsibility despite being intoxicated, as long as the intoxication caused the abnormality of mind. For example, the brain might have been damaged because the defendant is an alcoholic. However, alcohol simply having a transitory effect on the mind is not enough to trigger the defence. In the leading case of *R* v *Tandy* (1989), the defendant was an alcoholic who strangled her 11-year-old daughter after drinking a large amount of vodka. The Court of Appeal held that for drink to produce an abnormality of mind, the:

> *...alcoholism had to have reached such a level that the defendant's brain was damaged so that there was gross impairment of his judgement and emotional responses or the craving for drink had to be such as to render the defendant's use of drink involuntary because he was no longer able to resist the impulse to drink.*

The defendant stated that she was able to exercise a degree of control over her drinking and had taken the first drink of the day voluntarily. Consequently, she was unable to rely on the defence of diminished responsibility, and her appeal was dismissed.

However, in *R* v *Wood* (2008), Judge LJ (President of Queen's Bench Division) argued that:

> *...as a matter of practical reality the bar the defendant is required to surmount before diminished responsibility can be established in the context of chronic addiction to alcohol may have been set too high [in Tandy].*

He further stated that 'nothing in s.2 itself suggests that alcohol dependency syndrome [alcoholism] is excluded from consideration as a possible source of abnormality of mind'.

He concluded that this defence, when arising as a result of alcohol consumption, was a matter for the jury to decide, by determining whether or not the defendant's syndrome was of such an extent and nature that it constituted an abnormality of mind induced by illness or disease. If it was, then the defence was available; the next step was for the jury to consider whether the defendant's craving for alcohol was irresistible or not. The fact that some drink was consumed voluntarily would not necessarily deprive the defendant of this defence.

Note also the case of *R* v *Dietschmann* (2003). Here, the defendant killed the victim while both intoxicated *and* suffering from an abnormality of mind, but there was no evidence of alcoholism itself as an abnormality of mind. It was held that in such a situation, if a defendant satisfies the jury that, notwithstanding the role of the alcohol, his or her abnormality of mind substantially impaired his or her mental responsibility for the killing, the jury should find him or her not guilty of murder but guilty of voluntary manslaughter by reason of diminished responsibility. In this case, Lord Hutton stated that:

...the subsection [s.2(1) of the Homicide Act 1957] does not require the abnormality of mind to be the sole cause of the defendant's acts in doing the killing. In my opinion, even if the defendant would not have killed if he had not taken drink, the causative effect of the drink does not necessarily prevent an abnormality of mind suffered by the defendant from substantially impairing his mental responsibility for his fatal acts.

Questions

1 In *R* v *Byrne* (1960), how was 'abnormality of mind' defined?

2 What psychiatric conditions are covered by 'inherent causes'?

3 In *R* v *Lloyd* (1966), how is the issue of 'impairment of mental responsibility' explained?

4 Briefly explain the decision made in *R* v *Wood* (2008).

5 Briefly explain the decision made in *R* v *Dietschmann* (2003).

Provocation

If the jury finds that the defendant was provoked, his or her liability will be for manslaughter rather than murder. For all other offences, provocation may only be pleaded in mitigation of sentence.

Section 3 of the **Homicide Act 1957** states:

Where on a charge of murder there is evidence on which the jury can find that the person charged was provoked (whether by things done or by things said or by both together) to lose his self-control, the question whether the provocation was enough to make a reasonable man do as he did shall be left to be determined by the jury; and in determining that question the jury shall take into account everything both done and said according to the effect which, in their opinion, it would have on a reasonable man.

In summary, the defence can be broken down into three elements. It must be established that:

❖ the defendant was provoked 'by things done or by things said or by both together' (evidential test)

❖ this provocation caused the defendant to lose self-control (subjective test)

❖ the defendant reacted to the provocation in a way that a reasonable person may have ('reasonable man' test)

It is important to have a sound understanding of the legal tests and to be able to apply them to scenario facts in exam questions. Particular attention should be paid to the 'reasonable man' test.

Evidential test

The judge must initially decide if there is evidence capable of amounting to provocation. This is the limit of the judge's role, as the success or failure of the defence is left to the jury. Note that where there is some evidence of provocation, even if the defence does not specifically rely on it at trial, this must be put by the judge to the jury (see *R* v *Cambridge*, 1994). In *R* v *Acott* (1997), where there was evidence that the victim (the defendant's mother) had treated the defendant like a child and also drank excessively, it was held that as there was no specific evidence of provocation but merely speculation, the trial judge was right not to direct the jury on the issue of provocation. This was also confirmed in *R* v *Miao* (2003) and in *R* v *Serrano* (2006).

Provocation may result from things said or things done, or both together (whereas prior to the 1957 Act, only things done could amount in law to provocation). This means that any conduct or words can amount to provocation; in *R* v *Doughty* (1986), even the crying of a young baby was considered as provocative when his father killed him.

A court can also take into account cumulative provocation, which has taken place over a long period of time, as in *R* v *Humphreys* (1995). In this case, the defendant and the victim had a stormy relationship, and the victim had subjected the defendant to both physical and sexual abuse over a long period. While the 'final straw' incident of provocation was a comparatively minor taunt about the victim's attempted suicide, the Court of Appeal held that the jury should have been directed to consider not just that particular incident but also the wider relationship context. This means that the final provocation is considered not in isolation but in the context of all the provocative incidents that have gone before it.

Subjective test

The jury must ascertain whether, as a matter of fact, the defendant was provoked to lose his or her self-control; if the defendant, although provoked, lost his or her self-control for any other reason, the defence fails. This requirement involves more than being angry, or a loss of temper, but is less than a total loss of self-control. In *R* v *Duffy* (1949), Lord Devlin defined it as 'a sudden and temporary loss of self-control, rendering the defendant so subject to passion as to make him for the moment not the master of his mind'. This requirement avoids bringing revenge killings under the scope of the defence.

Note that evidence of provocation followed by premeditated action will result in this defence being lost. In *R* v *Ibrams and Gregory* (1981), for example, it was held that the existence of a 'cooling-off period' between the provocation and the pre-planned killing a few days later was evidence that the loss of self-control was not 'sudden and temporary'. However, the courts have recently taken a more generous approach to 'cooling-off periods', so that they will not necessarily exclude the defence. However, the longer the delay between the provocative act and the response, the stronger the evidence of premeditation. In *R* v *Baillie* (1995), the Court of Appeal stated that the

defence of provocation should have been put to the jury; in this case, the defendant, following the provocation, had gone to the attic to fetch a gun and then driven his car for 2 miles, filling up with petrol on the way, before shooting the victim.

It must be further noted that the existence of a 'cooling-off period' is not a matter of law. It is a piece of evidence that the jury may use to decide whether, at the time of the killing, the defendant was deprived of self-control, as in *R* v *Ahluwalia* (1992). Here, the defendant was married to a man who was frequently violent towards her. One night, after another abusive altercation where she was threatened with a hot iron, she waited until her husband was asleep in bed before pouring paraffin on him and setting it alight. He died 6 days later as a result of severe burns. She was convicted of murder, but at a subsequent appeal, it was held (per Lord Taylor CJ) that the delay in reacting would not necessarily negative the subjective loss of self-control, 'provided there was at the time of the killing a "sudden and temporary loss of self-control" caused by the alleged provocation'.

'Reasonable man' test

Once a jury is satisfied that the defendant did suffer a sudden and temporary loss of self-control, it must then be proved that not only would a reasonable person have been provoked, but also that such provocation would have made a reasonable person act as the defendant did — in other words, that the response was not out of proportion to the provocation. This is an objective test. For example, note the contrasting cases of *Bedder* (1954) and *DPP* v *Camplin* (1978) which overruled it. In *Bedder*, an impotent man killed a prostitute after she provoked him about his condition. However, at trial the judge refused the defence argument that the jury should consider the 'reasonable man' as also being impotent. In *Camplin* (details below), the judge refused to direct the jury to consider the 'reasonable' 15-year-old, but on appeal to the House of Lords it was held by Lord Diplock that the members of a jury should be told that the reasonable person is:

> ...a person having the power of self-control to be expected of an ordinary person of the sex and age of the accused, but in other respects sharing such of the accused's characteristics as they think would affect the gravity of the provocation to him; and that the question is not merely whether such a person would in like circumstances be provoked to lose his self-control but also whether he would react to the provo-cation as the accused did.

In *R* v *Roberts* (1990), a 23-year-old man who suffered from substantial deafness and impaired speech killed someone as a result of taunts about this condition. It was held that the judge had rightly directed that the hypothetical 'reasonable man' had those same characteristics.

Both *Ahluwalia* and *R* v *Thornton* (1992) have now confirmed that 'battered woman syndrome' might constitute a relevant characteristic.

This objective test was stretched further in *R* v *Morhall* (1996). The defendant was a glue-sniffer who was taunted by the victim about this addiction. A fight ensued and the defendant killed the other man. He was convicted of murder and appealed on the ground of provocation. The Court of Appeal rejected his submission on the grounds that 'repugnant characteristics' could not be attributed to the 'reasonable man'. The House of Lords overturned the decision of the Appeal Court, holding that such characteristics could and should be taken into account when applying the objective test, provided that the characteristic was the target of the provocation (the 'response' characteristic, as opposed to the 'control' characteristics that affect the defendant's self-control).

The controversial decision in *R* v *Morgan Smith* (2000), was greatly criticised for blurring the distinction between the subjective and objective tests. The defendant had been suffering from serious clinical depression, and the House of Lords held that in cases where the defendant suffered from a mental illness, the jury should be directed to consider whether it thought 'the behaviour of the accused had measured up to the standard of self-control which ought reasonably to have been expected of him' per Lord Hoffman.

In *Attorney General for Jersey* v *Holley* (2005), a panel of the Privy Council took the opportunity to 'clarify definitively the present state of English law on provocation'. Following a retrial at the Royal Court in Jersey, the defendant had been convicted of murder. He was a chronic alcoholic who admitted killing his longstanding girlfriend with an axe while under the influence of alcohol. The sole issue at trial was provocation. The Court of Appeal allowed his subsequent appeal and substituted a conviction for manslaughter on the ground that the deputy bailiff had misdirected the jury on the issue of provocation. The Attorney General appealed to the Privy Council, and Lord Nicholls gave the majority judgement of the nine-judge panel.

The main focus of the judgement was the 'reasonable man test' in s.3. Lord Nicholls stated that this 'has been the most difficult issue in the whole law of provocation'. It can be divided into two separate tests: the first calls for an assessment of the gravity of the provocation, the second requires an application of an external standard of self-control — 'whether the provocation was enough to make a reasonable man do as he did'. In *DPP* v *Camplin* (1978), Lord Diplock defined this person as:

> *...an ordinary person of either sex, not exceptionally excitable or pugnacious, but possessed of such powers of self-control as everyone is entitled to expect that his fellow citizens will exercise.*

In that case, the 15-year-old defendant killed the victim with a chapatti pan after he had been sexually abused and then taunted by his attacker. At the trial, the judge directed the jury to judge the defendant according to the standards of an adult male, and Camplin was convicted. However, both the Court of Appeal and the House of Lords allowed his appeal. It is now clear that the reasonable person must share the age, sex and race of the actual defendant, both with regard to the gravity of the provocation and the degree of self-control to be expected of him or her.

In the Privy Council judgement Lord Nicholls decisively overturned the majority judgement in *R* v *Morgan Smith* (2001) on the ground that 'the statute does not leave each jury free to set whatever standard they consider appropriate in the circumstances by which to judge whether the defendant's conduct is "excusable"'. He held:

> *...however much the contrary is asserted, the majority view [in* Smith*] does represent a departure from the law as declared in s.3 of the Homicide Act 1957. It involves a significant relaxation of the uniform, objective standard adopted by Parliament. Under the statute the sufficiency of the provocation is to be judged by one standard, not a standard which varies from defendant to defendant.*

He also held that, in cases such as *Morgan Smith*, the defendant should argue his or her case on the basis of diminished responsibility, not provocation. The reason was that 'that statutory provision [s.2] represents the legislature's view on how cases of mental abnormality are to be accommodated in the law of homicide'. (This was the view also of the Court of Appeal in *Ahluwalia,* where a defence of provocation failed and a retrial was ordered on the issue of diminished responsibility.)

Note, however, that in cases where the defendant is suffering from a mental abnormality and the focus of the provocation is directed at that abnormality, it would still be entirely proper for the defence of provocation to be led in addition to that of diminished responsibility, and the judge would be required to direct the jury to consider the effect of the provocative taunts on the gravity of the provocation.

The decision in *Holley* was confirmed as correct by the Court of Appeal in the later cases of *R* v *James* and *R* v *Karimi* (both 2006), where a 5-judge panel presided over by Lord Phillips CJ decided that the Privy Council decision should be followed rather than the House of Lords decision in *Smith*, a judgement which effectively meant that the Court of Appeal ruled that the Privy Council overruled the House of Lords.

Finally, note that for reasons of policy, intoxication cannot be taken into account. This is because of the common-law rule that intoxication does not of itself excuse a person from committing a criminal offence. In *R* v *Newell* (1980), the defendant was a chronic alcoholic who became depressed when his girlfriend left him. When the defendant and his friend were drunk, the friend make insulting remarks about the defendant's former girlfriend. This caused the defendant to lose self-control and fatally attack his friend. The trial judge directed the jury to ask whether a sober man, in relation to that drunken observation, would hit his friend over the head with a heavy ashtray. The Court of Appeal held that this was a correct direction.

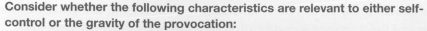

Questions

Consider whether the following characteristics are relevant to either self-control or the gravity of the provocation:

1 John has a hot-headed temperament. When his boss snaps at him, he stabs and kills him.

2 Peter is an alcoholic and thinks all Asians are terrorists. Asif shouts that he is a racist thug. Peter then hurls a brick at Asif, which hits him and results in fatal injuries.

3 Mary, aged 15, suffers from Down's Syndrome. She is taunted by Jane because she is slow to complete a class exercise. Mary reacts by grabbing a pair of scissors and stabbing Jane through the heart and killing her.

4 Bill has been treated recently for a mental illness. A workmate points at him and shouts that he is 'a loonie'. Bill grabs the workmate and strangles him.

The elements of the defence of provocation are summarised in Table 3.1.

Table 3.1 Summary of provocation

Introduction	Governed by the Homicide Act 1957 s.3.Partial defence to murder only.	
Evidential test	Provocation may be by words or actions or both combined. Jury can consider cumulative effect of more than one provocative incident.	*R* v *Cambridge* (1994) *R* v *Doughty* (1986) *R* v *Acott* (1997) *R* v *Humphreys* (1995)
Subjective test	Provocation must have caused D to lose self-control — must be 'sudden and immediate'. Delay *could be* 'cooling-off' period.	*R* v *Duffy* (1949) *R* v *Ibrams and Gregory* (1981) *R* v *Baillie* (1995)
'Reasonable man' test	Would the reasonable person also have lost self-control and then killed the victim? Personal characteristics of the defendant which are attributable to the reasonable person are age, gender or the 'focus' of the provocation, e.g. physical appearance or even 'repugnant characteristics' that affect the *gravity* of the provocation. But the reasonable person standard is an *objective* one. If the defendant is suffering from a mental abnormality which may make him more likely to lose self-control, the proper defence is diminished responsibility.	*DPP* v *Camplin* (1978) *Attorney General for Jersey* v *Holley* (2005) *R* v *James*, *R* v *Karimi* (2006) *R* v *Morhall* (1996)

Questions

1 Explain the evidential test for provocation.
2 What rule is illustrated by *R* v *Acott* (1997)?
3 What was decided in *R* v *Humphreys* (1995)?
4 Briefly explain the importance of the decision in *R* v *Morhall* (1996).
5 How did Lord Diplock define the 'reasonable man' in *DPP* v *Camplin* (1978)?
6 In which case was it decided that the defendant's intoxication cannot be taken into account when considering the 'reasonable man' test?

Sample exam question

While having a drink in a pub with his girlfriend, Victoria, Jim is annoyed by a torrent of rude comments from a noisy and drunken group of women sitting at the next table. Jenny is particularly vocal in making loud sexual jokes and, eventually, Victoria goes across to their table and throws a glass of water over Jenny.

Some time later, while Jenny is waiting for a taxi in the town centre, she sees Victoria and Jim walking on the other side of the road. Jenny immediately crosses the road and starts to shout at them. Victoria then tells Jenny that her behaviour is disgraceful and calls her a 'spotty cow'. Jenny suffers from severe acne and is very sensitive about this condition. She responds to the insult by grabbing Victoria's arm and pushing her into the road, where Victoria is struck and killed by a passing bus.

Discuss whether Jenny could plead provocation as a partial defence to the charge of Victoria's murder.

Chapter 4

Involuntary manslaughter

Involuntary manslaughter offences have the same *actus reus* as murder (unlawful killing) but are committed without specific intention to kill or commit grievous bodily harm. Of all kinds of homicide, involuntary manslaughter has always been the most difficult to define because of its explanation of *mens rea* in the negative. In *Andrews v DPP* (1937), Lord Atkin observed:

> *Of all crimes manslaughter appears to afford most difficulties of definition, for it concerns homicide in so many and so varying conditions...the law...recognises murder on the one hand based mainly, though not exclusively, on an intention to kill, and manslaughter on the other hand, based mainly, though not exclusively, on the absence of intent to kill, but with the presence of an element of 'unlawfulness' which is the elusive factor.*

As Andrew Ashworth writes in *Principles of Criminal Law* (3rd edition, 1999, p. 299):

> *In practice the category of involuntary manslaughter contains a large variety of killings...a killing in which the defendant merely pushed a person during an argument in the street and the person fell backwards, cracking his head on the kerb and dying from a brain haemorrhage, might fall within involuntary manslaughter. The sentence for such an offence would be low, whereas a killing in which the defendant knew there was a risk of death, but was held not to have intended death or grievous bodily harm, would also fall within involuntary manslaughter and might justify a high sentence.*

In a sense, manslaughter is therefore caught between murder at the extreme end of criminal liability and accidental death, where no criminal liability usually attaches.

At present, the law recognises three broad categories of involuntary manslaughter:
❖ manslaughter by an unlawful and dangerous act
❖ gross negligence manslaughter
❖ reckless manslaughter

Unlawful and dangerous act manslaughter

In order to be guilty of this type of involuntary manslaughter, the defendant must have killed by committing an unlawful and dangerous act. The *mens rea* for this offence is simply an intention (or recklessness) to perform that act.

Unlawful act

It is now established that to be unlawful for the purposes of this offence, the act must be a crime — a tort or breach of contract will not be sufficient. In *R* v *Franklin* (1883), a man on Brighton's West Pier took a large box from a refreshment stall and threw it into the sea. The box struck and killed a swimmer. The prosecution argued that the tort of trespass involved in seizing the box was an unlawful act, but the trial judge ruled that:

> *The mere fact of a civil wrong committed by one person against another ought not to be used as an incident which is a necessary step in a criminal case.*

The prosecution's case was rejected, although the defendant was found guilty of manslaughter by gross negligence.

The offence can only be committed by a positive unlawful act, as opposed to an omission. This is the key characteristic that distinguishes unlawful act manslaughter from gross negligence manslaughter.

R v *Lowe* (1973) seems to confirm that if the omission is no more than an act of negligence, this will not be the basis of unlawful dangerous act manslaughter, unless the omission is truly wilful. In this case, the defendant was a man of low intelligence, who was alleged to have neglected his infant daughter by failing to summon medical assistance when she became ill, resulting in her death. However, he did not realise that the aid was necessary and had failed to foresee the consequences of his neglect. Omissions that cause death should therefore be dealt with under the law on gross negligence manslaughter.

It seems to be settled law from the cases of *R* v *Lamb* (1967) and *R* v *Jennings* (1990) that a criminal act must be identified and proved, including the necessary *mens rea*. It was for this reason that Lamb's conviction was quashed on appeal: no initial crime was proved to have been committed (see also page 11). The defendant and his friend were playing with a gun. Both men believed the weapon posed no threat, because there was no bullet opposite the barrel. However, when in jest the defendant pointed the gun at his friend and pulled the trigger, the chamber rotated and the friend was killed. Since the victim was party to the joke and did not feel threatened, there was no assault and therefore no unlawful act.

In *R* v *Lamb* (1967), no initial crime was proved to have been committed

This was also the case in *R* v *Scarlett* (1993), where the defendant's conviction was quashed since the Crown had not been able to produce evidence that the use of force by the defendant had been unreasonable and therefore was unlawful. A pub landlord pushed a drunken customer, who had refused to leave, towards the door of the pub. The customer fell down some stairs and hit his head on the pavement, suffering fatal injuries.

It is vital to understand that the *mens rea* for involuntary manslaughter is the intention to commit the unlawful and dangerous act. Most cases involve some form of assault, but in *DPP* v *Newbury and Jones* (1976), the initial offence (which was not identified in the case) was surely that of criminal damage, which the defendants clearly intended to commit when they pushed a stone block off a railway bridge. The failure to refer to the *mens rea* in examination questions involving unlawful and dangerous act manslaughter is a common problem.

Dangerous act

The unlawful act must be considered dangerous. The test for this is objective, in that the ordinary reasonable person would see a risk of some harm. In *R* v *Church* (1967), Lord Edmund-Davies stated:

> ...the unlawful act must be such as all sober and reasonable people would inevitably recognise must subject the other person to, at least, the risk of some harm resulting therefrom, albeit not serious harm.

In this case, during an argument, the defendant knocked a woman unconscious and, thinking she was dead, threw her into a river to dispose of the body. She drowned in the river.

In *Newbury*, Lord Salmon confirmed the test in *Church*, stressing that:

> The test is still the objective test. In judging whether the act was dangerous the test is not 'did the accused recognise that it was dangerous' but 'would all sober and reasonable people recognise its danger'.

The question is further extended to consider whether the reasonable person would have appreciated that the act was dangerous in the light not only of the circumstances actually known to the defendant, but also of any additional circumstances of which the hypothetical person would have been aware. An example is the leading case of *R* v *Watson* (1989), although note that the defendant's conviction for the manslaughter during a burglary of an 87-year-old was later overturned on appeal on the ground that causation had not been proved. In *R* v *Dawson* (1985) (armed robbery of a petrol station, which led to the death of the attendant from a heart attack), the original conviction for manslaughter was also quashed on appeal because the attendant's heart disease would not have been obvious to a reasonable person with the same knowledge as the men attempting to commit the armed robbery.

It seems that the court assumed that, in the context of this offence, 'harm' includes 'injury to the person through the operation of shock emanating from fright'. As Professor J. C. Smith comments in *Criminal Law* (7th edn): 'It seems that it is not enough that the act is likely to frighten. It must be likely to cause such shock as to result in physical injury.' The question arises, however, why the 'thin skull' rule was not applied in this case.

Cause of death

The unlawful and dangerous act must be the cause of the victim's death. At one time, it was considered that the act had to be directed at the victim, but following *R* v *Goodfellow* (1986) it is now clear that provided the act satisfies both the normal factual and legal rules of causation, this will suffice for such a charge to be brought. In this case, the defendant deliberately set fire to his council house, in the hope of being rehoused. However, his wife and children were killed in the blaze. Although the defendant claimed that his unlawful act had not been directed at the victims, the court held that it was only necessary to prove the existence of an unlawful, intentional act that a reasonable person would feel was likely to result in serious injury.

This decision was confirmed by the decision of the House of Lords in *Attorney General's Reference No. 3* (1994). It was held here that not only is there no requirement for the unlawful act to be directed at the victim, but that there is also no requirement that the danger or risk of harm be perceived in respect of the actual victim; a risk of harm to someone else arising from the unlawful act will suffice.

In *R* v *Carey* (2006), the victim was punched by the defendants and ran away. Unfortunately, the victim had a weak heart, collapsing and dying. Medical evidence indicated that she might not have died if she had not been running. The Court of Appeal ruled that the manslaughter charge should have been withdrawn from the jury, as the physical harm to the victim did not cause her death.

Manslaughter by supplying drugs

It is not uncommon for death to result from taking illegal drugs, but this type of case has given rise to difficulties in the courts. It raises questions such as whether the person who provided the drugs committed an unlawful act, either in the supply or administration of the drug or in causing the victim to administer the drug, and whether the supply then caused the victim's death.

In *R* v *Dalby* (1982), the defendant who had supplied the victim with diaconal tablets had his conviction quashed on the ground that the unlawful supply did not cause the victim's death. However, in *R* v *Cato* (1976), where the defendant had both supplied and injected the victim with heroin, the conviction was upheld.

The recent case of *R* v *Kennedy* (2007) hopefully provides a definitive judgement, because the case was appealed to the House of Lords. The defendant had supplied, prepared and handed the victim a syringe containing heroin for immediate injection. The victim did inject himself and later died. The defendant was duly convicted of unlawful act manslaughter. The vexed issues of what constitutes the unlawful act and whether that unlawful act was the actual cause of death were at the centre of three appeals — two to the Court of Appeal, and the final one to the House of Lords on the question certified by the Court of Appeal:

> When is it appropriate to find someone guilty of manslaughter where that person has been involved in the supply of a Class A controlled drug, which is then freely and voluntarily self-administered by the victim, and that administration then causes his death?

The House of Lords held that while the appellant undoubtedly committed a criminal act by supplying the heroin to the deceased, this act was *not* the cause of the victim's death — the cause was the victim's own decision to self-administer the drug. Therefore, the answer to the certified question is 'in the case of a fully informed and responsible adult, never'.

Gross negligence manslaughter

Gross negligence manslaughter is based on the civil tort of negligence and is most commonly the result of an omission — a failure to act where there is a clear duty to act, as in *R* v *Stone and Dobinson* (1977), where the defendants had voluntarily assumed a duty to care for Stone's anorexic sister but had failed to provide even basic care or to summon medical assistance when it was clear her health was deteriorating.

The quotation of Lord Hewart CJ in *R* v *Bateman* (1925) is still important:

> In order to establish criminal liability the fact must be such that in the opinion of the jury, the negligence of the accused went beyond a mere matter of compensation

between subjects (civil tort liability) and showed such disregard for the life and safety of others as to amount to a crime against the state and conduct deserving punishment.

This was substantially repeated in Lord Mackay's judgement in *R* v *Adomako* (1995; see facts under 'Gross negligence' on pages 42–43). He stated:

The essence of the matter, which is supremely a jury question, is whether, having regard to the risk of death involved, the conduct of the D was so bad in all the circumstances as to amount in their judgement to a criminal act or omission.

The rules that the Crown is obliged to satisfy to obtain a conviction for gross negligence manslaughter are as follows.

Duty of care owed by the defendant to the victim

This issue has caused considerable difficulty but, following *Adomako*, it now appears to be the case that duty of care is simply based on the 'neighbour' test in *Donoghue* v *Stevenson* (1932) or the incremental approach in *Caparo Industries PLC* v *Dickman* (1990). Note, however, that a duty of care can also be established by using the rules on omission within *actus reus* (assumption of a duty, *Stone and Dobinson*, 1977; voluntarily creating a dangerous situation, *R* v *Miller*, 1983; and contractual liability, *R* v *Pittwood,* 1902*)*. The test is, therefore, whether it was **reasonably foreseeable** that the victim would be injured.

However, the more recent case of *R* v *Singh* (1999) laid down the current rule, whereby:

The circumstances must be such that a reasonably prudent person would have foreseen a serious and obvious risk not merely of injury or even of serious injury but of death.

In this case, the victim tenant died of carbon monoxide poisoning, and death was foreseeable by the landlord's son, who was in charge of maintenance. In *R* v *Misra and Srivastava* (2004), where two doctors were convicted of gross negligence manslaughter after a patient died from toxic shock syndrome (where a simple course of antibiotics would have saved his life), the Court of Appeal confirmed this test — that the risk to which the victim must be exposed is the risk of death. In *R* v *Brown* (2005), the Privy Council even suggested that only a very high risk of death would suffice.

This decision clarifies one of the major problems with the speech of Lord Mackay LC in *Adomako*. It requires the risk in respect of which the defendant was negligent to be one of death rather than any lesser degree of harm. If the defendant is reckless to a lesser degree of harm but does cause a victim's death, this may amount to reckless manslaughter — a category of manslaughter that Lord Mackay left open.

Examples of duty-of-care situations are doctor–patient and landlord–tenant. In *R* v *Becker* (Court of Appeal, unreported), the defendant was a doctor on an emergency house call. The victim was suffering from severe pain resulting from a kidney stone, and the defendant prescribed a painkiller, having made a correct diagnosis. However, the painkiller did not work fast enough and the defendant decided to prescribe an opiate as well. Though the victim indicated that the pain had now eased, the defendant went ahead with the injection of diamorphine (30 mg). The victim died later that day from the overdose. The defendant was convicted of gross negligence manslaughter. At the trial, it was common ground that the injection of that quantity of the drug (about three times the largest permissible dose) was conduct falling below the standard expected of a reasonably competent GP. The sole issue for the jury had been whether that amounted to gross negligence.

It would appear from *R* v *Khan and Khan* (1998) that judges are reluctant to extend the areas where there could be a duty of care. In this case, the defendants supplied a prostitute with twice the amount of heroin likely to be taken by a regular user. They left her unconscious in a flat, returning on the next day to discover she had died from the overdose. The trial judge invited the jury to consider liability of the basis of the defendants' failure to summon medical assistance. However, the conviction was quashed on appeal because the defendants had not accepted a duty of care.

It is now settled law that the issue of whether there is a duty of care is one for the jury, not the judge, to decide, as in *R* v *Willoughby* (2004). In this case, the defendant set fire to his business premises to solve financial difficulties. The petrol he used as an accelerant caused an explosion, resulting in the death of the victim who had been helping him. The Court of Appeal held that the duty of care arose because the defendant had enlisted the help of the victim, not because he was the owner of the premises.

Breach of duty of care causing the death of the victim

The test for breach of duty is again that found in tort: the defendant's conduct must have fallen below the standard of care expected of a reasonable person. This requires the various risk factors to be considered, such as probability of death, cost of taking precautions etc. Note the second part of this rule — that the breach must have caused death. In examination answers, it is necessary to consider both the factual 'but for' rule and the legal rules of causation under criminal law.

Gross negligence

This is the fault element or *mens rea* for the offence. As can be seen from the *Hewart* and *Adomako* judgements, it is a question for the jury to decide. It must consider whether, having regard to the risk of death involved, the conduct of the defendant was so bad in all the circumstances as to amount in its judgement to a criminal act or omission.

In the case of *R* v *Adomako*, Lord Taylor CJ indicated that 'gross negligence' could include the following:

* indifference to an obvious risk of injury to health
* actual foresight of the risk coupled with the determination nevertheless to run it
* an appreciation of the risk coupled with an intention to avoid it, but with such a high degree of negligence in the attempted avoidance that the jury considers conviction justified
* inattention or failure to address a serious risk, which went beyond 'mere inadvertence' in respect of an obvious and important matter which the defendant's duty demanded he or she should address

In *Adomako*, the defendant was an anaesthetist during an eye operation. An oxygen tube became disconnected from the ventilator, which he failed to notice for 6 minutes, despite the patient turning blue through anoxia, the gas gauges on the anaesthetic machine oscillating wildly, and the audible warning signal which the machine emitted. An expert witness stated that this problem would have been obvious to any competent anaesthetist within 15 seconds. When this

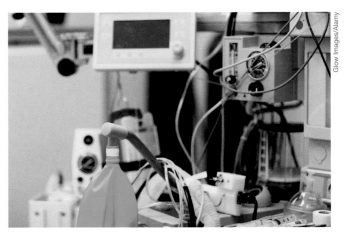

In *R* v *Adomako* (1995), the defendant anaesthetist failed to notice that an oxygen tube had become disconnected from the ventilator

case went to appeal, the House of Lords' ruling effectively returned this branch of the law to the traditional rules laid down in *Bateman* and *Andrews* v *DPP* (1937), after a 'wrong turn' had been taken in both *R* v *Lawrence* (1981) and *R* v *Seymour* (1983). In *Lawrence*, the defendant was convicted of causing death by reckless driving, and the Court of Appeal confirmed that objective (Caldwell) recklessness was sufficient for the conviction. Seymour was convicted of 'motor manslaughter', also on the grounds of objective recklessness.

Subjective reckless manslaughter

Following *R* v *Adomako*, it was believed that the category of reckless manslaughter no longer existed but had been absorbed by gross negligence manslaughter. However, in *R* v *Lidar* (1999), the Court of Appeal developed the current test for this type of involuntary manslaughter.

The defendant was the driver of a moving car onto which the victim was clinging while fighting with the defendant. The victim fell, and was killed when the car ran him over. The test for reckless manslaughter is whether the defendant was aware of a risk of death or serious injury and nonetheless proceeded unreasonably to take that risk — provided his or her action was the cause of death. The test for recklessness is subjective.

As Janet Loveless writes in *Complete Criminal Law* (2008, p. 303):

> *The main difficulty here is to distinguish recklessness from oblique intention. If you think back to* Hyam *for instance, in pouring paraffin through a letter-box and igniting it, the defendant foresaw a highly probable risk of death/GBH but no certainty. The court considered that such foresight was sufficient* mens rea *for murder… Now Mrs Hyam would be considered subjectively reckless and guilty of either reckless or unlawful and dangerous act manslaughter but not murder.*

Questions

Study the following brief scenarios. Explain which type of involuntary manslaughter the killer in each case may have committed.

1 John is a loader at an airport. He fails to close a cargo door properly and the door bursts open in flight, causing the plane to crash, killing all on board.

2 Sharon allows a dog she knows to be vicious to run loose in her garden. One day it escapes and savages a toddler, who dies.

3 Bill tries to grab an elderly lady's handbag; he doesn't know that she has it attached to a chain round her waist. He pulls her over and she fractures her skull and dies.

4 Fred and Jean have a 6-year-old child who is ill. Her condition is diagnosed as diabetes and the doctor advises an immediate course of insulin. The parents decide to seek help from a herbal doctor instead. After a short time, their child goes into a coma, from which she later dies.

5 Julian, a footballer, gets over-excited during a match and lunges wildly at the goalkeeper. The goalkeeper suffers a ruptured spleen, and dies while undergoing surgery.

6 Derek and William own a fishing boat. They hire a crew to take it on a trip, even though it has inadequate safety equipment and does not have a current certificate of seaworthiness. The previous crew refused to sail it because it was unseaworthy. The boat capsizes and all hands drown.

7 Alan is a lorry driver who has refused to pay maintenance to his ex-wife. One day she parks her car in front of his lorry and refuses to move until he agrees to pay. In a rage, he drives the lorry at the car, intending to push it out of the way. She is trapped between the vehicles and dies.

8 Jock, who is a doctor, has several drinks on New Year's Eve, even though he is on duty. As a result, he fails to recognise the symptoms of a serious illness, despite them being so obvious that a nurse is worried and asks him to examine the patient again. He refuses, and the patient dies. What difference would it make if the patient was already terminally ill and no treatment could have saved him?

9 Alan is a soldier in the Territorial Army. He picks up a rifle that has been left lying around during an exercise. When laid down by the soldier who had been using it, the rifle was switched to single-shot mode and the safety catch was on. Alan aims the rifle at a third soldier and pulls the trigger; *two* bullets kill him instantly. In evidence, Alan admits to 'fiddling with the safety catch'. He maintains that the shooting was an accident.

10 Ann and Linda run a café. They suspect that some of the food may be contaminated with salmonella. Because they are afraid they will lose business if they close the café to confirm the contamination, they continue to serve customers, one of whom contracts acute food poisoning and dies.

Sample exam question

Farrah, who is 14 years old, begins to receive notes through the post that contain drawings of dead bodies and statements such as 'This will be you'. In consequence, she becomes reluctant to leave the house and has to have specialist counselling for depression and panic attacks. Eventually, Farrah's mother, Gill, discovers that the notes are being sent by Isi, a girl in Farrah's class at school, and she goes round to confront Isi at her house. When she does so, a furious argument breaks out on the doorstep, during which Isi grabs Gill's hair and slaps her hard three or four times. Gill then manages to push Isi, who trips over the doorstep and falls backwards through a glass door panel, suffering deep cuts to her arm and face.

Isi's father, Jack, is angry about these events. While driving through town, he sees Farrah's 13-year-old brother, Karl, walking along the street. He rapidly brakes, forces Karl into the car and drives away into the countryside. When the car stops at a junction, Karl manages to jump out and run away. Jack panics and drives off, and so does not see that, almost immediately, Karl is struck by a car driven by Leon as it comes round a bend. Karl is thrown into a ditch and Leon drives away without stopping. Karl is not discovered until the next day, by which time he has died from his injuries.

Discuss the criminal liability of Jack and of Leon for the involuntary manslaughter of Karl.

Adapted from AQA Unit 4 paper, January 2008

Questions

1 What is the definition of involuntary manslaughter?

2 Which case confirmed that that the unlawful act must be a criminal offence?

3 What is the test for 'dangerousness'?

4 What rule is illustrated by *R v Dawson* (1985)?

5 Give two case examples of the 'dangerous' rule.

6 What is the *mens rea* for unlawful and dangerous act manslaughter?

7 What causation rule did *R v Goodfellow* (1986) establish?

8 Distinguish the cases of *Dalby* (1982) and *Cato* (1986).

9 Why was Kennedy's conviction quashed by the House of Lords?

10 What was Lord Hewart's definition of gross negligence in *R v Bateman* (1925)?

11 What test did *R v Singh* (1999) lay down?

12 In *R v Adomako* (1995), Lord Taylor CJ gave four examples of conduct that could constitute gross negligence. Which of these could be applied to *Adomako*?

13 Which case 're-established' reckless manslaughter?

14 What is the definition of reckless manslaughter?

Further reading

Ashworth, A. (1999) *Principles of Criminal Law* (3rd edn), Oxford University Press.

Elliott, C. and Quinn, F. (2006) *Criminal Law* (6th edn), Pearson Longman.

Loveless, J. (2008) *Complete Criminal Law*, Oxford University Press.

McAlhone, C. and Huxley-Binns, R. (2007) *Criminal Law: The Fundamentals*, Sweet & Maxwell.

Storey, T. and Lidbury, A. (2007) *Criminal Law*, Willan.

Chapter 5

General defences

From Chapter 1 on criminal liability, we know that offences (except those of strict liability) require both *actus reus* and *mens rea* to be proved. For murder, there are partial defences, such as provocation and diminished responsibility, which operate to reduce the conviction to one of voluntary manslaughter. This provides the judge with the opportunity to impose a lower tariff than the mandatory life sentence, to reflect the defendant's reduced level of fault.

The defence of consent, if successfully pleaded, negates the *actus reus* element of unlawfulness in any assault. However, this defence has restricted and controlled applications, and it is important to remember how limited it is. It only applies to non-fatal offences, and is therefore covered in Chapter 2.

This chapter explains the defences that can be used for *all* crimes: insanity, automatism, self-defence/prevention of crime, mistake and intoxication. These operate in different ways: some negate the *actus reus* or *mens rea*, others justify the defendant's actions or excuse him or her from liability.

In exam responses, if the question asks you to 'discuss the defendant's criminal liability', you must consider arguments for both the prosecution and the defence. Indeed, in some questions, especially those dealing with murder, defence material is often more important than explaining the offence.

Insanity

A defendant who argues that he or she was insane when the offence was committed may rely on the common-law defence of insanity, also referred to as insane automatism. If pleaded successfully, the defendant will be deemed 'not guilty by reason of insanity'. This amounts to an acquittal, but may result (and in murder cases *will* result) in a compulsory hospital treatment order being imposed under the **Criminal Procedure (Insanity) Act 1991**.

The **M'Naghten rules** were laid down by a committee of Law Lords following the case of *R* v *M'Naghten* (1843), where the defendant had attempted to kill the prime minister, Sir Robert Peel, but killed his secretary by mistake. His acquittal of murder on the grounds of insanity provoked controversy and was debated in the House of Lords, which sought the advice of judges. That advice became these famous rules, which have formed the basis of the defence ever since.

The starting point is that everyone is presumed sane, otherwise the burden would be too great if the prosecution had to prove a defendant's sanity or otherwise in every case. The rules continue that:

> *...to establish a defence on the ground of insanity, it must be clearly proved that, at the time of the committing of the act, the party accused was labouring under such a defect of reason, from disease of the mind, as not to know the nature and quality of the act he was doing, or, if he did know it, that he did not know he was doing what was wrong.*

As with the partial defence of diminished responsibility, the burden of proof rests on the defendant, and the standard of proof is 'on the balance of probabilities'.

There are two lines of defence open:

- The defendant must be acquitted if, because of a disease of the mind, he or she did not know the nature/quality of his or her act.
- Even if the defendant did know the nature/quality of his or her act, he or she must be acquitted if, because of a disease of the mind, he or she did not know it was 'wrong'.

Note that after the introduction of the partial defence of diminished responsibility under s.2 of the **Homicide Act 1957**, this defence became rare. However, in the 5 years following the operation of the **Criminal Procedure (Insanity) Act 1991**, there were 44 findings of 'not guilty by reason of insanity'.

It is often seen as a major flaw in the defence that the courts use a legal definition of insanity rather than a medical one. Smith and Hogan in *Criminal Law* (7th edition) write:

> *When a D puts his state of mind in issue, the question of whether he has raised the defence of insanity is one of law for the judge. Whether D, or indeed his medical witnesses would call the condition on which he relies 'insanity' is immaterial. The expert witnesses may testify as to the factual nature of the condition but it is for the judge to say whether that is evidence of a 'defect of reason from disease of the mind' because these are legal, not medical concepts.*

Disease of the mind

The term 'disease of the mind' does not only cover mental disorders; any disease that produces a malfunctioning of the mind falls into this category, including physical conditions such as arteriosclerosis (hardening of the arteries), a brain tumour, epilepsy, sleep-walking and diabetes. A malfunctioning of the mind is *not* a disease of the mind when it is caused by some external factor, such as a blow on the head causing concussion or the consumption of alcohol or drugs.

In *Bratty* v *Attorney General for Northern Ireland* (1963), the defendant strangled his victim during an epileptic seizure. In this case, Lord Denning stated that: 'It seems to me that any mental disorder which has manifested itself in violence and is prone to recur is a disease of the mind.'

In *R* v *Kemp* (1957), the defendant, who was suffering from arteriosclerosis, made a savage attack on his wife with a hammer. It was argued that his defect of reason arose from a purely physical condition and not from any mental disease. It was further argued that, if a physical disease caused the brain to degenerate, it would be a disease of the mind, but that otherwise the disorder was a temporary interference with the working of the brain, like concussion, and not a disease of the mind. Lord Devlin rejected this argument and ruled that the defendant was suffering from a disease of the mind:

The law is not concerned with the brain but with the mind, in the sense that 'mind' is ordinarily used, the mental faculties of reason, memory and understanding... In my judgement the condition of the brain is irrelevant and so is the question of whether the condition of the mind is curable or incurable, transitory or permanent.

Diabetes

This medical condition has given rise to a confusing and controversial situation; diabetes can lead to either insane or non-insane automatism, depending on the *cause* of the diabetic symptoms. The two cases of *R* v *Hennessy* (1989) and *R* v *Quick* (1973) can be compared.

In *Hennessy*, the diabetic defendant was charged with stealing a car and driving while disqualified. He pleaded (non-insane) automatism, claiming he had acted involuntarily, having forgotten to take his insulin due to stress, anxiety and depression. Consequently, he was suffering hyperglycaemia (high blood-sugar levels). The trial judge ruled that this condition was the result of diabetes, an internal cause of involuntary action, and that his defence was therefore insanity. To avoid detention in a mental institution, the defendant pleaded guilty, and

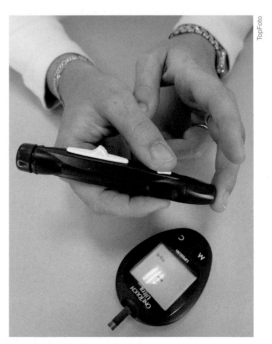

Diabetes can lead to either insane or non-insane automatism, depending on the cause of the symptoms

appealed on the grounds that his depression and anxiety (caused by relationship problems) were external factors that justified his defence as non-insane automatism. His appeal was dismissed; Lord Lane CJ stated that his stress and depression constituted a state of mind that was prone to recur.

In *Quick*, the defendant was a nurse convicted of assault occasioning actual bodily harm on a patient. The nurse had been diabetic since childhood and had taken his insulin that day. He had eaten a small breakfast but no lunch. He had no memory of the assault and pleaded not guilty on the basis of (non-insane) automatism and hypoglycaemia (low blood-sugar levels). Although the trial judge ruled that his condition was insanity because the diabetes was an internal disease of the mind, his appeal was successful as the Court of Appeal held that the cause of his involuntary action was not his underlying diabetes but the use of the insulin — an external factor.

Defect of reason

The basis of the M'Naghten rules is that the disease of the mind must have given rise to a defect of reason. This means that the defendant's powers of reasoning must have been impaired; a defendant who possesses those powers but fails to use them cannot be classed as insane.

An example is *R* v *Clarke* (1972), where the defendant was charged with theft after she took articles from a supermarket without paying for them. She claimed she was suffering from depression, which had caused her to become absent minded, and therefore did not remember putting the items in her bag. It was held that, even if she was suffering from a disease of the mind, she had not raised the defence of insanity but was simply denying that she had *mens rea*. She still possessed powers of reasoning but failed to use them on this occasion.

The concept of 'defect of reason' is vague and could apply to many people who are either forgetful or confused, but when allied to 'disease of the mind' it clearly indicates something more serious.

Not knowing the nature and quality of the act

The defendant must not have known what he or she was physically doing, and what the physical consequences of his or her actions would be. This issue concerns the physical, rather than the moral, nature of the act; it applies, for example, to the madman who cuts a victim's throat believing he is cutting a loaf of bread, or the nurse who throws a baby into a fire thinking it is a log. Persons who kill under such delusions cannot be convicted of murder, as they lack the required *mens rea*.

Knowledge that the act was wrong

It is established law that this means legally wrong, not morally wrong. Even if the defendant did not know that his or her action was against the law, he or she will still be liable if he or she knew it was wrong 'according to the ordinary standard adopted by reasonable men'. In the case of *R* v *Windle* (1952), the defendant killed his wife, who was certifiably insane and who was always speaking of committing suicide. He then phoned the police, and when he was arrested said: 'I suppose they will hang me for this.' At his trial, the defence of insanity was not allowed to go to the jury since the words he used indicated that he knew killing his wife was legally wrong. Research by Mackay, Mitchell and Howe ('Yet more facts about the insanity defence') in *Criminal Law Review* (2007, p. 399) suggests that psychiatrists have extended this limb of the defence to include situations where, although the defendant recognised his or her actions were unlawful, he or she thought they were morally justified.

Automatism

Criminal responsibility generally requires voluntary conduct on the part of the defendant. However, when pleading the defence of automatism, the defendant claims that his or her actions were involuntary and beyond his or her control. Typical examples are sleepwalking, acts carried out in a hypnotic trance, reflex actions and convulsions.

The rationale for this defence is clear: the defendant in such a situation is not responsible for the consequences of his or her actions. The act is, in a sense, not his or her own. He or she does not deserve to be punished, nor would punishment serve any useful or rational purpose. Although automatism has been referred to as a 'defence', it is more accurate to say that a basic ingredient of criminal liability is the voluntary nature of the *actus reus*. The onus, therefore, is on the prosecution to prove beyond reasonable doubt that the acts of the defendant were voluntary. Note, however, that the prosecution only has to do this if the defendant has laid an evidential foundation (generally of a medical type) that he or she was an automaton at the relevant time.

Lord Denning in *Bratty* v *Attorney General for Northern Ireland* (1963) stated:

The requirement that it should be a voluntary act is essential...in every criminal case. No act is punishable if it is done involuntarily; and an involuntary act in this context — some people...prefer to speak of it as 'automatism' — means an act which is done by the muscles without any control by the mind such as a spasm, a reflex action or a convulsion; or an act done by a person who is not conscious of what he is doing, such as an act done whilst suffering from concussion or whilst sleepwalking.

He went on to stress that an act is not to be regarded as involuntary if the person was conscious of what he or she was doing but nevertheless could not control his or her actions (irresistible impulse), or could not remember after the event exactly what had taken place.

In *Broome* v *Perkins* (1987), the defendant was charged with driving without due care and attention. He drove the vehicle erratically for some 6 miles. It was held that even though there was some evidence to establish that he was suffering from hypo-glycaemia, he must have been exercising conscious control of the vehicle even though imperfectly, in order to have manoeuvred it reasonably successfully over such a distance. See also *Attorney General's Reference No. 2* (1992), where the defence of 'partial awareness' was disallowed by the Court of Appeal. Both these cases emphasised the need for total loss of control; however, it has also been suggested that effective loss of control would suffice (Law Commission Draft Criminal Code).

Note that where the defendant has been aware that he or she might lose conscious control of his or her actions, the defence is likely to be rejected by the jury, assuming that an adequate evidential foundation has been laid.

Insane automatism

If the automatism results from a 'disease of the mind' under the M'Naghten rules, the condition amounts to what in law is known as insanity. In such circumstances, the defendant is entitled to a qualified acquittal by the special verdict of 'not guilty by reason of insanity', and the judge must make one of various orders under the **Criminal Procedure (Insanity) Act 1991**.

In *Bratty*, it was held, following *R* v *Kemp*, that if the defendant leads evidence of automatism, the prosecution is allowed to lead evidence that the condition giving rise to the automatism is a 'disease of the mind' and that the defendant is entitled only to a qualified acquittal. If the trial judge agrees, from the evidence, that the condition is a disease of the mind, he or she is entitled to refuse to let the defence of non-insane automatism go to the jury. In these circumstances, he or she must instruct the jury that insanity is the only defence available.

As seen above for insanity, any disease that impairs the functioning of the mind may amount to a 'disease'. It does not matter whether the cause of the impairment is organic, as in epilepsy, or functional, as in schizophrenia. Nor does it matter whether the impairment is permanent, or transient and intermittent, provided that it was operative at the time of the alleged offence. In *R* v *Sullivan* (1983), the defendant was charged with s.47 actual bodily harm (ABH) after he attacked his victim while recovering from a minor epileptic seizure and did not know what he was doing. The House of Lords held that the trial judge was correct when he ruled that this raised the defence of insanity.

Non-insane automatism

This requires that an *external* cause induced the automatism, such as concussion resulting from a blow to the head or a reflex spasm (as in the hypothetical example given in *Hill* v *Baxter* (1958), of being stung by bees). This test has given rise to results that have been criticised as unjust, as in cases of epilepsy and sleepwalking, which would have to be considered as forms of insane automatism. Diabetes (discussed above) has been the subject of particular criticism, where, depending on whether the diagnosis is hypo- or hyperglycaemia, the defence is judged to be non-insane or insane automatism respectively. In *Quick*, the defendant who took his insulin but failed to eat was able to plead non-insane automatism, but in *Hennessy*, the defendant who failed to take sufficient insulin was held to have the defence of insane automatism (which caused him to change his plea to guilty).

In *R* v *T* (1990), the application of the internal/external-factor test led to a just and fair decision. The defendant, who suffered from post-traumatic stress disorder as a consequence of being raped, stabbed the victim during a robbery. The trial judge ruled that the stress had been caused by the external factor of the rape and accordingly the defence was that of non-insane automatism.

Note that where the defendant's automatism has been caused by the consumption of alcohol or dangerous drugs, the defence becomes intoxication.

Self-defence/prevention of crime

In *R* v *Palmer* (1971), Lord Morris stated:

> *Where an attack of a violent, unlawful or indecent nature is made so that the person under attack fears for his life or safety of his person from injury etc., then the person is entitled to protect himself and to repel such attack by force, provided that he uses no more force than is reasonable in the circumstances.*

There is a common-law right of self-defence, as well as the right enshrined in s.3 of the **Criminal Law Act 1967**, which states:

> *A person may use such force as is reasonable in the circumstances in the prevention of crime, or in effecting or assisting in the lawful arrest of offenders/suspected offenders or of persons unlawfully at large.*

Note that the common law and s.3 may overlap, as the use of reasonable force in defending oneself from a murderous assault is also preventing a crime. The statutory defence is wider, however, because it entitles the defendant to use force to prevent any crime, including property offences. Where it is justified, self-defence can provide a complete defence to charges of murder or any non-fatal offence. It operates by negating the unlawfulness of the homicide/assault by in effect rendering the circumstances that surround the act not unlawful.

As Janet Loveless points out in *Complete Criminal Law* (2008, p. 423), the general requirement is that:

> *...defensive force will only be lawful if it is necessary, and it will only be necessary if it is used to resist, repel or ward off an unjust imminent threat. The act of self-defence cannot be retaliatory or revengeful.*

The jury rejected Tony Martin's plea of self-defence after he shot dead an intruder

An attack at some future point will not be sufficiently imminent — this means 'fairly immediate'.

The second requirement is that the degree of force must be reasonable. Excessive force is usually evidence that the killing was retaliatory and therefore not in self-defence, as in *R* v *Martin* (2001). In that case, the defendant was a farmer living in an isolated Norfolk farmhouse who shot at two teenage burglars who had entered his house, killing one and injuring the other. At his trial, the jury rejected his plea of self-defence. At his appeal to the Court of Appeal, Lord Wool CJ ruled that the jury was entitled to reject his plea if it thought he had used an unreasonable amount of force.

Factors that may be taken into account in determining what is reasonable force in the context of both common-law and statutory defences are:

❖ the nature and degree of force used
❖ the gravity of the crime or evil to be prevented
❖ the relative strength of the parties concerned and the number of persons involved

The law does not require 'proportionate' force, but the degree of force must be capable of being seen as only as great as is necessary to repel an attack. In *R* v *Scarlett* (1993), a pub landlord was charged with manslaughter following his forceful ejection of a drunk man from his pub. The drunk, described as a 'large, heavily built man', arrived shortly after closing time, and the landlord told him to leave. The victim refused to leave and tried to punch the defendant, who then bundled the victim towards the door. What happened next was disputed: the prosecution argued that the defendant pushed the victim down some stairs using excessive force. The victim hit his head on the pavement and suffered fatal injuries. Although convicted of manslaughter, Beldam LJ stated that the defendant's appeal was allowed on the basis that:

> *...the jury ought not to convict unless they are satisfied that the degree of force used was plainly more than was called for by the circumstances as they believed them to be.*

The concept of reasonable force, by definition, requires an element of objectivity. That is, in order to reject it as a defence, the jury must be satisfied that no reasonable person put in the position of the defendant, with the time for reflection that was available in the actual case, would consider the violence used by the defendant to be justifiable. However, this objectivity must be tempered by the personal situation of the actual defendant. The test is whether or not the defendant's use of force was reasonable in the 'agony of the situation', and not whether it would be considered reasonable by the defendant or a reasonable person viewing the situation in cool isolation.

In *R* v *Owino* (1995), the Court of Appeal confirmed that when the jury assesses whether the amount of force was reasonable, the jury members should put themselves in the situation that the defendant supposed (rightly or wrongly, reasonably or unreasonably) to exist. The test of reasonableness is therefore both objective *and* subjective. In this case, the defendant was convicted of causing ABH to his wife. He argued that he had acted in self-defence, and that his wife's injuries were caused by his use of reasonable force to restrain her from assaulting him. Although the trial judge directed the jury that the prosecution must prove that the defendant did not believe he was using reasonable force, the Court of Appeal held that the correct statement of the law is that a person may use such force as is (objectively) reasonable in the circumstances as he or she (subjectively) believes them to be.

In *R* v *Whyte* (1987), Lord Lane CJ stated:

> ...in most cases...the jury should be reminded that the defendant's...view of the danger threatening him at the time of the incident is material. The test of reason-ableness is not...a purely objective test.

Further points to consider

- ❖ Where the defendant has used excessive (and therefore unreasonable) force, neither common-law nor statutory defences are open to him or her, and his or her criminal liability will be determined by his or her *mens rea* and the harm he or she has inflicted.
- ❖ The law has no sympathy with people who are drunk. An honest mistake made by a drunken defendant will render a plea of self-defence inadmissible (as in *R* v *O'Grady* (1987), where the voluntarily intoxicated defendant killed his friend when retaliating to his friend hitting him).
- ❖ It was held in *R* v *Bird* (1985) that proof that the defendant tried to retreat was a method of showing that the defendant was not an attacker, but not the only method. The defendant in this case retaliated to her ex-boyfriend hitting her, lashing out while forgetting she had a glass in her hand. The trial judge said that she could only rely on self-defence if she had shown an unwillingness to fight. The

Court of Appeal disagreed, and decided that there may be situations when the defendant might react immediately without retreating. This matter was for the jury to consider. This established that the defendant is not under a duty to retreat and may strike first in self-defence.

❖ It also appears that in certain circumstances a person is not obliged to wait until he or she is attacked before taking steps to protect himself or herself. In *R v Beckford* (1988), Lord Griffiths said: 'A man about to be attacked does not have to wait for the assailant to strike the first blow — circumstances may justify a pre-emptive strike.' This confirmed the decision in *Attorney General's Reference No. 2* (1983), where the defendant's shop had been attacked by rioters. Fearing further attacks, he made petrol bombs and was then charged with possessing an explosive substance. He pleaded self-defence, which the jury accepted. On a reference appeal by the Attorney General, the Court of Appeal confirmed that this was correct.

❖ As regards the defence of property, the use of force is not so highly regarded, so this defence is limited. Professor Ashworth comments in *Principles of Criminal Law* (2006; p. 143):

> *What is crucial is that it should rule out the infliction or risk of considerable physical harm merely to apprehend a fleeing thief, to stop minor property loss or damage, etc… The proper approach is to compare the relative value of the rights involved, and not to give special weight to the rights of the property owner simply because the other party is in the wrong (i.e. committing a crime).*

Mistake

The defence of mistake can be relevant in two contexts. First, in most cases of mistake, the defendant argues that it negates the *mens rea* required for the crime. It is clearly established that the mistake must be one of fact and not of law if it is to afford a defence. This is shown in *R v Reid* (1973), for example, where a driver refused to take a breath test because he mistakenly believed the policeman had no right to require him to do so. The defence was disallowed on the ground that ignorance of law cannot amount to a mistake.

Second, within self-defence, it must be noted that if the defendant honestly but mistakenly believed himself or herself to be under attack, he or she must be judged according to his or her mistaken view of the facts, regardless of whether the mistake was reasonable or not. In *R v Williams* (1984), a passer-by called Mason saw a youth rob a woman. He chased after the man and knocked him to the ground. At this point, the defendant came on the scene. He had not seen the earlier robbery and mistakenly thought that Mason was the attacker. Mason told the defendant that he

was a police officer (which was untrue) and that he was arresting the youth. The defendant asked to see the warrant card, and when this could not be produced, a struggle ensued, during which the defendant punched Mason in the face. In his defence, he claimed that he honestly believed Mason was unlawfully assaulting the youth and that he was trying to rescue him. He was convicted of s.47 ABH following a direction to the jury that his mistake would only be relevant if it was honest and based on reasonable grounds. On appeal, Lord Lane CJ stated:

> *The reasonableness or unreasonableness of the D's belief is material to the question of whether the belief was held by the D at all. If the belief was in fact held, its unreasonableness, so far as guilt or innocence is concerned, is neither here nor there. It is irrelevant... The jury should be directed first of all that the prosecution have the burden of proving the unlawfulness of the D's actions; secondly, if the D may have been labouring under a mistake as to the facts, he must be judged according to his mistaken view of the facts, and thirdly, that is so whether the mistake was, on an objective view, a reasonable mistake or not... Even if the jury come to the conclusion that the mistake was an unreasonable one, if the D may genuinely have been labouring under it, he is entitled to rely on it.*

The Judicial Studies Board has produced a model direction on self-defence, which states the following:

> *Whether the plea is self-defence or defence of another, if the D may have been labouring under a mistake as to the facts, he must be judged according to his mistaken view of the facts: that is so whether the mistake was, on an objective view, a reasonable mistake or not.*

Intoxication

Students often find this defence difficult to deal with, as the way in which it operates, if it operates at all, depends on:

❖ whether the intoxication is voluntary or involuntary
❖ whether it is by alcohol and illegal drugs or by sedative/prescribed drugs
❖ whether the particular offence charged is an offence of basic or specific intent

The first general rule to learn is that, as Smith and Hogan write in *Criminal Law* (1999, p. 219):

> *Intoxication is not, and never has been, a defence in itself. It is never a defence for D to say, however convincingly, that but for the drink he would not have behaved as he did. Because alcohol and other drugs weaken the restraints and inhibitions which normally govern our conduct, a man may do things when drunk that he*

would never dream of doing when sober. If, however, he had the mens rea *for the crime charged he is guilty, even though drink impaired or negatived his ability to judge between right and wrong or to resist temptation or provocation and even though, in his drunken state, he found the impulse to act as he did irresistible.*

Voluntary intoxication by alcohol or illegal drugs

The legal rule is that voluntary intoxication is, at best, only a partial defence to offences of specific intent, i.e. those crimes for which the only *mens rea* is intention, such as murder and s.18 malicious wounding/causing grievous bodily harm with intent. That intention also has to be directed at achieving a particular end result ('ulterior intent'). Following the leading case of *DPP* v *Beard* (1920), if the defendant is able prove that at the time of committing the crime he or she was so drunk as to be unable to form the necessary *mens rea* of intent for the crime, he or she will be acquitted of that offence. He or she will instead be convicted of the basic intent offence (which can be committed with intention *or* recklessness).

So, if the defendant is charged with murder and successfully pleads intoxication, he or she may be charged with the basic intent crime of manslaughter instead. If the defendant is not guilty of s.18 OAPA due to voluntary intoxication, he or she may be guilty of s.20 OAPA instead. That rule has been slightly relaxed: it is now firmly accepted that the defendant need not be *incapable* of forming the required specific intent — it is sufficient if he or she does not *do* so.

In *DPP* v *Majewski* (1977), this approach was confirmed. The defendant was charged with the assault of a policeman — an offence of basic intent — and his defence of drunkenness was rejected. Lord Elwyn-Jones LC said that 'self-induced intoxication, however gross and even if it has produced a condition akin to automatism, cannot excuse crimes of basic intent such as assault'. He also stated that 'his course of conduct in reducing himself by drink to that condition...supplies the evidence of *mens rea* certainly sufficient for crimes of basic intent'. In other words, the recklessness required for basic intent crimes is derived from the defendant's recklessness in voluntarily becoming drunk.

As for intoxication by illegal drugs, the same position applies. The leading case is *R* v *Lipman* (1970), where the defendant killed his girlfriend. Having taken a quantity of LSD and believing as a result that he was being attacked by snakes, he killed the girl, cramming a sheet into her mouth. At his trial, he was acquitted of murder, but his plea of intoxication was not accepted as a defence to manslaughter. The Court of Appeal stated that when the killing results from an unlawful act of the defendant, no specific intent has to be proved to convict of manslaughter. Self-induced intoxication is no defence, and since the acts complained of were obviously likely to cause harm to the victim, the verdict of manslaughter was inevitable.

Voluntary intoxication using sedative drugs

If the defendant has an unexpected reaction to drugs that normally have a sedative or soporific (sleep-inducing) effect, he or she will usually be treated as being involuntarily intoxicated. In *R* v *Hardie* (1984), the defendant took Valium tablets prescribed for the woman with whom he shared a flat, and then started a fire when she asked him to leave. He was charged and convicted under the **Criminal Damage Act 1971**. However, the Court of Appeal, quashing this conviction, overturned the trial judge's direction to the jury because he had not mentioned the distinction the law draws between dangerous/illegal and prescription/sedative drugs. Parker LJ stated:

> *Valium…is wholly different from drugs which are liable to cause unpredictability or aggressiveness…if the effect of a drug is merely soporific or sedative the taking of it, even in some excessive quantity, cannot in the ordinary way raise a conclusive presumption against the admission of proof of intoxication such as would be the case with alcoholic intoxication or incapacity resulting from the self-administration of dangerous drugs.*

Of course, there could be situations where the defendant does realise that the sedative drug, instead of calming him or her down, might cause 'aggressive or unpredictable conduct'. If the jury believes that this is the case, and that the defendant went on to take that risk, he or she could be found to have acted recklessly.

Involuntary intoxication

This deals with the situation where the defendant claims not to have known that he or she was taking alcohol or an intoxicating drug, as in cases where food or drink is laced without the defendant's knowledge. The legal rule here is that, if this negates the *mens rea* of the offence, it will provide a full defence to any offence, whether one of specific or basic intent. For either type of offence, the defendant is not automatically acquitted, but is entitled to have the evidence of intoxication considered. If the intoxication negatives *mens rea*, the defendant may be acquitted; if not, he or she remains liable, even though the defendant would not have acted in such a way if he or she remained sober.

This is illustrated in the difficult case of *R* v *Kingston* (1994), where the defendant was attracted to young boys. His co-defendant, a business associate, set out to blackmail him and invited him round to his flat. Once there, the defendant's drink was spiked and he was taken to a room where a 15-year-old boy was asleep and told to abuse him. The defendant did so, and the associate photographed the attack. His defence to a charge of indecent assault was that the involuntary intoxication effectively disinhibited him, and that, if sober, he would not have carried out these acts. The Court of Appeal allowed his appeal, holding that if a surreptitiously administered drug causes a person to lose his or her self-control and so form an intent he or she would not otherwise have formed, the law should not hold him or her liable, as the operative fault is not his or hers. This novel argument was rejected by the House of Lords, which approved the trial judge's direction to the jury that an intoxicated intent was still intent, and the fact that the intoxication was involuntary made no difference.

Intoxication causing insanity or abnormality of mind

It is settled law that where excessively heavy drinking causes actual insanity, such as the condition of *delirium tremens*, then the M'Naghten rules apply and the defence becomes one of insanity.

Another point concerns the issue of abnormality of mind, which gives rise to the possible (partial) defence to murder of diminished responsibility (**Homicide Act 1956**, s.2). It is clear that self-induced intoxication must be ignored in deciding whether the defendant was suffering from such an abnormality of mind as to amount to diminished responsibility, unless it can be proved either that the defendant suffered from alcohol dependency syndrome, which caused an abnormality of mind, or that the craving for drink or drugs was itself an abnormality of mind (see *R v Wood*, 2008, and *R v Dietschmann*, 2003, both discussed in Chapter 3).

'Dutch courage'

If a defendant deliberately gets intoxicated in order to give himself or herself 'Dutch courage' to commit a crime, his or her self-induced intoxication will not be a defence to any crime. This was confirmed in *Attorney General for Northern Ireland v Gallagher* (1963), where the defendant decided to kill his wife. He bought a knife and a bottle of whisky, which he drank to provide him with Dutch courage, and then stabbed her to death. He was convicted of murder, as the jury believed that he had the required specific intent at the time of the stabbing. On appeal, Lord Denning, in *obiter dictum* remarks, considered that even if the defendant were too drunk to form that specific intent when he stabbed his wife, he still would not be able to use his voluntary intoxication as a defence, even to reduce the level of conviction to manslaughter.

Sample exam question

Early one morning, Alan is standing on a stepladder, washing the windows of his house with a powerful detergent solution. Bob and Chris come walking noisily up the street, having spent all night out, drinking alcohol. Bob shouts something and suddenly veers across the street in Alan's direction, followed by Chris, who is trying to take hold of his arm. Alan is convinced that Bob is coming to knock him off the ladder, and quickly gets down and throws the bucket of detergent solution over Bob. Some of the solution also goes over Chris, causing him to suffer an extreme allergic reaction, which requires hospital treatment for damage to the skin on his face. In fact, though very drunk, Bob merely wanted to have a friendly talk to Alan.

Adapted from AQA Unit 4 paper, January 2008

1 Explain whether Bob could plead intoxication in relation to the above incident.

2 Explain whether Alan could plead self-defence in relation to the above incident.

Further reading

Smith, J. C. and Hogan, B. (1999) *Criminal Law*, chapter 10, Butterworths.

Chapter **6**

Evaluation of criminal law

In Unit 3, part (c) examination questions ask you to criticise or evaluate a particular area of criminal law, such as murder (including provocation and diminished responsibility), non-fatal offences, or defences. The same question is asked in both scenarios; there is no choice of questions as in the previous specification.

Be aware of the difference between criticism and evaluation: criticism asks 'what is wrong with this area of law?'; evaluation, while requiring a well-explained analysis of weaknesses in the law, also requires you to consider which aspects of that law are broadly satisfactory, and then give a reasoned conclusion. Do not simply repeat the rules of law that you have already explained or applied in earlier answers. Ideally, you should suggest improvements or reforms that address some of the criticisms, especially the recommendations of the Law Commission. However, do not be afraid to include your own ideas, especially if these are based on topical debates.

This type of answer requires careful planning, both in terms of content and how long you should spend writing. These questions comprise a third of the overall marks for the paper, and you should allocate your time accordingly.

Non-fatal offences

Criticisms

Terminology

Non-fatal offences are poorly defined. There are no clear statutory definitions of assault and battery, while the definitions of the more serious offences are contained

in an Act passed well over 100 years ago, described by Lord Lane CJ in *R* v *Williams* (1987) as:

> *...a rag-bag of offences brought together from a wide variety of sources with no attempt, as the draftsman frankly acknowledged, to introduce consistency as to substance or as to form.*

Much of the vocabulary is old-fashioned and even misleading. 'Assault', for example, is commonly understood to involve some form of physical attack, whereas it is technically defined as causing a victim to *apprehend* some form of attack. However, for a s.47 offence — assault occasioning actual bodily harm — in the vast majority of cases, the assault is actually battery.

The offence of battery is also misleading, insofar as there is no need for there to be any injury, and, until the case of *Wilson* v *Pringle* (1986), there was no requirement that the touching or contact was hostile. This considerably widened the extent of this offence.

The word 'maliciously', used in both s.20 and s.18 offences, creates further problems. In s.18, 'maliciously' means nothing in its primary use, because the *mens rea* is already defined as 'with intent'. In s.20, however, the same word means recklessness or basic intent as to inflicting some harm.

The word 'wounding' also has a technical rather than common definition. Although the Joint Charging Standards substantially clarify which charge to bring for different levels of injury, nonetheless any injury that penetrates both layers of skin could potentially be charged as wounding, irrespective of its seriousness.

Actus reus

The accepted definition of assault refers to an apprehension of 'immediate' unlawful personal violence, but there are problems in interpreting this concept of immediacy. In *Smith* v *Superintendent of Woking Police* (1983), it was held on appeal that an assault had been committed where the victim was frightened by seeing a man looking at her through a window, although there was little evidence that the defendant was in any way threatening to use force against her.

The case of *Logdon* v *DPP* (1976) also seems to suggest a broad interpretation, where the defendant showed a replica gun to the victim. Despite not handling the gun or pointing it at the victim, the defendant was still held to have committed an assault.

The offence of battery appears to be more satisfactory, particularly since it is now accepted that the application of force must be hostile. Also, although the *actus reus* does not require there to be any injury, the Joint Charging Standards make it clear that some minor harm should have been caused, such as reddening of the skin or a graze.

In the past, the use of the words 'inflict' in s.20 and 'cause' in s.18 was criticised. It has been argued that 'inflict' requires a battery to take place for the full offence to be committed. This was the central issue raised in the case of *R* v *Burstow* (1997; psychiatric injury), which was decided by the House of Lords after the Court of Appeal had certified the question as to whether an offence of inflicting grievous bodily harm under s.20 could be committed where no physical violence was applied directly or indirectly. Here, it was argued that it is inherent in the word 'inflict' that there must be some application of force to the body. Lord Steyn, in the leading judgement, ruled that 'there is no radical difference between the meaning of the words "cause" and "inflict"'. Lord Hope went even further when he stated: 'For all practical purposes there is, in my opinion, no difference between these two words.'

Another *actus reus* problem is that wounding can be sufficient for a s.20 offence. It is clearly unhelpful and confusing that a minor cut that could be treated as ABH could technically result in a s.20 offence, when compared to the much more serious level of injury required for GBH. There could be a complete lack of balance between the respective elements of 'wounding' and 'inflicting grievous bodily harm'.

In its 1991 report on reform of non-fatal offences, the Law Commission recommended that a serious wound should be included within a new offence of causing serious harm.

Mens rea

Possibly the most serious criticism that can be directed against the present law on non-fatal offences is the issue of constructive intent — what the Law Commission refers to as 'the lack of coherence in sections 20 and 47 between the consequences for which the accused is punished and the mental state that is sufficient for his conviction'. In both these offences, the defendant is liable to a possible 5-year sentence, more because of the outcome of the offence (which, in many cases, will have been unforeseen and unintended) than the degree of *mens rea*. This runs counter to the basic requirement that criminal liability should depend on and reflect the amount of fault possessed by the defendant.

In s.20, for example, the defendant who foresees only minor physical harm is nevertheless criminally liable for causing serious harm that may have been quite unforeseeable. So, for example, the defendant could roughly push someone aside in the street, but if the victim then stumbled over a crack in the pavement, fell over and broke an arm, the defendant could be convicted of a s.20 GBH offence.

In a s.47 offence, the accused only has to foresee any physical contact; the actual bodily harm for which he or she is convicted and punished could easily have been caused unforeseeably. Thus in *Savage* (1991), the defendant would have been liable

even if it had been proved that the injury to the victim occurred only because of an entirely unforeseeable weakness that caused the glass to splinter.

One further problem, this time in s.18, concerns the issue of proving intent to cause serious psychiatric injury. The decision in *Burstow* (1998) created the opportunity for both sections 18 and 20 to include serious psychiatric injury, but it is difficult for prosecutors to establish that the defendant intended to cause such injury. After all, it is usually only possible for the prosecution to establish the specific intent to cause physical GBH if the defendant has used a weapon, and that method would not be available for psychiatric injury.

Sentencing

The hierarchy of the non-fatal offences according to seriousness can also be criticised. While assault and battery are punished with a maximum of 6 months' imprisonment, s.47 ABH receives a custodial sentence of up to 5 years. However, the only real difference between the offences is that actual bodily harm is caused, yet this can mean as little as causing discomfort to the person.

Further, the s.20 offence is defined as much more serious than s.47, in both its *actus reus* and *mens rea,* and yet they share the same maximum sentence. This was described by Professor Clarkson in 'Violence and the Law Commission' (*Criminal Law Review* 324, 1994) as 'a serious distortion of the relative seriousness of the offences'. Although it is accepted judicial practice that the maximum sentence is rarely imposed, and then only for the most severe offence, it remains manifestly unfair that the s.47 and s.20 maximum sentences are identical, when both the *actus reus* and the *mens rea* required for a s.20 conviction are much greater.

Another problem is that arguably the only significant difference between s.20 and s.18 is a slightly more serious *mens rea*, yet the maximum sentence leaps from 5 years to life. While there are many reasons for this, one clear factor is the difficulty in proving the required specific intention for s.18. This can perhaps be justified by the fact that a defendant who intends to cause GBH within s.18 has the *mens rea* of murder; it is merely chance that dictates whether the victim of a stabbing survives or dies.

Development of statutory offences through case law

The final criticism concerning the present state of the law on non-fatal offences is how statutory offences in the **Offences Against the Person Act 1861** are redefined through reported cases.

It is extraordinary that the *mens rea* for both s.47 and s.20 offences had to be defined as a result of case law. In s.47, there is no *mens rea* stated at all, and for s.20, the only *mens rea* reference is the word 'malicious', which has had to be interpreted by courts.

It is unsatisfactory for so many changes (including basic definitions) to be made to statutory offences by means of case law, which by its nature can be amended by later cases being appealed to the Court of Appeal or the House of Lords. This is both an unnecessary and expensive appeals process, arising from wrong decisions on questions of law. In its consultation document, the Law Commission stated that 'in recent years, the attempts of the courts at appellate level to elucidate the 1861 Act have led to a series of inconsistent or contradictory decisions'.

The cases of *Burstow* and *Ireland* (1998) have considerably extended the law on assault and s.20 GBH, and *Dica* (2004) seems to have created a further major extension to the definition of GBH. In this case, the defendant, who knowingly had HIV, was convicted of causing biological GBH when he tricked two women into having unprotected sexual intercourse with him.

As described in Chapter 2 (page 17), the *Dica* ruling in the Court of Appeal clearly overruled the case of *R v Clarence* (1888), where a husband was prosecuted for infecting his unsuspecting wife with gonorrhoea. His conviction was quashed by a House of Lords ruling that s.20 required an assault or some form of direct bodily violence.

the box studio/Alamy

The case of *R v Smith* (2006), where the defendant cut off his ex-girlfriend's ponytail, resulted in an expensive appeal to the Queen's Bench Divisional Court, following his acquittal by magistrates, to determine whether this could constitute ABH. The court decided this was ABH, and the case then had to be remitted back to the Magistrates' Court with a direction to convict.

In *R v Smith* (2006), the defendant who cut off his ex-girlfriend's ponytail was convicted of ABH

Proposed law reform

The Draft Criminal Law Bill, issued by the Home Office in 1998 (and based on the Law Commission's 1991 recommendations), updates the language used for non-fatal offences by referring to 'serious injury' rather than 'grievous bodily harm', and avoiding the words 'maliciously' and 'wounding' altogether.

Under the bill, s.18 is replaced by 'intentionally causing serious injury' (maximum sentence: life); s.20 by 'recklessly causing serious injury' (maximum sentence: 7 years); and s.47 by 'intentionally or recklessly causing injury' (maximum sentence: 5 years). However, the bill continues to use the term 'assault' for the two separate offences of assault and battery.

Murder

It is evident that our existing homicide laws are in urgent need of reform when even Ken Macdonald QC, a former Director of Public Prosecutions, has criticised them — and has been echoed in turn by most senior judges. In an interview in *The Times*, Mr Macdonald proposed that there should be degrees of homicide, 'not just murder and manslaughter, but three or four degrees'. The government has acknowledged this and asked the Law Commission to widen its approach from just examining the law on provocation to considering the whole law on homicide. In its 2004 report on partial defences to murder, the Law Commission itself described the law of murder as 'a mess'.

Criticisms

Structure

In its report on murder, manslaughter and infanticide (LAW COM 304), the Law Commission frankly acknowledged:

> The law governing homicide in England and Wales is a rickety structure set upon shaky foundations. Some of its rules have remained unaltered since the seventeenth century, even though it has long been acknowledged that they are in dire need of reform. Other rules are of uncertain content, often because they have been constantly changed to the point that they can no longer be stated with any certainty or clarity. At the end of the nineteenth century there was a valuable attempt at wholesale reform. This was thwarted largely by quite unconnected political problems. The consequence was that the Homicide Bill did not progress beyond its second reading in Parliament. Moreover, certain piecemeal reforms effected by Parliament, although valuable at the time, are now beginning to show their age or have been overtaken by other legal changes and, yet, have been left unreformed.

For such a critical statement to be made about any offence would be serious enough; for it to be directed at the most serious of all offences is almost incredible.

In England and Wales, murder has never been a statutory offence but has instead been developed by judges over centuries through case law, with 'each new case sometimes generating further case law to resolve ambiguities left behind by the last one' (Law Commission).

Until the present government asked the Law Commission to examine this offence in 2005, it had never been comprehensively analysed and researched. Other countries within the Anglo-American common law system, such as the USA, Australia and Canada, have long adopted a statutory criminal code that recognises that the different levels of fault with which murder can be committed need to be reflected in different degrees of murder. This is the single most important recommendation of this Law Commission report — that the offence of murder should be subdivided into two separate offences:

❖ **First-degree murder** would deal only with intentional killing, or killing through an intention to cause serious injury with an awareness of a serious risk of causing death. It would carry the mandatory life sentence.
❖ **Second-degree murder** would include killing through an intention to cause serious injury (even without an awareness of a serious risk of causing death), or killing where there was an awareness of a serious risk of causing death, coupled with an intention to cause either some injury, a fear of injury or a risk of injury.

This recommendation addresses the most serious criticism of the present law on murder. Second-degree murder would also include the present offence of voluntary manslaughter, where what would otherwise be a murder conviction is reduced to that of manslaughter because of the partial defences under the **Homicide Act 1957**: provocation, diminished responsibility and suicide pact.

The principal reason for this is that 'the primary importance of partial defences should be seen as lying in the impact they have on sentence rather than on verdict' — the 'sentence mitigation' principle. The Law Commission argues that the issue of 'fair labelling' — avoiding the term 'murderer' — is less important than the issue of mitigating the sentence.

Mandatory life sentence

It is often argued that the mandatory life sentence means that the trial judge cannot discriminate between different kinds of murder when imposing a sentence. A mass murderer — such as Peter Sutcliffe (the Yorkshire Ripper) — receives the same sentence as a caring relative who, as an act of mercy, kills a loved one who is dying of a painful terminal illness.

However, in many exam answers this issue is insufficiently analysed. In most 'mercy-killing' cases, the defendant is usually convicted of voluntary manslaughter through diminished responsibility; were such a defendant to be convicted of murder, the minimum tariff sentence imposed by the trial judge would be much shorter than that in other murder cases. Such a criticism also fails to recognise that it is rare for a 'whole life' tariff to be imposed where the defendant will die in prison.

A more effective contrast would be with a defendant who participates in a murder by providing only some minor act of assistance, for example by informing the killers of the victim's imminent arrival on the scene. Under the existing law, that person too would be convicted of murder and face a lengthy life sentence.

Most judges are opposed to the mandatory life sentence on the grounds that they cannot properly discriminate between different types of murderers in terms of the individual level of fault with which each murder has been committed. This opinion was strongly reinforced by the House of Lords Select Committee on Murder and Imprisonment (1988–89), which agreed that this sentence should be abolished. The recommendation of the Law Commission that only first-degree murder should in future carry this mandatory sentence largely resolves this issue.

Intention: malice aforethought

The words 'malice aforethought' are misleading. 'Malice' has been defined by judges to refer to 'intention to kill or commit grievous bodily harm', although as recently as the 1970s, judges disagreed whether 'malice' included causing death through some kinds of reckless conduct. As for 'aforethought', it has long been clear there is no need for premeditation.

Glanville Williams summed up the problem of intention clearly when he wrote:

> Why is it that intention, or intent, one of the basic concepts of the criminal law, remains so unclear? Judges decline to define it, and they appear to adjust it from one case to another.

Since the case of *DPP* v *Smith* (1961), this key element of intention has undergone considerable changes in definition in terms of the foreseeability and probability of death (see the cases of *Hyam* v *DPP*, 1974, *R* v *Hancock and Shankland*, 1986, *R* v *Nedrick*, 1986, and, more recently, *R* v *Woollin*, 1998). Because this aspect has been case-law led, it is always open to the House of Lords (or even the Court of Appeal) to vary the definition. As Professor Clarkson writes in his book *Understanding Criminal Law* (2005):

> ...these decisions...leave the law in a state of confusion and uncertainty and open the door to inconsistency in jury verdicts...this lack of definition and certainty is highly undesirable and simply invites prejudice, discrimination and abuse.

The present 'definition' of oblique intent — the defendant's foresight of death or GBH as *virtually certain* (as illustrated by both *Nedrick* and *Woollin*) — also makes it difficult for the prosecution to obtain a murder conviction. Note the importance of s.8 of the **Criminal Justice Act 1967**:

*A court or jury, in determining whether a person has committed an offence —
(a) shall not be bound in law to infer that he intended or foresaw a result of his
actions by reason only of its being a natural and probable consequence of those
actions; but (b) shall decide whether he did intend that result by reference to all the
evidence, drawing such inferences as appear proper in the circumstances.*

This section effectively ensures that the question of intention is essentially a jury
issue, to be decided on the basis of the evidence, and is therefore incapable of
judicial definition. It must therefore be the strict position that a jury directed along
the lines of *Nedrick/Woollin* could hold that the defendant did foresee death or
serious injury as 'being virtually certain' but decide that the defendant nonetheless
did not intend to kill or commit GBH, and is therefore not guilty of murder. This was
confirmed by *R* v *Matthews and Alleyne* (2003).

Implied malice

Intention to cause grievous bodily harm is at present included as *mens rea* of murder,
but this has long been a key focus of criticism. The following quotations lay out the
respective positions.

In *R* v *Vickers* (1957), Lord Goddard CJ stated:

*If a person does an act which amounts to the infliction of GBH he cannot say that
he only intended to cause a certain degree of harm — he must take the consequences. If he intends to inflict GBH and that person dies, that has always been held
in English law sufficient to imply the malice aforethought which is a necessary
constituent of murder.*

This judgement regarding implied malice was confirmed by *R* v *Cunningham*
(1981). However, Lord Edmund-Davies in a dissenting judgement argued:

*...the view I favour is that there should be no conviction for murder unless an intent
to kill is established, the wide range of punishment for manslaughter being fully
adequate to deal with all less heinous forms of homicide. I find it passing strange
that a person can be convicted of murder if death results from, say, his intentional
breaking of another's arm, an action which, while undoubtedly involving the
infliction of 'really serious harm' and, as such, calling for severe punishment,
would in most cases be unlikely to kill.*

In *Principles of Criminal Law* (1999), Andrew Ashworth elaborates on this issue of
constructive liability:

*Does the grievous bodily harm (implied malice) rule extend the definition of murder
too far? If the point of distinguishing murder from manslaughter is to mark out the
most heinous group of killings for the extra stigma of a murder conviction, it can
be argued that this rule draws the line too low. In terms of principle, the rule*

requires justification because it departs from the principle of correspondence, namely that the fault element in a crime should relate to the consequences prohibited by that crime.

Partial defences

Provocation

Provocation has been described as a concession to human frailty, whereby the law recognises that a defendant who has killed as a result of losing self-control from being provoked should not be regarded as wholly responsible for that killing. In such cases, the defendant is instead convicted of voluntary manslaughter, which gives the trial judge discretion as to the sentence he or she will impose. Most jurisdictions allow provocation to be pleaded as a partial defence to murder, as it reflects the moral view that if a defendant is not in control of his or her actions, he or she should not be held fully liable for the consequences of his or her actions in killing (usually) the person who provoked him or her. To that extent, provocation appears to be fair and moral. However, there are a number of serious criticisms that can be directed against provocation.

Criticisms

Male-oriented

First, it has been argued that provocation is a male-oriented defence, which is difficult for women to use. This is because men are thought more prone to react immediately and violently to provocation than women. This has been an issue where a female defendant has finally 'snapped' after a series of provocative acts and killed her male partner. In *R* v *Thornton* (1992) and *R* v *Ahluwalia* (1992), both female defendants argued that the delay between the provocative action of their husbands and the killing should not bar them from pleading provocation.

The courts have accepted this argument to some extent by use of the 'slow burn' issue, and also, in *R* v *Humphreys* (1995), the principle of 'cumulative provocation'.

In *R* v *Ahluwalia* (1992), the defendant argued that the delay between her husband's provocative action and her killing him should not bar her from pleading provocation as a defence to murder

Too wide

A further criticism is that the present law on provocation is too wide — that any evidence of provocation, however limited, effectively forces the defence to be put before the jury. The obvious case to illustrate this problem is *R v Doughty* (1986), where a baby's cries were held by the Court of Appeal to constitute provocation.

Subjective test

The subjective test (loss of self-control as a result of the provocation) can also be criticised, because the rule established in *R v Duffy* (1949) — that the defendant's loss of self-control has to be 'sudden and immediate', requiring the retaliation to occur fairly quickly after the provocation has been received — is inconsistent with *R v Baillie* (1995). Here it was held that the defence of provocation should have been put to the jury, where after the provocation the defendant had gone to the attic to fetch a gun and then driven his car for 2 miles (filling up with petrol on the way) before shooting his victim.

'Reasonable man' test

The most significant criticisms must be directed at the 'reasonable man' test.

First, this test is paradoxical — the reasonable person would never kill in reaction to provocation, however serious. The law, therefore, despite reference to the 'reasonable person', does not require a reasonable reaction.

Second, this test has been subject to a great deal of judicial reinterpretation — from *Bedder* (1954) and *Camplin* (1978), to *Morhall* (1996) and the issue of 'repugnant characteristics', to *Smith* (2000) and the recently decided cases of *R v Karimi* and *R v James (2006),* which confirmed the Privy Council decision in *Holley* (2005), over-turning the earlier *Smith* judgement.

As this is (or should be) the main test applied by juries in determining whether a plea of provocation succeeds, it may be asked how a jury is meant to understand it when so many judges have differing interpretations. Lord Hoffman's view in *Smith* is completely at odds with that of Lord Nicholls in *Holley*. The difficulty for the jury in differentiating between those characteristics that affect the gravity of the provoca-tion, and other characteristics that affect the defendant's ability to control his response, was one of the main reasons that persuaded Lord Hoffman to rewrite the *Camplin* rule in *Smith*.

Proposed law reforms

❖ Provocation would, in future, reduce the defendant's conviction to one of second-degree murder, not manslaughter.

❖ The defendant would be required to prove that he or she acted in response to *gross* provocation that caused him or her to have a justifiable sense of being seriously wronged.

❖ The 'reasonable man' test is also revised as follows: in deciding whether a person of the defendant's age and of ordinary temperament in the circumstances of the defendant might have acted in the same way, the court should take into account the defendant's age and all the circumstances of the defendant, other than matters whose only relevance is that they bear simply on his general capacity for self-control.

Diminished responsibility

The defence of diminished responsibility plays a significant but declining role in murder trials — in the period from 1997 to 2001, this defence was raised in 157 murder trials. Interestingly, in 77% of cases the prosecution accepted the defendant's plea of guilty to manslaughter on the grounds of diminished responsibility.

Public opinion broadly supports treating in a tolerant way those who kill because of serious mental abnormality. The principal argument in favour of retaining the defence of diminished responsibility, which the Law Commission recommends, is that of 'fair and just labelling' — the view that it is 'unjust to label as murderers those not fully liable for their actions'. Professor Mackay stated that 'there is, in my view, a clear moral distinction between murder and a diminished responsibility killing despite the presence of the *mens rea* of the former offence'.

It is further argued that this partial defence is needed because the full defence of insanity is outdated; if diminished responsibility were not available, juries might in some cases acquit the defendant altogether.

However, two key criticisms can be made in relation to this partial defence to murder.

Criticisms

Burden of proof

The legal burden of proof rests on the defendant to prove the defence, albeit on the balance of probabilities. This breaches the 'golden rule' that the prosecution should prove the defendant's guilt. For any other defence, the defendant only has to produce evidence of it, and it is then up to the prosecution to prove its absence.

It has also been argued that this requirement is in contravention of the European Convention on Human Rights (ECHR) Article 6(2), which guarantees the presumption of innocence and the imposition of the burden of proof on the prosecution.

In *R* v *Ali* and *R* v *Jordan* (2001), however, the Court of Appeal ruled that this does not contravene the ECHR because a person charged with murder is not required to prove anything unless he or she seeks to rely on diminished responsibility and this, since it is a defence, is to the defendant's advantage.

Despite widespread criticism on this issue of burden of proof, the Law Commission recommended no change on the basis that:

> ...in contrast to provocation, the defence depends not on external facts which might be investigated and challenged independently of the defendant but on the defendant's state of mind, a matter which can only be investigated with his cooperation.

Categories of mental abnormality

The second serious criticism is directed at the categories that may produce a mental abnormality. According to Janet Loveless in *Complete Criminal Law* (2008), these are:

> ...vague and problematic because psychiatrists have to testify to the presence of an abnormality of mind the formulation of which is not linked to a medical definition of mental illness. It is not a psychiatric term...the specified causes, as strictly interpreted, are rigid and would exclude the mercy-killer who kills through compassion under a temporary condition of mental imbalance, usually severe depression.

The Law Commission also observed that:

> ...diagnostic practice...has long since developed beyond identification of the narrow range of permissible 'causes' of an abnormality of mind...and, in any event, the stipulated permissible causes have never had an agreed psychiatric meaning.

It is also the case that in many murder trials where diminished responsibility is pleaded, there will be dispute between expert medical witnesses called by the defence and the prosecution as to whether the defendant was suffering from an abnormality of mind, especially since that phrase is not usually used by psychiatrists. In such cases, how is a jury composed of lay people supposed to decide which set of psychiatrists is correct? Furthermore, even in the absence of such professional disagreements on the question of 'abnormality of mind', how is the jury to assess whether that abnormality has 'sufficiently impaired the mental responsibility' of the defendant in relation to the killing? The definition of diminished responsibility in s.2 contains no guidance as to what may constitute a 'substantial impairment of mental responsibility'.

The Law Commission, in its 2005 report on homicide, considered this concept to be fundamentally flawed. One is either responsible for killing or not; 'responsibility cannot be either enhanced or diminished'.

Proposed law reforms

The Law Commission recommended that the following definition be adopted:

> ...a person who would otherwise be guilty of first-degree murder is guilty of second-degree murder if, at the time he or she played his or her part in the killing, his or her capacity to:

(i) understand the nature of his or her conduct; or

(ii) form a rational judgment; or

(iii) control him or herself,

was substantially impaired by an abnormality of mental functioning arising from a recognised medical condition, developmental immaturity in a defendant under the age of eighteen, or a combination of both; and the abnormality, the developmental immaturity, or the combination of both provides an explanation for the defendant's conduct in carrying out or taking part in the killing.

Questions

1 How is first-degree murder defined in the Law Commission report on homicide?

2 Briefly explain what criticism of murder this recommendation largely addresses.

3 Explain why implied malice should be so heavily criticised.

4 Why did the Law Commission recommend that provocation and diminished responsibility, as partial defences, should only reduce first-degree murder to second-degree murder and not manslaughter?

5 What criticism of the present law on provocation is illustrated by *R* v *Doughty* (1986)? What specific recommendation did the Law Commission make to deal with this problem?

6 What criticism of the 'reasonable man' test in provocation can be derived from *R* v *Morhall* (1996)?

7 What is the justification for the partial defence of diminished responsibility?

8 To which criticism of diminished responsibility does Janet Loveless refer?

General defences

Self-defence

At present, self-defence is an 'all or nothing' defence. If successfully pleaded, the defendant is acquitted. If not, he or she is convicted of the crime charged, and if that is murder, the mandatory life sentence must be imposed.

In *R* v *Clegg* (1995), defence counsel argued before the House of Lords that in cases involving police officers or, as in that particular case, military personnel assisting the civil powers, it should be possible to mitigate the offence by pleading that the defendant had used unreasonable force in self-defence. This would reduce what would otherwise be a murder conviction to involuntary manslaughter. This had been recommended by the Nathan Committee (House of Lords, 1989). The argument was rejected, as the Law Lords decided such a change in the law could only be made by Parliament.

The mistaken shooting of Jean Charles de Menezes in 2005 drew to the public's attention the use of lethal force by the police in defence of state security

In its 2006 report on murder, manslaughter and infanticide, the Law Commission rejected making excessive-force self-defence a partial defence to murder, instead suggesting that a wider defence of provocation could address this argument by reducing first-degree murder to second-degree murder.

There has also been considerable public concern about the use of lethal force by the police in defence of state security. The mistaken shooting of Jean Charles de Menezes in London in 2005 clearly illustrates the reasons for this concern — could such killings be defended using the law on self-defence, and, if so, is such a law compatible with ECHR Article 2 — the right to life? This Article could also make it difficult to use self-defence to justify killing a person in defence of property or in the more general prevention of crime. As McAlhone and Huxley-Binns comment in *Criminal Law: The Fundamentals* (2007): 'It is difficult to imagine where a proportionate response to a threat to property is to kill.'

The case of *R* v *Martin* (2001; see page 54) prompted considerable controversy over the extent to which a householder can use force to protect his or her home. In that case, the defendant's plea of self-defence was rejected by the jury. However, there have been several cases where the occupier has used a firearm or knife against a burglar with fatal consequences and either no prosecution has been mounted or the self-defence plea has been successful. This raises the problem that Article 2 of the ECHR does not allow an exception to the right to life in favour of the prevention of crime, unless the crime is 'unlawful violence' or a riot. English law apparently conflicts with this fundamental right, insofar as it allows the acquittal of a householder who uses fatal force against an intruder who has not done or threatened 'unlawful violence'.

Insanity

A major criticism of the insanity defence is that the M'Naghten rules were created by judges in 1843, when psychiatric illness was hardly understood, and they remain unchanged. Despite huge developments in understanding, diagnosing and treating psychiatric illness, an insanity plea must still satisfy the same legal rules as interpreted by those judges. In 1953, the Royal Commission on Capital Punishment described these rules as obsolete and misleading, and the category of 'disease of the mind' as outdated and inaccurate.

The present law can also be criticised for being too wide, as it includes epilepsy, sleepwalking and diabetes (see *Sullivan*, 1983, *Burgess*, 1991, and *Hennessy*, 1989). However, it is also too narrow, as it can exclude many who are clinically (but not legally) insane — the 'defect of reason' test excludes those who know what they are doing but who cannot help themselves.

Psychiatric medicine no longer defines mental disorders as 'insanity'; rather, a psychiatrist would argue that a person may understand what he or she is doing and still be mentally ill. A judge, on the other hand, would hold that a person who is partially rational is not insane and therefore must be held accountable. It is often the case that psychiatric reports, while concluding the defendant is insane, fail to mention or do not explain his or her mental condition in relation to the M'Naghten rules.

As is the position with diminished responsibility, it is common for there to be conflicting expert evidence led at trial by the prosecution and the defence. If left to the jury by the trial judge, the decision of whether or not the defendant is legally insane is made by medically unqualified jurors who have to choose between expert psychiatrists.

To detain under the **Criminal Procedure (Insanity) Act 1991** defendants who are epileptics, diabetics or sleepwalkers could be in breach of ECHR Article 5 — the right to liberty. In *Winterwerp* v *Netherlands* (1979), the European Court of Human Rights ruled that whether someone was of unsound mind was a matter of objective medical expertise, and that detention is unlawful unless the mental disorder warrants compulsory hospitalisation. This ruling conflicts with the fact that the test of insanity in England is still formally a legal one.

It can also be argued that the M'Naghten rules are contrary to the presumption of innocence enshrined in ECHR Article 6 — the right to a fair trial — because the burden of proof is reversed. Since the prosecution is not required to prove *mens rea* in insanity cases, the criticism arises that if the defendant fails to prove insanity, yet the prosecution proves the *actus reus*, the defendant can still be convicted, despite the existence of reasonable doubt concerning the *mens rea*.

An interesting and challenging argument concerns whether the insanity verdict should be retained. About one-third of all prisoners are believed to suffer from some form of mental disorder, but for those prisoners the insanity verdict was not available. If mental illness is an excusing condition, the law is clearly being applied in a grossly uneven manner. But more fundamentally, *ought* mental illness to be an excusing condition at all? Many people might be mentally ill and commit a crime, but there is little evidence to suggest, far less prove, that the one *causes* the other. The classic position is that the insane are 'mad' and not 'bad'. But why cannot the same person be both mad and bad?

At a different level, it has been argued that while there might be a relationship of sorts between mental illness and crime, a far stronger relationship exists between adverse social circumstances and criminal behaviour. Why, then, is there an insanity defence but no defence of 'social adversity'?

Intoxication

In discussing the rules concerning intoxication as a defence, McAlhone and Huxley-Binns write in *Criminal Law: The Fundamentals* (2007): 'The law is a mass of inconsistency, lacks any logic and is rooted firmly in policy.' The problem is that the defence of intoxication means creating a defence out of circumstances that can by themselves be a criminal offence — drunk and disorderly conduct or drink-driving. This can only result in policy-driven rules to restrict the availability of such a defence, particularly when it is voluntary. It makes good sense to argue that intoxication should not lead to a defendant being acquitted when he or she has caused harm to people or damage to property while drunk. One of the main functions of criminal law, after all, is to protect major social and individual interests and, as Andrew Ashworth writes in *Principles of Criminal Law*:

> ...any legal system which allows intoxication to negative mens rea would present citizens with an easy route to impunity. Indeed, the more intoxicated they became, the less likely they would be to be held criminally liable for any harm caused.

Janet Loveless argues in *Complete Criminal Law* that 'the *Majewski* rule is contrary to three fundamental principles of criminal liability', on the grounds that it assumes that the defendant behaved recklessly in becoming intoxicated, and then that 'recklessness' is effectively 'transferred' to the crime, thus providing the *mens rea* for a basic intent offence.

The problem here is that recklessness, in its legal sense, requires the defendant to be aware of the unjustified risk he or she is taking, and as Andrew Ashworth comments (in *Principles of Criminal Law*), 'in most cases it is far-fetched to argue that a person who is getting drunk is aware of the type of conduct he or she might later

indulge in'. More straightforwardly, Loveless also states that in such cases there is no coincidence of *actus reus* and *mens rea*, since the recklessness involved in getting drunk usually occurs before the crime is committed. Finally, she argues that:

> It is contrary to the general principle that mens rea *must be proved by the prosecution. It also runs counter to s.8 Criminal Justice Act 1967 which requires juries to consider the D's subjective state of mind. Clearly, if the D is so intoxicated as to not know what he is doing or fails to foresee something that they ordinarily would not miss, D will have no 'state of mind' that could be described as one of* mens rea.

A further criticism of the rule from *DPP* v *Majewski* (1977) lies in the distinction it makes between crimes of basic and specific intent. It assumes that this distinction is always easy to draw, but this is not the case. Another problem arises with that part of the rule that allows the defendant to be convicted of a basic-intent offence if intoxication is accepted as a partial defence to a specific-intent crime. This functions practically in murder, where the defendant can be convicted of involuntary manslaughter, but in theft — a crime of specific intent — there is no lesser basic-intent offence.

A telling point in support of the argument that the *Majewski* rules are unfair is that there are a number of common-law jurisdictions, such as Canada, Australia and New Zealand, where these rules do not operate, but, nevertheless, the conviction rate in cases involving drunk defendants is no lower than in the UK.

Questions

1 In which case was the House of Lords invited to allow excessive force in self-defence to act as a partial defence for police officers and military personnel in support of the civil powers? Why did the House of Lords refuse to do this?

2 What 'solution' to this problem has been recommended by the Law Commission?

3 Explain why the present rules on self-defence may conflict with the right to life in Article 2 of the ECHR.

4 Explain why the present rules on insanity may conflict with the right to liberty in Article 5 of the ECHR.

5 What is the key criticism of the decision in *DPP* v *Majewski* (1977) concerning recklessness?

Sample exam question

Critically analyse the present law on murder and voluntary manslaughter.

Further reading

Ashworth, A. (1999) *Principles of Criminal Law* (3rd edn), Oxford University Press.

Elliott, C. and Quinn, F. (2006) *Criminal Law* (6th edn), Pearson Longman.

Loveless, J. (2008) *Complete Criminal Law*, Oxford University Press.

McAlhone, C. and Huxley-Binns, R. (2007) *Criminal Law: The Fundamentals*, Sweet & Maxwell.

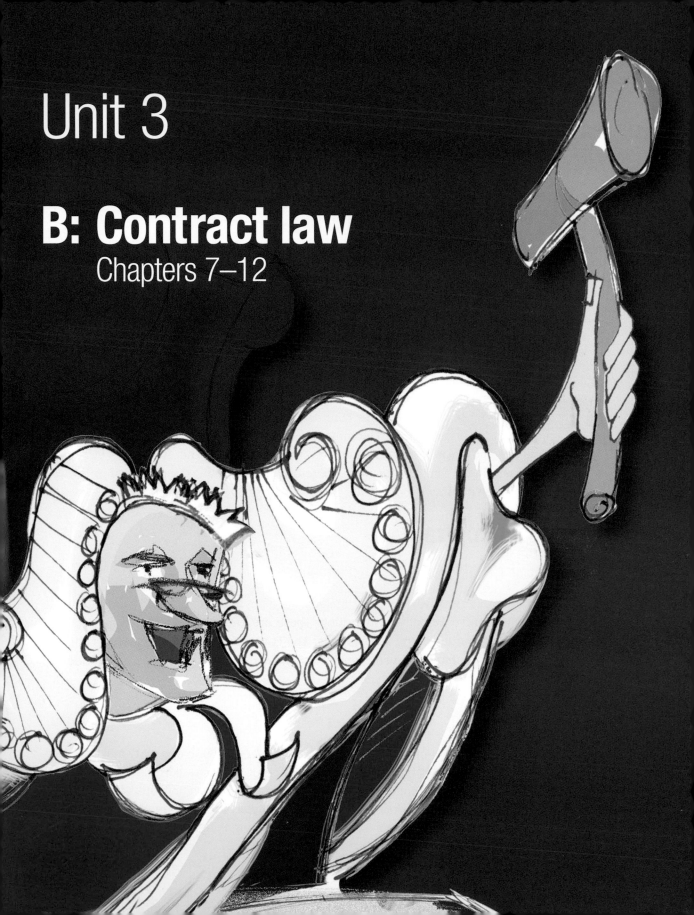

Unit 3

B: Contract law
Chapters 7–12

Chapter **7**

Formation of contract

In order to be valid, a contract must meet certain conditions, and these have to be present when the contract is formed.

There can be several parties to a contract, and contracts can be made by individuals, groups or organisations. The same rules apply, however complex the arrangements are and regardless of the number of people involved, but it is easier to see them operating in simple situations. Therefore, most of the examples used in this chapter involve just two individuals.

Types of contract

Bilateral contracts

Many contracts involve one party making an offer and another party indicating acceptance, either verbally or in writing. These are known as **bilateral** contracts, because both parties promise something. The contract is valid at the moment the promises are exchanged, even though at this stage neither party may have done anything to implement the agreement.

Unilateral contracts

In a situation like that in *Carlill* v *Carbolic Smoke Ball Co.* (1893), one party makes an offer but acceptance is through the performance of an act rather than through a formal indication of acceptance. Such contracts are known as unilateral contracts, because only one party makes a promise. An example would be a promise to pay a reward to anyone who finds a missing cat. The person making the promise is obliged

7

to pay the reward to anyone who finds the cat, but nobody has to undertake to find it.

An agreement between a person wanting to sell his or her house and an estate agent would also be an example of a unilateral contract. The seller promises to pay a specified percentage of the house price to the estate agent as commission if the house is sold, but the estate agent does not have promise anything in return.

An agreement between a person wanting to sell his or her house and an estate agent is a unilateral contract

Offers and invitations to treat

Offer and acceptance

Offer and acceptance are the most basic and arguably most important requirements when forming a contract. An 'offer' has been defined as an expression of willingness to contract on certain terms, made with the intention that a binding agreement will exist once the offer is accepted. The person making the offer is known as the **offeror**, and the person to whom the offer is made is called the **offeree**.

An offer can be **specific** — made to one person or group of people, in which case it can only be accepted by that person or group. An offer can also be **general** and not limited in whom it is directed at. An offer of a reward would be a good example, which could be accepted by anyone who met the conditions. The case of *Carlill* (1893) (discussed in more detail on page 86) is an example of an offer made to the public at large. A more recent example is *Bowerman* v *ABTA* (1996), when a promise by ABTA to reimburse monies paid when a tour operator went out of business was held to be an offer to the public at large, which is accepted whenever someone contracts with an ABTA member.

An offer may be **express** (made orally or in writing) or it may be **implied from conduct**, as when taking goods to the checkout in a supermarket.

Invitations to treat

It is important that you are able to distinguish between offers and invitations to treat:
❖ For an offer, all that is required from the other party is acceptance.
❖ For an invitation to treat, the other party is invited to make an offer, leaving the person who issued the invitation able to decide whether or not to accept.

Suppose, for example, something is advertised at £100, but this is actually a mistake and it should be £1,000. If this is an offer, and someone accepts it, it becomes a legally binding agreement, but if the advertisement is an invitation to treat, the person issuing the advertisement has the opportunity to reject any offers made to buy at that price.

Whether something is an offer or an invitation depends on all the circumstances. The following are invitations.

Displays of goods in shop windows

In *Fisher* v *Bell* (1961), a prosecution under the **Offensive Weapons Act 1959** failed because the offence was to 'offer for sale' prohibited weapons. Although the shopkeeper was displaying a flick knife in his window with a price tag, the court decided that this amounted to an invitation to treat and not an offer for sale.

Goods on display in supermarkets and self-service stores

This principle was established before the appearance of modern supermarkets in *Pharmaceutical Society of Great Britain* v *Boots* (1953). Boots had opened a shop in which customers selected the products they wanted from displays and paid for them at a cash point. The court decided that the contract was made when the goods were presented at the cash desk and accepted by the cashier, and not when they were taken from the shelves. The goods on display were an invitation to treat.

Small advertisements (e.g. in magazines or newspapers)

The law makes a distinction between advertisements for unilateral contracts, such as those offering rewards, and advertisements offering specified goods at a certain price. The former are usually treated as offers, because acceptance is possible without the need for any further negotiation between the parties, while the latter are often considered invitations to treat, on the grounds that there may be further bargaining about price etc.

The leading case is *Partridge* v *Crittenden* (1968). An advertisement reading 'Bramblefinch cocks, bramblefinch hens, 25s each' was an invitation, not an offer, and so a prosecution for offering for sale a wild bird under the **Protection of Birds Act 1954** failed.

Price lists, catalogues etc.

The same principle applies to catalogues, circulars, timetables and price lists. Lord Herschell in *Grainger* v *Gough* (1896) commented that 'the transmission of a price list does not amount to an offer to supply'.

Responses to requests for information

In *Harvey* v *Facey* (1893), Harvey telegraphed Facey and asked: 'Will you sell me Bumper Hall Pen? Telegraph lowest cash price.' Facey replied by telegram: 'Lowest cash price for Bumper Hall Pen £900.' Harvey sent a second telegram: 'We agree to

buy Bumper Hall Pen at £900 asked by you.' It was held that Facey's telegram was not an offer but merely a statement of the price.

The courts have adopted quite a narrow interpretation of what constitutes an offer when information is being supplied. For example, in *Gibson* v *Manchester City Council* (1979), a statement that the council 'may be prepared to sell the house to you' at a certain price was held to be an invitation to treat, not an offer.

Auction sales

In *British Car Auctions* v *Wright* (1972), a prosecution for offering to sell an unroadworthy car at auction failed because putting goods into an auction is an invitation, not an offer for sale. The offer is made by the person making the bid. This allows the auctioneer to withdraw the goods if the offers are not high enough.

Sometimes, however, an auction is 'without reserve', which means that the auctioneer will sell to the highest bidder, however low the bid might be. It was held in *Warlow* v *Harrison* (1859) that auctioning an item in this way constitutes an offer, which is accepted by the person making the highest bid. This was confirmed in *Barry* v *Davies* (2000).

Invitations to tender

Normally, an invitation to tender for the supply of goods or services is an invitation to treat. It was held in *Spencer* v *Harding* (1870) that the person inviting the tenders is free to accept any of them, and not necessarily the cheapest. However, the wording of the invitation is important and may restrict the freedom to choose between rival bids. For example, in *Harvela Investments* v *Royal Trust Co. of Canada* (1986), a statement that the highest bid would be accepted was held to be binding.

However, in *Blackpool and Fylde Aero Club* v *Blackpool Borough Council* (1990), it was made clear that an invitation to tender is also a unilateral offer to consider all tenders correctly submitted.

Questions

1 What is a bilateral contract?

2 What is a unilateral contract? Give an example.

3 Give a definition of 'offer'.

4 Give an example of a general offer.

5 What is an invitation to treat?

6 Make a list of all the situations that are considered invitations rather than offers, and name one case for each.

7 Under what circumstances might an advertisement in a newspaper amount to an offer?

8 Under what circumstances might an invitation to tender amount to an offer?

> **9** Explain the principles of law illustrated by the following cases:
> - ❖ *Bowerman* v *ABTA* (1996)
> - ❖ *Barry* v *Davies* (2000)
> - ❖ *Blackpool and Fylde Aero Club* v *Blackpool Borough Council* (1990)

Offers

Reward posters/advertisements

Reward posters and advertisements can constitute offers, as long as it is clear that all that needs to be done is to fulfil certain conditions. This was established in the celebrated case of *Carlill* v *Carbolic Smoke Ball Co.* (1893).

The Carbolic Smoke Ball Company issued a newspaper advertisement in which it said it would pay £100 to any person who contracted influenza after using one of its smoke balls in a specified manner for a specified period. It also stated that it had deposited £1,000 with a named bank, to show its sincerity in the matter. The court held that there was an express promise to pay £100 in certain events, expressed in language that was perfectly unmistakeable, and the deposit placed with the bank was proof of the intention to pay the £100 in the events that the company had specified. This is an unusual example of an advertisement that amounted to an offer, but it does show that this is possible if the wording makes it clear that it is intended to be an offer.

The Carbolic Smoke Ball Company's advertisement amounted to an offer rather than an invitation to treat

Promotional campaigns

A supermarket might encourage customers to buy one product and get another free, or it might offer two items for the price of one. As with reward posters, all that is required is that certain conditions are fulfilled.

Timetables and tickets for transport

There is no single rule covering all the potential situations that may arise in this area, and the law remains unclear.

In *Wilkie* v *London Passenger Transport Board* (1947), it was suggested that the offer is made by running the service and accepted when the passenger gets on board. It could perhaps also be argued that by asking for a ticket, the passenger is making an offer that the company accepts by issuing the ticket.

Further rules about offers

- **The offer must be certain.** Its terms must be clear and definite, without any ambiguity. For example, in *Guthing* v *Lynn* (1831), a promise to pay an extra £5 'if the horse is lucky' was considered too vague to constitute an offer.
- **The offer may be made by any method.** There is no requirement that an offer is in a particular form. It can be made in writing, verbally or by conduct (e.g. by picking up an item and taking it to the cash desk).
- **The offer can be made to anyone:** an individual, a group, a company or organisation, and even, as in *Carlill* v *Carbolic Smoke Ball Co.,* the whole world. Lord Justice Lindley commented in *Carlill*: 'The offer is to anybody who performs the conditions named in the advertisement. Anybody who does perform the conditions accepts the offer.'
- **It must be communicated.** A person cannot accept what he or she does not know about. In practice, this is not likely to happen often, but one example might be an offer of a reward for the return of a missing dog. If someone finds the dog and returns it, but that person did not know about the reward, technically he or she is not entitled to the reward because the offer was never received and therefore cannot be accepted.
- **It must still be in existence when it is accepted.** A number of problems might arise, for example when no time limit is agreed for acceptance/rejection, or if the person making the offer wants to revoke it. The principle here is that **the revocation must be received before the acceptance is made.** This is discussed in the next section.

Termination of offers

An offer can be brought to an end at any point before acceptance and in a number of different ways.

Acceptance or refusal

These are the most obvious and straightforward ways of terminating an offer. Acceptance may be issued in writing, verbally or by conduct. If an offer is refused, it is ended, which means that it cannot be accepted later if there is a change of mind.

Failure of a precondition

Some offers are made subject to certain conditions, for example when someone offers to sell his or her car if he or she is given a company car through a new job.

Counter-offer

In *Hyde* v *Wrench* (1840), Wrench offered to sell his farm to Hyde for £1,000. Hyde offered to pay £950, which Wrench rejected. When Hyde then tried to accept the original offer, it was held that his counter-offer of £950 had ended that offer. This case confirms that all the terms of an offer must be accepted and an attempt to change any of them becomes a counter-offer.

Revocation

Revocation (withdrawal of the offer) must be communicated, although this could be by a third party, as in *Dickinson* v *Dodds* (1876). Dodds offered to sell his house to Dickinson, and the offer was expressed to be 'left open till Friday'. On Thursday afternoon, Dickinson heard from a third party that Dodds had sold the property to someone else. On the Friday morning, Dickinson delivered a formal acceptance to Dodds and then commenced legal proceedings against him. The court held that the offer made to Dickinson had been withdrawn on the Thursday and was no longer capable of being accepted.

The revocation must actually be received before the acceptance is made. In *Byrne* v *Van Tienhoven* (1880), Van Tienhoven wrote to Byrne on 1 October, making an offer, but changed his mind and wrote again on 8 October, withdrawing his offer. However, Byrne accepted the offer in a telegram on 11 October, before he received the revocation letter, and therefore the acceptance was valid.

However, it seems that a revocation would be also valid if it is delivered to the last-known address, or it is sent by fax or telex during office hours, but is not read until some time later.

One practical issue is that in most offices, the post is opened by clerical staff, who then distribute it to the relevant people. The courts have not ruled on this point, but it would certainly be easier in practice to decide that communication takes place when the letter is opened, rather than trying to trace the letter through to its final recipient.

Where the offer is to enter into a unilateral contract, the revocation must take place before performance has commenced. It is clear from *Luxor (Eastbourne) Ltd* (1941) that the promise can be revoked at any time before sale, even if the estate agent has already started work on finding a buyer.

In order to revoke an offer made to the public at large, it is probably sufficient to take reasonable steps to draw it to the attention of those to whom the original offer was directed. For example, if the offer was made through a newspaper advertisement, it would be sufficient to publish a revocation notice in the same newspaper, even though there could clearly be no guarantee that those who saw the first advert would also see the revocation.

Lapse of time

Where no time limit is specified, the offer will remain open for a reasonable time. What is considered reasonable depends on the circumstances. For example, an offer to sell perishable goods may lapse in a few days, while an offer to sell land would last considerably longer. In *Ramsgate Victoria Hotel* v *Montefiore* (1866), an offer to buy shares in June had lapsed by November. If a time limit is specified, it must be complied with.

Death of the person making the offer

It has been suggested that the death of either party terminates the offer, as it makes it impossible for the parties to reach agreement. The position is not entirely clear, although it appears from *Bradbury* v *Morgan* (1862) that if the offeree knows the offeror has died, the offer will lapse, but if the offeree is unaware of the offeror's death, it probably will not. If the contract involves personal services, such as a singer giving a performance, the death of the offeror will necessarily end the offer.

There are no legal authorities dealing with a situation where the offeree has died.

Questions

1 Which features in the Carbolic Smoke Ball advertisement persuaded the court that it was an offer and not an invitation?

2 Give an example of a promotional campaign. How does the law treat it?

3 Suggest two possible views as to when a contract to travel on a bus is made.

4 List five further rules about offers.

5 List the circumstances in which an offer might be terminated.

6 Explain the principles of law illustrated by the following cases:
  ❖ *Guthing* v *Lynn* (1831)
  ❖ *Hyde* v *Wrench* (1840)
  ❖ *Dickinson* v *Dodds* (1876)

Acceptance

Acceptance is **unqualified and unconditional agreement** to all the terms of the offer by words or conduct. If conditions or qualifications are added, a counter-offer is created. For example, in *Tinn* v *Hoffman* (1873), where an offer was made to sell 1,200 tons of iron, an order for 800 tons was not acceptance.

Rules on acceptance

Acceptance must be communicated

Mere silence cannot amount to acceptance, unless it is absolutely clear that acceptance was intended.

In *Felthouse* v *Bindley* (1862), the defendant auctioneer had been charged with selling the farming stock of John Felthouse. The claimant, Felthouse's uncle, offered to buy a horse from his nephew, adding: 'If I hear no more about him, I shall consider the horse mine at £30.15s.' It was evident from the nephew's conduct that he intended to accept the offer, as he instructed the auctioneer to withdraw the horse from the auction, but he did not reply to his uncle. By mistake, the horse was put up for sale and sold, and the uncle began an action against the defendant. However, the court held that the uncle had no property in the horse, as the silence of his nephew could not amount to acceptance of the uncle's offer.

It is possible for the person making the offer to state that acceptance need not be communicated and therefore to bind him- or herself to the risk of unknowingly entering a contract, but he or she cannot in law impose this risk on someone else.

Acceptance can be inferred from conduct

The principle seems to be that when you start to implement what is in the offer, you have provided acceptance, although the courts will only adopt this interpretation if it seems reasonable to infer that acceptance was intended. For example, in *Brogden v Metropolitan Rail Co.* (1877), the parties were discussing an agreement for the supply of coal to the railway company. Brogden returned a draft agreement to the defendants with a new term inserted. This document was then filed by them and forgotten; meanwhile, Brogden continued to supply the coal. The House of Lords held that by adding a new term, Brogden was making a counter-offer, which was then accepted by conduct, either when the company next placed an order for coal or when it accepted delivery.

Questions

1 Explain what acceptance is.

2 Explain the principles of law illustrated by the following cases:

❖ *Tinn* v *Hoffman* (1873)

❖ *Felthouse* v *Bindley* (1862)

❖ *Brogden* v *Metropolitan Railway Co.* (1877)

Methods of acceptance

The general rule is that if a method of acceptance is specified, it must be complied with, although in some circumstances, another equally good method might suffice. In *Tinn* v *Hoffman* (1873), acceptance was requested by return of post. Honeyman J said:

> *That does not mean exclusively a reply by letter or return of post, but you may reply by telegram or by verbal message or by any other means not later than a letter written by return of post.*

If no method is specified, any method will do, as long as it is effective. However, where an offer is made by an instantaneous method, such as e-mail, fax or telephone, acceptance by post would not usually be considered reasonable.

The 'postal rule' maintains that acceptance by means of the post is effective as soon as the letter of acceptance is posted, even if the letter is lost in the post. However, as we saw earlier, revocation of an offer is only valid when it is received. The practical basis of the rule is that it is presumably easier to prove that a letter has been posted than it is to prove that it has been received and drawn to the attention of the relevant person. The principle that acceptance is valid when posted was first laid down in *Adams* v *Lindsell* (1818). In *Household Fire* v *Grant* (1879), a letter was lost in the post, but there was nevertheless a proper acceptance and a binding contract.

The 'postal rule' maintains that acceptance by means of the post is effective as soon as the letter of acceptance is posted

In *Henthorn* v *Fraser* (1892), the plaintiff, who lived in Birkenhead, was handed a note at the defendant's office in Liverpool, giving him an option to purchase certain property within 14 days. The next day, the defendant posted a letter withdrawing the offer, which did not reach Birkenhead until 5 p.m. Meanwhile, the plaintiff had posted a letter at 3.50 p.m. accepting the offer. That letter was delivered after the defendant's office was closed and was opened the following morning. It was held that a valid contract had been concluded at 3.50 p.m.

An obvious difficulty is trying to determine the application of the postal rule to modern methods of communication. In *The Law of Contract* (2007), Treitel suggests that where a communication such as a fax has arrived but is for some reason illegible, 'it might well be effective in such circumstances'.

The postal rule does not apply where the offeror has specified that acceptance must be communicated directly. In *Holwell Securities Ltd* v *Hughes* (1974), the offer required acceptance to be 'by notice in writing'. It was held that these words negated the effect of the postal rule so that a letter of acceptance posted but not received by the offeror was insufficient to form a contract.

Instantaneous methods

When instantaneous methods such as telephone or telex are used, acceptance is immediate as long as it is communicated, i.e. the message gets through.

In *Entores* v *Miles Far East* (1955), an English company in London was in communication by telex with a Dutch company in Amsterdam. The English company received an offer of goods from the Dutch company and made a counter-offer, which the Dutch company accepted — all by telex. For purposes of jurisdiction, it was held that the contract was made in London, where the English company received the acceptance. Denning LJ suggested that the person receiving the acceptance will be bound even if he or she does not read the telex until much later.

However, in *Brinkibon Ltd* v *Stahag Stahl* (1983), one of the issues was a telex being received when the office was closed. The House of Lords held that the acceptance could only become effective when the office reopened.

In essence, it is all about reasonableness. In *Brinkibon,* Lord Wilberforce said:

> *No universal rule can cover all such cases; they must be resolved by reference to the intentions of the parties, by sound business practice and in some cases by a judgement where the risks should lie.*

As yet, there have been no cases on e-mails, but there seems no reason why the same rule on electronic transfers should not apply to them.

Standard form contracts

If an offer is made by a business using its own standard form but the business receiving the offer alters the terms by sending back its own form, this amounts to a counter-offer. What may then follow is a series of communications with each party referring to its own terms. The general rule in such cases is that the 'last shot' wins the battle. Each new document is seen as a counter-offer, and when one party performs its obligations under the contract, for example by delivering the goods, this is seen as acceptance of the terms in the last document to be sent.

This is illustrated by the case of *British Road Services* v *Crutchley* (1968), in which whisky was delivered by BRS to Crutchley for storage. The BRS driver handed over a delivery note referring to his company's terms, but Crutchley stamped the note with the words 'received under our conditions', before handing it back to the driver. It was held that these words amounted to a counter-offer, which BRS accepted when it handed over the goods; the contract therefore incorporated these conditions rather than those of BRS.

The outcome in *Butler Machine Tool Co. Ltd* v *Ex-Cell-O Corporation* (1979) was different, in that the last document to be sent was *not* treated as a counter-offer. This case demonstrates that the courts look at the circumstances of each case and do not automatically assume that the last document sent is the one upon which the contract will be based.

Questions

1 To what extent is it true that if a method of acceptance is specified, it must be complied with?

2 Explain the postal rule. In which case was the principle first laid down?

3 What happens if the letter is lost in the post?

4 In what circumstances might the postal rule be relevant to modern methods of communication?

5 What does *Holwell Securities* v *Hughes* (1974) say about the postal rule?

6 What is the rule concerning instantaneous methods of communication?

7 What happens if the communication arrives when the office is closed?

8 What principle does Lord Wilberforce suggest should apply in all these cases?

9 What is the general rule when the parties are using standard form contracts? Which case illustrates this?

10 Why was the outcome different in *Butler Machine Tool Co. Ltd* v *Ex-Cell-O Corporation* (1979)?

Consideration

Consideration means that each side must promise to give or do something for the other. For example, if A promises to paint B's house, the promise will only be enforceable as a contract if B has provided consideration. B's consideration in this situation would usually take the form of a payment of money or the promise of a future payment, but it could also consist of some other service or future service to which A agrees.

It is possible to have a valid contract even if one party does not provide consideration, for example a promise to make a gift, but only if the contract is made by deed.

Definition

Consideration was defined in *Currie* v *Misa* (1875) as:

> *...some right, interest, profit or benefit accruing to one party, or some forbearance, detriment, loss or responsibility given, suffered or undertaken by the other.*

In *Dunlop* v *Selfridge Ltd* (1915), it was stated that:

> *...an act or forbearance of one party, or the promise thereof, is the price for which the promise of the other is bought, and the promise thus given for value is enforceable.*

For our purposes, it may be helpful to think of consideration as something of value being offered by each party. As you will see, sometimes it can be of little value and it certainly does not have to correspond to what something is actually worth.

Types of consideration

Consideration can, and often does, involve a promise by the parties to do something in the future, and this exchange of promises is called **executory consideration**.

Either party can sue the other in the event of it not doing what it has promised. In unilateral contracts, however, the party making the offer (e.g. of a reward) is under no obligation until the other party performs (executes) its part of the agreement. This is called **executed consideration**.

The rules of consideration

Something of value must be given by all parties

This is the basic principle and it distinguishes a contract from a purely gratuitous agreement (i.e. a promise to make a gift). The law says that consideration must be sufficient. This means that it must be real and tangible and have some actual value. In *White* v *Bluett* (1853), a promise not to complain about the contents of a will in return for the cancelling of a debt was considered to be intangible. It was not offering anything of real value or substance to the bargain.

It does not have to be adequate

The courts will not investigate adequacy, nor will they investigate contracts to see if the parties have got equal value.

In *Thomas* v *Thomas* (1842), an executor agreed that a widow could continue to live in a house in return for a promise that she would pay £1 a year and keep the house in good repair. This was accepted by the court as good consideration.

In *Chappell and Co. Ltd* v *Nestlé Co. Ltd* (1960), it was held that the three wrappers were part of the consideration, even though on receipt the wrappers were thrown away.

It must not be past

This means that any consideration must come after the agreement, rather than being something that has already been done. For example, if A paints B's house and then, when the work is finished, B promises to pay £100 for the work, this promise is un-enforceable because A's consideration is past.

In *Re McArdle* (1951), repairs were made to a property, and afterwards people who were to inherit the property were asked to sign an agreement that they would reimburse the cost of the repairs. This agreement was not enforceable because the repairs had been done before the agreement was made.

The law recognises, however, that there are situations in which something, for example a restaurant meal or a taxi ride, is provided on the unspoken expectation that ultimately it will be paid for.

In *Lampleigh* v *Braithwaite* (1615), it was held that there was a contract because at the time the original request was made, both parties would have contemplated a payment. This principle is known as the '**rule in *Lampleigh* v *Braithwaite***' and was applied in *Re Casey's Patents* (1892), where the claimant was the manager of a patent

for an invention and had worked on it for 2 years. The joint owners of the patent then promised him a one-third share in the invention for his help in developing it. It was held that it was understood by both sides that he would be paid, and the subsequent promise to pay merely fixed the amount.

Modern confirmation of this rule was given by Lord Scarman in *Pao On* v *Lau Yiu Long* (1980).

It must not be an existing duty

Doing something that you are already bound to do cannot amount to good consideration. The basic rule can be seen operating in *Stilk* v *Myrick* (1809), when two out of eleven sailors deserted a ship. The captain promised to pay the remaining crew extra money if they sailed the ship back, but later refused to pay. It was held that as the sailors were already bound by their contract to sail back and to meet such emergencies of the voyage, promising to sail back was not valid consideration. Thus the captain did not have to pay the extra money.

However, in *Hartley* v *Ponsonby* (1857), when 19 out of the 36 crew of a ship deserted, the captain promised to pay the remaining crew extra money to sail back, but later refused to pay, saying that they were only doing their normal jobs. In this case, the ship was so seriously undermanned that the rest of the journey became extremely hazardous. It was held that sailing the ship back in such dangerous conditions was over and above their normal duties.

The modern example of *Williams* v *Roffey* (1990) seems to indicate that in business contracts the courts will try to find consideration in circumstances where on the face of it the consideration appears to part of an existing duty. Roffey had a contract to refurbish a block of flats and had subcontracted the carpentry work to Williams. After the work had begun, it became apparent that Williams had underestimated the cost of the work and was in financial difficulties. Roffey, concerned that the work would not be completed on time and that as a result it would incur a financial penalty under his contract with the owner, agreed to pay Williams an extra payment per flat. Williams completed the work on more flats but did not receive full payment. He stopped work and brought an action for damages.

It was held by the Court of Appeal that where a party to an existing contract later agrees to pay an extra 'bonus' in order to ensure that the other party performs his or her obligations under the contract, that agreement is binding if the party agreeing to pay the bonus has thereby obtained some new practical advantage or avoided a disadvantage. In the present case there were benefits to Roffey, including (a) making sure Williams continued his work, (b) avoiding payment under a damages clause of the main contract if Williams was late, and (c) avoiding the expense and trouble of hiring someone else. Therefore, Williams was entitled to payment.

The courts have also been prepared to find evidence of consideration in other duty situations. In *Harris* v *Sheffield United Football Club* (1988), the court ruled that the

In *Harris* v *Sheffield United Football Club* (1988), the court ruled that the large police presence at the football ground for home matches was an extra service going beyond the existing duty of the police

large police presence at the football ground for home matches was an extra service going beyond the existing duty of the police and would have to be paid for by the club.

The courts have also accepted that a promise to do something as part of a contract, which the party is already obliged to do under a contract with a third party, can be good consideration. In *Scotson* v *Pegg* (1861), Scotson was asked by a third party to deliver coal to Pegg. He then contacted Pegg and agreed to deliver the coal, which he was already legally obliged to do, if Pegg would agree to unload it. It was held that this promise to deliver the coal was good consideration.

Part-payment of a debt cannot be consideration for the whole debt

On the basis that consideration must be something going beyond any existing obligations, it follows that part-payment of a debt cannot be satisfaction for the whole debt, unless something else is offered as consideration. *Pinnel's Case* (1602) is the authority for this general principle. In that case, which remains good law, it was held that payment of a lesser sum on the day the debt was due would not be accepted as payment of the whole debt.

There are a number of exceptions to this rule:

❖ when, at the request of the creditor, something else is added to the payment
❖ when, at the request of the creditor, a lesser sum is paid before the date on which it is due (the situation in *Pinnel's Case*)

❖ when, at the request of the creditor, the method of payment is changed; it was held in *D and C Builders* v *Rees* (1965) that payment of a lesser amount by cheque rather than cash is not a sufficient difference to discharge the debt

❖ when there is a composition agreement with the creditors (when the debtor is insolvent, all the creditors might make an agreement to accept a proportion of what they are owed)

❖ when a lesser amount is accepted from a third party, the original debtor cannot then be sued for the full amount; in *Hirachand Punamchand* v *Temple* (1911), it was held that payment of a lesser sum by the debtor's uncle was a full settlement of the debt

❖ the doctrine of promissory estoppel, developed by Lord Denning — the idea that a person is stopped from withdrawing a promise to excuse a party from contractual obligations

Consideration must be provided by any beneficiary under a contract

Some contracts involve an agreement to benefit someone other than the parties to the agreement. For example, in *Tweddle* v *Atkinson* (1861), an agreement was made between William Guy and John Tweddle that each would give a sum of money to William Tweddle, who had married William Guy's daughter. Unfortunately William Guy died before making the payment and William Tweddle sued Guy's estate for the money. His claim failed. The modern law as set out in the **Contracts (Rights of Third Parties) Act 1999** has significantly altered the position of third parties, allowing them to enforce agreements where they are expressly identified as beneficiaries. It is likely that cases such as *Tweddle* v *Atkinson* would be decided differently now.

Questions

1 Give a definition of consideration.

2 Explain what is meant by executory consideration and executed consideration.

3 Make a list of five rules of consideration. Name a case to illustrate each rule.

4 In your own words, explain in what circumstances past consideration may be used in a contract.

5 How was past consideration justified in *Re Casey's Patents* (1892)?

6 In *Pao On* v *Lau Yiu Long* (1980), what conditions did Lord Scarman say should apply in order for past consideration to be valid?

7 Under what circumstances have the courts accepted an existing duty as good consideration?

8 Suggest three exceptions to the rule that part-payment of a debt cannot be satisfaction for the whole debt.

9 What is the effect of the rule that 'consideration must move from the promisee'?

Privity of contract

The basic rule in contract law is that a person who is not a party to a contract can neither sue nor be sued under it. We have already seen in *Tweddle* v *Atkinson* how this rule operates in respect of consideration.

The modern law on privity of contract was set out by Lord Haldane in *Dunlop Pneumatic Tyre Co.* v *Selfridge and Co.* (1915). There was a contract between Dunlop and another company containing a provision that tyres would not be sold on below a fixed price. The tyres were then sold on to Selfridge, with the same stipulation applying. Selfridge then disregarded the stipulation and sold them at a lower price. Dunlop was not able prevent this because 'only a person who is a party to a contract can sue on it' (Lord Haldane) and Dunlop was not a party to the agreement with Selfridge. The party who had contracted with Selfridge could have sued, but it chose not to.

The rule provides important protection for third parties who might otherwise face obligations that they had not agreed to, but it can often appear to frustrate the intentions of those who have entered into a contract. This was clearly the situation in the *Dunlop* case, and it led Lord Dunedin to remark that the effect was to 'make it possible for a person to snap his fingers at a bargain definitely made'.

The rule also creates difficulty in cases where gifts or bequests are made. A person receiving goods as a gift would be unable to sue personally in the event that the goods were defective, and would have to rely on the person who made the gift bringing an action on his or her behalf. Even then, the rule would prevent recovery of losses that were those of a third party rather than those of the person who made the contract. We have already seen in *Tweddle* v *Atkinson* how the rule can defeat the intentions of a testator.

The law has recognised these problems and there are a number of **exceptions to the rule**, as follows.

Legislation for third-party rights

Parliament is able to legislate to create third-party rights, as it did for example in s.148(7) of the **Road Traffic Act 1988**, which requires motorists to take out third-party insurance. This can then be enforced against them by other motorists in the case of injury resulting from an accident.

Restrictive covenants

Land law provides a further exception in the form of restrictive covenants, which bind subsequent purchasers, even though they were not parties to the original agreement. A covenant not to build on a garden area in the centre of Leicester Square, London, was enforced against a subsequent purchaser in *Tulk* v *Moxhay* (1948).

Trusts

Creating a trust is another way of avoiding the strict application of privity of contract, but the courts have been reluctant to accept that a trust exists when it is not explicitly stated.

Collateral contracts

A further way of avoiding privity of contract is to claim that a collateral contract exists. In *Shanklin Pier* v *Detel Products Ltd* (1951), the owners of the pier were assured that the paint supplied by Detel was suitable, and they employed contractors to paint the pier using it. The paint was unsuitable and the court held that a collateral contract existed between Detel and the pier owners.

Lenient interpretation

The House of Lords in *Woodar Investment Development Ltd* v *Wimpey Construction Ltd* (1980) followed the decision in *Jackson* v *Horizon Holidays* (1975) and identified a special group of contracts involving families and other groups, where it was clearly intended that benefits under the contract were to be shared.

Contracts (Rights of Third Parties) Act 1999

The **Contracts (Rights of Third Parties) Act 1999**, which was based on Law Commission recommendations, addresses a number of the issues raised in earlier case law and allows for a wide range of third-party interests to be enforced.

In s.1(1), the Act allows a third party to enforce a contract if it:

❖ contains an express term to that effect, or
❖ purports to confer a benefit on a third party

Note that the Act only allows enforcement where the benefit is intended for a specific person or for a member of a specific group, and where it is clear that the parties intended the benefit to be enforceable by the third party.

The statute has the important consequence of creating certain exceptions to the general rule of privity of contract. Cases such as *Jackson* v *Horizon Holidays*, *Tweddle* v *Atkinson* and *Beswick* v *Beswick* would all presumably qualify today as situations falling within the requirements of s.1 of the Act, and therefore it arguably removes some of the most glaring injustices of the strict application of the doctrine.

In *Nisshin Shipping* v *Cleaves* (2003), a charter contract between ship owners and hirers provided for commission to be paid to brokers. The court held that the contract purported to confer a benefit as required by s.1(i)(b) of the Act and the brokers were therefore able to enforce it. On the face of it, the facts seem similar to those of *Les Affreteurs SA* v *Walford* (1919), where the common law reached a similar conclusion. However, by providing statutory rules, Parliament has made it easier for third parties in a variety of situations to be more confident of enforcing their rights without having to face the uncertainty of judicial interpretation of common-law rules.

Questions

1 In which case was the modern law on privity of contract set out?
2 What is the potential benefit of the rule?
3 Suggest two problems with the rule.
4 Identify three exceptions to the rule.
5 What does s.1(1) of the Contracts (Rights of Third Parties) Act 1999 allow?
6 What important consequences does this provision have?

Intention to create legal relations

In practice, it is easy for agreements to be made that contain offer and acceptance, and in which both parties provide consideration. However, the law recognises that often the parties do not intend to create a legally binding contract. This is particularly so within families and between friends. The law therefore says that there must be an intention to create legal relations. It makes a distinction between social and domestic agreements (where the assumption is that there is no intention to create legal relations) and commercial and business agreements (where the law assumes that the parties intend the agreement to be legally binding).

Social and domestic agreements

Case law suggests that agreements within families will generally be treated as not legally binding. For example, in *Jones* v *Padavatton* (1969), Jones offered a monthly allowance to her daughter if she would give up her job in the USA, come to England and study to become a barrister. Because of accommodation problems, Jones bought a house in London, where the daughter lived and received rents from other tenants. Jones then attempted to back out of the agreement and repossess the house. The court decided that there was no intention to create legal relations and that all the arrangements were just part of ordinary family life.

In *Balfour* v *Balfour* (1919), the issue was the promise made by a husband to pay his wife an allowance while he was abroad. He failed to keep up the payments when the marriage broke down. The wife sued but was unsuccessful, as it was held that arrangements between husbands and wives are not contracts because the parties do not intend them to be legally binding. The court also decided that she had given no consideration for the husband's promise.

In contrast is the case of *Merritt* v *Merritt* (1970). The husband had already left his wife and they met to make arrangements for the future. The husband agreed to pay £40 per month maintenance, out of which the wife would pay the mortgage. When the mortgage was paid off, he would transfer the house from joint names to the wife's name. He wrote this down and signed the paper, but later refused to transfer the house. The court held that when the agreement was made, the husband and wife were no longer living together, therefore they must have intended the agreement to be binding, and their intention to base their future actions on the agreement was evidenced by the writing.

The courts have also had to consider cases that do not just involve members of the same family, and here the principle they apply is that the presumption that the arrangement is purely social will be rebutted if money has changed hands.

For instance, in *Simpkins* v *Pays* (1955), a lodger and two members of a household entered a competition in the lodger's name and paid equal shares. It was held that the presence of the outsider rebutted the presumption that it was a family agreement and not intended to be binding. The mutual arrangement was a joint enterprise, to which cash was contributed on the understanding that any prize would be shared.

Similarly, in *Peck* v *Lateu* (1973), where two women had agreed to share any money won by either of them at bingo, it was held that there was an intention to create legal relations.

In *Parker* v *Clarke* (1960), a young couple, the Parkers, were persuaded by an older couple to sell their house and move in with them. They would share the bills and the younger couple would inherit the house. It was held that the actions of the parties showed that they were serious and the agreement was intended to be legally binding. Therefore the Parkers were entitled to damages.

Commercial and business agreements

There is a strong presumption in commercial agreements that the parties intend to be legally bound. In *Esso Petroleum* v *Customs and Excise Commissioners* (1976), Esso ran a sales promotion that involved giving away tokens showing members of the England World Cup squad. It was held by the House of Lords that there was an intention to create legal relations because 'the whole transaction took place in a setting of business relations', and therefore Esso was bound to keep the promises it made in its advertisements.

An agreement made in a business context is presumed to be legally binding, unless a different intent can be shown, and there are a number of circumstances in which this may occur.

Some agreements contain an 'honourable pledge clause', in which it is specifically stated that the parties do not intend to be legally bound. In *Rose and Frank* v *Crompton Bros* (1925), paper manufacturers entered into an agreement with the claimant to act as sole agents for the sale of their paper in the USA. The written agreement contained a clause that it was not entered into as a formal or legal agreement and would not be subject to legal jurisdiction in the courts, but was a record of the purpose and intention of the parties to which they honourably pledged themselves. It was held that the sole agency agreement was not binding owing to the inclusion of the 'honourable pledge clause'.

Football pools are a specific exception to the rule that agreements of a commercial nature are presumed to be legally binding. In *Jones* v *Vernon Pools* (1938) and *Appleson* v *Littlewoods* (1939), the courts ruled that the statement on the coupon that the transaction was 'binding in honour only' meant that it was not legally binding.

On the other hand, situations where free gifts or prizes are promised *are* deemed to be legally binding, because the purpose is generally to promote the commercial interests of the body offering the gift or prize. In *McGowan* v *Radio Buxton* (2001), a prize in a radio competition was stated to be a Renault Clio car, but when the prize was awarded it was a model car rather than a real one. The radio company claimed that there was no legally binding contract because it was not a commercial arrange-ment. The court, however, held that there was intention to create legal relations and also that, from the transcript of the broadcast, the competition entrants would expect the prize to be a real car.

In *Edwards* v *Skyways* (1964), an airline pilot was made redundant and was informed by his pilots' association that he would be given an *ex gratia* payment (i.e. a gift) by the airline. The airline failed to pay and argued that the use of the words '*ex gratia*' showed that there was no intention to create legal relations. It was held that this agreement related to business matters and was presumed to be binding. The court stated that the words '*ex gratia*' or 'without admission of liability' are used simply to indicate that the party agreeing to pay does not admit any pre-existing liability. It cannot preclude the legal enforceability of the settlement itself by describing the payment as '*ex gratia*'.

Questions

1 Explain how the rules on intention to create legal relations were applied in each of the following cases:

❖ *Jones* v *Padavatton* (1969)

❖ *Balfour* v *Balfour* (1919)

❖ *Merritt* v *Merritt* (1970)

❖ *Simpkins* v *Pays* (1955)

❖ *Parker* v *Clarke* (1960)

2 Identify a case illustrating the presumption that commercial transactions are intended to create legal relations.

3 Suggest two circumstances that would be exceptions to the rule that agreements in a business context are intended to be legally binding.

4 Explain what decisions the courts reached in *McGowan* v *Radio Buxton* (2001) and *Edwards* v *Skyways* (1964).

Sample exam questions

Past and specimen questions (and mark schemes) for this specification are available on the AQA website (www.aqa.org.uk). You are advised to look at these and to write answers to them.

The following questions will also provide practice in answering the kind of problem-solving questions that are likely to be asked.

1 Jim wants to sell his car. He telephones William and offers it to him for £3,000. William says he will think about it. Three days later, William sends an e-mail to Jim, telling him that he will buy the car. Unfortunately, Jim's daughter accidentally deletes the e-mail before he sees it. Meanwhile, Jim advertises the car in the local paper and Mary leaves a message on his answering machine, agreeing to buy the car for the asking price. The next day, both William and Mary arrive with the cash, expecting to take the car away.

With regard to the relevant rules on formation of contracts, consider whether there is a valid contract with either William or Mary.

2 Jane and Cyril are neighbours and often do jobs for each other. When Cyril is away on holiday, his greenhouse is damaged by vandals and Jane knows that his plants will be affected by the cold weather. Jane buys new materials and repairs the greenhouse before Cyril comes back from holiday. On his return, Cyril pays Jane for the materials and he also promises to decorate the back of her house without charge. Jane buys the materials for the decorating, but Cyril tells her a week later that he has changed his mind and will not do the decorating.

Consider what rights and remedies, if any, are available to Jane in connection with Cyril's refusal to keep his promise to decorate the back of her house.

3 X Ltd, a manufacturer, owes its supplier £20,000 for materials. It is unable to pay this because, as a result of an economic downturn, its sales have slumped and it has a lot of unsold stock. The supplier agrees to accept £10,000 to stop himself going out of business. Three months later, the supplier discovers that X Ltd has secured a government contract worth £1 million. The supplier asks X Ltd to pay the remaining £10,000 owed to him, but X Ltd refuses.

Consider what rights and remedies, if any, are available to the supplier.

Further reading

Blood, P. (2007) 'Contract law: bilateral and unilateral contracts', *A-Level Law Review*, Vol. 2, No. 3, pp. 6–7.

Charman, M. (2007) *Contract Law*, chapters 2–4, Willan.

Elliott, C. and Quinn, F. (2007) *Contract Law*, chapters 1, 3, 5 and 6, Pearson Longman.

Smith, D. (2008) 'Acceptance in the formation of contracts', *A-Level Law Review*, Vol. 3, No. 3, pp. 22–25.

Treitel, G. H. (2007) *The Law of Contract*, chapter 2, Sweet & Maxwell.

Chapter 8

Contract terms

Contracts are often the result of negotiations between the parties, and terms that are expressly agreed are based on statements that the parties have made during these negotiations. These statements are known as **representations**. Pre-contractual statements are usually oral, but they could be written or implied from conduct. Representations often have the purpose of inducing or persuading the other party to enter the contract, but as long as they are not incorporated into the contract, they remain representations.

Statements incorporated into the contract, by which the parties intend to be bound, become terms.

In the past, it was more important to distinguish between terms and representations because it was difficult to obtain legal redress from misrepresentations (false or misleading representations) unless they were made fraudulently. Following the passing of the **Misrepresentation Act 1967** and the House of Lords judgement in *Hedley Byrne* v *Heller* (1964), it has become easier to recover damages in cases of misrepresentation, so it is now less important to prove that a statement has become a term of the contract.

Representations that are true present few problems, but false statements can often result in parties forming contracts on terms that they ultimately come to regret and which they may try to challenge.

Whether a statement becomes a term

In order to become a term, a statement must be incorporated and form part of the contract. Whether or not it is incorporated depends on a number of factors.

The importance attached to the statement

It is likely that if a party attaches importance to a statement and relies on it when deciding to enter the contract, the statement will be treated as forming part of the contract. An example is the case of *Birch v Paramount Estates (Liverpool) Ltd* (1956), in which a statement describing a house as being 'as good as the show house' was so central to the agreement that the court held it to have been incorporated.

Special knowledge or skill

The law is more likely to treat a statement by an expert as incorporated into the contract than a statement by a person without specialist knowledge. This can be demonstrated through the contrasting cases of *Oscar Chess Ltd v Williams* (1957) and *Dick Bentley Productions Ltd v Harold Smith Motors Ltd* (1965). In the first case, a statement about a car made by an ordinary person without expertise or specialist skill was treated as a representation, while in the second case, a statement by car dealers about the mileage driven by a car was treated by the court as having been incorporated.

When the statement was made

The nearer in time the statement was to the formation of the contract, the more likely the court is to treat it as having been incorporated. In *Routledge v McKay* (1954), a statement about the manufacture date of a motorbike was made a week before the actual sale. The contract made no mention of age and the court decided that the time delay meant that the statement had not been incorporated.

Whether the statement/agreement was in writing

A statement in writing is usually regarded as a term. If there is a written agreement, any statements made before it was drawn up but not included in it are likely to be treated as representations.

The extent to which the statement is drawn to the other party's attention

Sometimes, a party may want to include something in the agreement that the other party claims not to be aware of. In such cases, the statement only becomes incorporated into the contract if the other party has notice of it. Further discussion of the rules on incorporation is included later in this chapter (pages 121–23).

The 'parol evidence' rule

Under this rule, where an agreement is in writing, oral or other evidence that a party tries to introduce is not admissible if used to add to, vary or contradict the terms in the written contract. This seems reasonable, because it might be assumed that in putting an agreement in writing the parties deliberately choose to exclude other things that may have been discussed prior to the agreement.

An example is the case of *Henderson* v *Arthur* (1907), concerning a lease agreement that included the statement that rent was to be paid in advance. The Court of Appeal held that a previous oral agreement that rent could be paid in arrears could not be substituted for the term now in writing.

However, there are occasions when strict enforcement of this rule is inappropriate. For example, in *Webster* v *Cecil* (1861), a written document showed a price as £1,250, but it was evident from negotiations that preceded the contract that this amount was inaccurate.

Collateral contracts are another way in which an oral statement can be deemed binding, even though it conflicts with a written statement. These arise where verbal assurances have been given that clearly constitute an important reason for a party entering a contract. In *J. Evans* v *Andrea Merzario* (1976), an oral assurance was given that machinery being carried on a ship would be stored below decks. In error, the machinery was stored on deck and was lost overboard. The Court of Appeal allowed the inclusion of the oral assurance in what was otherwise a written contract on standard terms.

Conditions, warranties and innominate terms

It is clear that not all terms in a contract are of the same importance. For example, if a car were delivered with a faulty petrol cap, it is likely that an offer by the seller to replace the petrol cap with a new one would be seen as an acceptable solution. However, if the car had a faulty engine, this would be seen as a breach of a much more important term. The purchaser may well be reluctant to continue with the contract, fearing that repair or even replacement of the engine may still leave him or her with an unreliable car. The law recognises this distinction and identifies important terms as conditions and less important ones as warranties.

Conditions

These are terms that are fundamental to the contract, going to the root of the agreement. A breach of condition will give the injured party the choice of either repudiating (ending) the contract or continuing with it and claiming damages.

Warranties

These are less important terms and entitle the injured party only to damages. The distinction between conditions and warranties can be illustrated by two cases involving opera singers. In *Bettini* v *Gye* (1876), an opera singer was ill and only attended three of the six rehearsal days. However, he recovered in good time for the performance and therefore his breach did not go to the root of the contract and could be treated as a breach of warranty. On the other hand, in *Poussard* v *Spiers and Pond* (1876), the singer missed the final rehearsals and the first 4 nights of a 3-month engagement. It was held that this was a breach of condition, allowing for repudiation of the contract.

Condition or warranty?

The courts decide whether a term is a condition or a warranty in the following ways.

The terms may be specified by the parties

Written contracts may well specify particular terms as conditions, and this is likely to reflect the intention of the parties to treat certain terms as more important than others. In *Lombard North Central* v *Butterworth* (1987), a clause in a contract for the lease of a computer made punctual payments of the hire instalments 'of the essence' of the agreement. The Court of Appeal agreed that when the hirer was late with four of the first six payments, the suppliers were entitled to repudiate the agreement because they had made their intentions concerning the term quite clear at the outset.

However, the court is not bound to treat the term in the way that it is described. For example, in *L Schuler AG* v *Wickham Machine Tool* (1974), a term in an agency agreement that a representative would visit each of the manufacturers each week was referred to in the contract as a condition. Despite this, the House of Lords noted that over the 4 years of the contract some 1,400 visits were scheduled to be made, and that it was almost inevitable that at some point maintaining the schedule of visits might become difficult. It decided that to accept the term as a condition would be unreasonable, because it would allow the contract to be terminated if just one visit out of 1,400 were missed, an event unlikely to be regarded as going to the root of the contract.

Definition in a statute

The implied terms in sections 12 to 15 of the Sale of Goods Act 1979 are described in the statute as conditions. These statutory provisions are not negotiable and it is not open to the parties or the courts to alter their status.

Resolution by the courts

If the parties themselves do not label terms as conditions or warranties, the courts have to decide on a case-by-case basis. In situations where the parties have traded with each other before, or have traded within the same type of business, it is likely

that they will have developed in the 'course of dealing' an understanding of which are the most important terms.

In *British Crane Hire* v *Ipswich Plant Hire* (1975), the court held that it could refer to normal trade practice when deciding how to treat a term that the hirer of equipment should be responsible for returning it to the place of hire.

Innominate terms

The Court of Appeal in *Hong Kong Fir Shipping Co.* v *Kawasaki Kisen Kaisha Ltd* (1962) stated that the traditional approach to classification is suitable for simple contractual undertakings, but that on occasions there are clauses too complicated to be treated in this way. For example, a term might be wide in meaning, such as a claim that something is 'in good condition'. This could be breached in a serious way or in a much more minor way. In effect, the importance of a term only becomes apparent when it is breached in a particular way. Where the status of a term is unknown, it is referred to as an 'innominate term'.

Interpretation of express terms

The courts sometimes have to determine the meaning of a contractual term. Where possible, words are given their natural and ordinary meaning, but sometimes the courts look beyond this when a strict reading goes against what seems to be a sensible interpretation.

In a number of recent decisions, the House of Lords (and Lord Hoffman in particular) has developed an approach characterised by flexibility and a desire to find the meaning that would make sense to a reasonable person.

In *Sirius International Insurance Co.* v *FAI General Insurance Ltd* (2004), it was stated that literalism should be resisted in the interpretive process. Similarly, in *Mannai Investment Co. Ltd* v *Eagle Star Life Assurance Co.* (1997), Lord Hoffman argued that it was necessary to distinguish between the meaning of words in a technical dictionary sense, and what would be understood if the background against which the statement was made were taken into account.

This background information and the circumstances surrounding the making of the contract were described by Lord Wilberforce in *Prenn* v *Simmonds* (1971) as the 'matrix of fact'. Lord Hoffman developed this idea in *Investors Compensation Scheme* v *West Bromwich Building Society* (1998) and said that this matrix of fact includes 'absolutely everything which would have affected the way in which the language of the document would have been understood by a reasonable man'.

It appears from *Prenn* v *Simmonds* and *P and S Platt Ltd* v *Crouch* (2003), however, that pre-contractual negotiations are not part of this background information, and therefore the courts will not look at what was said in the course of negotiations when interpreting the meaning of the words used in the contract.

Implied terms

As well as express terms agreed by the parties, in some circumstances further terms may be read into contracts by the courts. There are different kinds of implied terms:

❖ terms implied by the courts on the facts of the case
❖ terms implied by the courts based on custom and trade usage
❖ terms implied into contracts by statute; the most significant of such terms for our purposes are those in the various **Sale of Goods Acts**

Terms implied as fact

Terms implied as fact are imputed from the intentions of the parties. They may have thought that a particular term was so obvious that it was not necessary to refer to it specifically, or they may have left it out by mistake.

The law has developed two tests to determine whether a term should be written into a contract.

The 'officious bystander' test

The 'officious bystander' test originates from remarks by Mackinon LJ in *Shirlaw* v *Southern Foundries* (1939) that a term may be implied 'if it is so obvious that it goes without saying'.

The officious bystander test cannot be used when one party is unaware of the term. In *Spring* v *National Amalgamated Stevedores and Dockers Society* (1956), a trade union claimed that it was an implied term of a contract with one of the union members that it would comply with the 'Bridlington Agreement', which laid down rules for when members transferred from one union to another. The court rejected this view and said that, if asked by an officious bystander, a member would be likely to have no idea what the 'Bridlington Agreement' was.

The test also does not apply where it is clear that one of the parties would not have agreed to the term if it had been discussed. The Court of Appeal in *Shell (UK)* v *Lostock Garage* (1977) rejected the argument by the garage that in an agreement to buy oil from Shell, a term should be implied to the effect that Shell would not discriminate against it by selling at a lower price to other garages. The court said that Shell would never have agreed to this term.

The business efficiency test

The business efficiency test is used when one party claims that a term must be implied in order for the contract to work as an effective business arrangement. The

leading case is *The Moorcock* (1889), in which the contract was for the unloading of a ship at a wharf on the Thames. Both parties knew that at low tide the ship would have to rest on the river bed; when this happened, it was damaged by a piece of hard rock. The Court of Appeal implied into the contract a term that the ship would be moored safely without damage, because such a term was necessary to give the contract business efficiency.

It was made clear by Lord Pearson in *Trollope and Colls Ltd* v *North West Hospital Board* (1973) that it is not enough that the term is one that would have been adopted by reasonable people if it had been suggested to them; it must be something that they intended to include, 'a term that went without saying' and without which the contract would not work.

In *Liverpool City Council* v *Irwin* (1976), Lord Denning suggested that a term should be implied if it is reasonable in the circumstances. The House of Lords, however, rejected this approach.

Terms implied by custom or trade usage

Terms can be implied if there is evidence that under local custom they would normally be there. For example, in *Smith* v *Wilson* (1832), under local custom 1,000 rabbits meant 1,200 rabbits. However, custom should only support the general purpose and not contradict express terms. This happened in *Les Affreteurs Reunis SA* v *Walford* (1919), where a custom that commission was payable only when a ship was actually hired was contradicted by an express clause in the agreement.

Terms may also be implied if they would routinely be part of a contract in a particular type of trade or business. In *British Crane Hire Corp. Ltd* v *Ipswich Plant Hire Ltd* (1975), for example, the court accepted that the owners' terms for the hire of a crane were based on a model common in the trade and could therefore be implied into the contract.

In *British Crane Hire Corp. Ltd* v *Ipswich Plant Hire Ltd* (1975), the court accepted that the owners' terms for hire of a crane were based on a model common in the trade and could therefore be implied into the contract

Questions

1 Explain the difference between a term and a representation.

2 Why was it more important in the past to distinguish between terms and representations?

3 List three factors that determine whether a statement has become a term, and name a case for each.

4 What approach does the House of Lords appear to have taken in recent cases when interpreting express terms?

5 What is meant by 'matrix of fact'?

6 What is an implied term? What different kinds are there?

7 What are the two tests used to determine whether or not a term should be written into a contract? Identify the leading cases for each.

8 Explain two circumstances in which the first test could not be used.

9 Give an example of a case illustrating local custom and one illustrating trade usage.

Exam hint

It is unlikely that whole questions will be asked on this material, but the ideas discussed here recur in other parts of the specification. For example, incorporation of terms is relevant to whether or not exemption clauses are valid, and the difference between representations and terms is important when considering misrepresentation. The distinction between conditions and warranties is relevant to any discussion of remedies.

Implied terms created by statute

Some terms graduate from being terms implied by the courts to terms implied by statute. For example, many of the implied terms set out in the **Sale of Goods Act 1893** had been habitually implied by the courts in the years before 1893, and so the statute was simply declaring the existing common law. This Act was re-enacted with some amendments in 1979. The general principle of the Act remains that the terms are implied unless there is something that indicates that the parties intend otherwise. However, it is now clear law that, in the interests of consumer protection, certain terms may not be excluded.

The **Sale of Goods Act 1979** applies to a sale of goods, defined in s.2(1) as a 'contract by which the seller transfers or agrees to transfer the property in goods to the buyer for a money consideration, called the price'. It therefore only applies to goods sold for money and does not cover other kinds of transaction, such as the exchanging of goods. The term 'goods' has been interpreted to include packaging and any instructions appearing on the packaging.

Certain provisions of the Act only apply when goods are sold 'in the course of a business', and difficulties have sometimes arisen in determining how far this term extends. It clearly does not apply to private sales by members of the public, such as when a car is sold through an advertisement in a newspaper. However, there are also situations where goods are sold by a business but the sale does not fall within the normal business activity of the company.

In *Stevenson* v *Rogers* (1998), a fisherman, whose normal business was selling fish, sold his boat. The Court of Appeal held that this was still a sale in the course of a business. Having looked at the legislative history of the 1979 Act, the court considered that it was the intention of the legislators to give a wider meaning to this term than in previous versions of the Act, and that it was intended to catch all sales of goods made by businesses, whether or not they were part of their usual type of business.

Terms implied by the Sale of Goods Act 1979

The Sale of Goods Act 1979 adds a number of implied terms to contracts for the sale of goods. Colin Scott and Julia Black, in *Cranston's Consumers and the Law,* point out that Professor Patrick Atiyah describes the provisions in sections 13 to 15 as a gradation in the standards required for products:

❖ Correspondence with description is the lowest standard — a product might be what it claims to be but also be highly defective.
❖ Satisfactory quality is the default requirement applying to all goods.
❖ The highest standard — fitness for a particular purpose — can be applied by the consumer, specifying to the seller the purpose for which the goods are required. This standard may be more demanding than fitness for normal purposes.

Title

Section 12 contains a basic term that is written into all sale of goods contracts: the seller has the right to sell the goods and is able to pass good title. If this term is broken, the purchaser is entitled to his or her money back, even if he or she has used the goods for some time.

In *Rowland* v *Divall* (1923), the claimant bought a car that (it later emerged) had been stolen. The person who sold it was not therefore the legal owner and did not have the right to sell the goods.

Description

Section 13 provides that where there is a sale by description, there is an implied term that goods must correspond with their description.

This section is increasingly important in self-service shopping, where most sales are, in practice, sales by description, with the shopper reliant on signs and descriptions on packaging. It is also relevant whenever goods are not seen before sale, for example with mail order sales or sales over the internet. In practice, it is only where consumers buy a product as a specific thing on their own assessment of its value that there is not a sale by description.

In *Beale* v *Taylor* (1967), a car advertised as 'Herald, convertible white 1961' was actually two half-cars joined together. In *Varley* v *Whipp* (1900), a piece of farming equipment was described as having been used for only one season. On delivery, it was evident that it was old and had been repaired.

There must be reliance on the description. In *Harlington* v *Christopher Hull Fine Art* (1990), there was no reliance on the description of a painting because it was bought at own risk.

Enforcement of s.13 is strict, as illustrated by *Re Moore and Landauer* (1921), in which a quantity of canned fruit was sold 'to be packed in cases of thirty'. On delivery, the quantity was correct, but about half were packed in cases of 24. The court held that the description of the goods — 'packed in cases of *thirty*' — had not been complied with and thus the buyers were entitled to reject. More recently, the House of Lords in *Reardon Smith Line* v *Hansen Tangen* (1976) has suggested that the better approach is not to give the buyer a remedy, however trivial the breach of description, but to ask whether a particular item in a description constitutes a substantial ingredient in the identity of the thing being sold.

Note that the term is not limited to sales in the course of business and therefore also applies to private sales.

Satisfactory quality

Section 14(2) contains an implied term that goods are of satisfactory quality. It applies only to sales in the course of a business and not to private sales.

In the original 1893 Act and in the 1979 Act, the term 'merchantable quality' was used. This was changed to 'satisfactory quality' by s.1 of the **Sale and Supply of Goods Act 1994**. Most of the leading cases are based on the old wording. 'Merchantable quality' implies that the goods are fit to be sold, while 'satisfactory quality' may suggest the state in which the customer is happy to receive the goods and is closer in nature to what consumers would expect of goods they purchase. Section 14(2)(a) of the 1994 Act adds some clarification on the meaning of 'satisfactory', stating that goods are satisfactory if:

> *...they meet the standard that a reasonable person would regard as satisfactory, taking account of any description of the goods, the price (if relevant) and all other relevant circumstances.*

Potentially relevant factors outlined under s.14(2)(b) include:
* fitness for the purpose for which goods of this kind are commonly supplied
* finish and appearance
* freedom from minor defect
* safety
* durability

In *Priest* v *Last* (1903), a hot-water bottle burst. It was clear that it had only one purpose, so this was a breach of 14(2) (as well as 14(3): see below). Another case is *Bartlett* v *Sidney Marcus* (1965), concerning a second-hand Jaguar car. It was pointed out at the time of the sale that the clutch needed some repair. The clutch failed after

300 miles and cost about £80 to fix. The court said that, bearing in mind the description of the car as having a defective clutch and being serviceable in every other way, that it was of 'merchantable' (now 'satisfactory') quality. As a second-hand car, it did not have to be in perfect condition and some defects were to be expected.

In *Brown* v *Craiks* (1970), Lord Reid commented that if you pay a higher price, you can expect higher quality. This was confirmed in *Clegg* v *Andersson* (2002).

The goods need to be satisfactory in their entirety. In *Wilson* v *Rickett Cockerell and Co. Ltd* (1954), coal had an explosive substance mixed with it. The coal on its own was satisfactory, but not when supplied with the explosive substance.

Under s.14(2)(c), you cannot claim that goods are unsatisfactory if:
* the relevant matter is specifically brought to your attention
* you examine the goods and the defect is one that you should have discovered

What this suggests is that no inspection at all may be better than one conducted carelessly. In *Bramhill* v *Edwards* (2004), the claimants bought a motor caravan. They inspected it and commented on how spacious it seemed. They later discovered that it was wider than the maximum permitted under UK law. Their claim failed because having inspected it, they should have checked the measurements, knowing as they did the maximum width allowed by law.

Fitness for purpose

Section 14(3) states there is an implied term that goods are fit for any purpose specifically made known to the seller, unless the buyer does not rely on the seller's judgement or it would be unreasonable for him or her to do so.

Griffiths v *Peter Conway* (1939) is a classic example. Here, a lady who had abnormally sensitive skin purchased a Harris tweed coat that caused her to suffer dermatitis. Her action for breach of fitness for purpose failed because she had not made known her abnormally sensitive skin.

Similarly, the particular purpose was not made clear in *Brown and Son Ltd* v *Craiks* (1970). Cloth manufacturers made woven material for cloth merchants to a detailed specification and it was bought. The merchants intended to resell the cloth for dress material, though this purpose was not intimated to the manufacturers. In fact, it was unsuitable for dress material but nevertheless it was good cloth, and a claim under s.14(2) also failed.

This section, like s.14(2), only applies to sales in the course of a business. It does not apply to private sales.

Sample

Section 15 contains an implied term that where goods are sold by sample, the bulk must correspond to the sample. Also, the buyer must have the opportunity to examine the bulk. Goods supplied must be free from defects that would have been apparent on examination of the sample.

Exclusion of implied terms

Under the Unfair Contract Terms Act 1977, s.12 cannot be excluded from any contract, while sections 13 to 15 cannot be excluded from consumer contracts (where a buyer is not 'in the course of business'), and can only be excluded from other contracts if this is reasonable.

Questions

1 In what sense was the original Sale of Goods Act simply declaring the existing common law?

2 How are 'goods' defined in the 1979 Act?

3 How has the phrase 'in the course of business' been interpreted?

4 Write out a list of the implied terms in the 1979 Act with their section numbers.

5 What does 'passing good title' mean?

6 Why is s.13 becoming more important?

Remedies

The remedies available for breach of these implied terms have been strengthened for consumers by the Sale and Supply of Goods to Consumers Regulations 2002. Before 2002, the law provided two remedies for consumers who receive faulty products in breach of the implied terms: the right to reject the goods and the right to damages.

Right to reject contract and demand return of purchase price

A breach of an implied term is a breach of condition, and this allows the purchaser to reject the goods.

However, this right to reject is lost once the goods have been accepted, and the claim would then be limited to damages. This is the effect of s.11(4) of the 1979 Act, which says that where the buyer has accepted the goods or any part of them, the breach is to be treated as one of warranty. Section 61 provides that the remedy for breach of warranty is damages.

Sections 34 and 35 explain how acceptance occurs:

❖ when the buyer intimates acceptance to the seller

❖ when the buyer does something inconsistent with the seller's ownership after he has had a chance to examine goods, such as in *Perkins v Bell* (1893), where the purchaser inspected a sample of barley, then resold it

❖ when the buyer retains the goods for a reasonable time without indicating he or she is rejecting them

Section 2(6) of the Sale and Supply of Goods Act 1994 states that the buyer must have reasonable opportunity to examine goods, and even having something repaired

may not amount to acceptance. It seems that simply signing a receipt to acknowledge delivery does not amount to acceptance.

Often, the problem is that a product may have a latent defect that does not emerge until some time after the consumer starts to use it. Because acceptance puts an end to the right to reject the goods, this remedy is only available for a short time.

The courts do not seem to have been entirely consistent in the way they have treated acceptance. In *Bernstein* v *Pamson Motors* (1987), the purchaser was deemed to have accepted a car when he had had it for 3 weeks and driven it for 140 miles, while in *Rogers* v *Parish (Scarborough)* (1987), the buyer had the car for several months and it had been replaced, but the Court of Appeal held that it had not been accepted.

Under the 1994 Act, there is a right of partial rejection, where a defect only affects some of the goods and the buyer accepts the remainder. The Act also added the provision that in consumer sales the right to reject is lost when the breach is so slight that rejection would be unreasonable.

Damages

Three situations can be identified where consumers might seek damages rather than reject the product:

* Supplies of the product are limited, so buying an alternative might be difficult.
* A consumer has suffered personal injury because of a faulty product and wishes to sue for consequential loss. The consumer will often be awarded sums far exceeding the value of the product itself. Examples are *Grant* v *Australian Knitting Mills* (1936), where an award of £2,450 was made for dermatitis contracted from underwear, and *Godley* v *Perry* (1960), where an award of £2,500 was made for the loss of an eye caused by a faulty catapult.
* The consumer has lost the right to reject by virtue of accepting the product.

Additional remedies

The **Sale and Supply of Goods to Consumers Regulations 2002** implemented the 1999 European Union **Directive on the Sale of Consumer Goods** and came into effect on 31 March 2003. Under the regulations, consumers have available further remedies.

They can request either **repair** of the goods or **replacement**. The retailer can decline either of these if he or she can show that they are disproportionately costly in comparison with the alternative. However, any remedy must also be completed without significant inconvenience to the consumer.

If neither repair nor replacement is realistically possible, consumers can request instead a **partial or full refund**, depending on what is reasonable in the circumstances. It may be the case that a full refund is not the reasonable option, because the consumer will have enjoyed some benefit from the goods before the problem appeared. This needs to be taken into account before a reasonable partial refund can be assessed. A full refund is referred to as **rescission** and, unlike the remedy of rejection of the contract, is not affected by acceptance of the goods. It is theoretically available for up to 6 years (the full limitation period).

Consumers can switch between certain remedies if they find they are getting nowhere down the route originally selected. However, they would have to give a retailer a reasonable time to honour a request before they tried to switch, and they could never pursue two remedies at the same time.

Questions

1 What were the two remedies available before 2002 for breach of statutory implied terms?

2 Explain the effect of acceptance and how this has been modified by the 1994 Act.

3 Under which three circumstances might a consumer seek damages rather than repudiation of the contract?

4 Explain the additional remedies now available under the 2002 regulations.

Terms implied by the Supply of Goods and Services Act 1982

The **Supply of Goods and Services Act 1982** was designed to cover situations that are not sales of goods. It extends the protection of the implied terms in the **Sale of Goods Act 1979** (SOGA) to goods supplied as part of a service and also to goods that are hired. In addition, the Act sets out implied terms in relation to contracts for services.

Supply of goods

Where goods are supplied as part of a service, the SOGA implied terms apply to the goods. For example, the paint and wallpaper used by a decorator or the fittings installed by a plumber would now be covered by the SOGA implied terms, which are restated in the 1982 Act, so that title is covered by s.2, description by s.3, satisfactory quality and fitness for purpose by s.4 and sample by s.5.

In sections 7 to 10, the same implied terms are extended to any contract for the hire of goods, for example the hire of a car or a television.

Supply of services

Section 12 of this Act defines a contract for the supply of services as 'a contract under which a person (the supplier) agrees to carry out a service'. This means that a wide range of contracts for services is included within the definition, from hair-dressers and shoe repairers to solicitors, architects and doctors providing private medical treatment, and from high-street consumer deals to industrial services such as cleaning and security. Therefore, the Act will apply to such things as electrical

8

David R. Frazier Photolibrary, Inc./Alamy

In *Lockett* v *A and M Charles Ltd* (1938), the court held that the supply of a meal in a restaurant was a sale of goods

rewiring, fitting central heating, installing new windows, dry cleaning, hairdressing, processing photos and holiday accommodation, and it will also apply to professional services such as accountancy, surveying or legal work.

There are some situations where it is not clear whether the contract is for the sale of goods or for services. In *Lockett* v *A and M Charles Ltd* (1938), the court held that the supply of a meal in a restaurant was a sale of goods, but in *Robinson* v *Graves* (1935), the painting of a portrait was held to be a contract of service because the buyer was essentially purchasing the artist's skill and labour, though of course it could be claimed that this would also be true when people ate in a particular restaurant because of the reputation of the chef.

Under sections 13 to 15, certain specific terms are automatically implied in service contracts. These are referred to in the Act simply as terms rather than as conditions. They are therefore treated by the courts as innominate terms, and the consequences of a breach depend on how serious that breach is.

Care and skill

Section 13 provides that in a contract for the supply of a service, where the supplier is acting in the course of a business, there is an implied term that the supplier will carry out the service with reasonable care and skill.

This provision applies to all contracts for services, and is the central implied term of this Act. This is the common-law standard incorporated into legislation. At common law, the duty requires that a business must use the skill appropriate to a reasonably competent member of the relevant trade. For example, a lower standard is required of a jeweller piercing ears than of a doctor.

Expert carpet-layers were held to be in breach of this standard when they left a hall carpet in such a condition that it constituted a danger to anyone occupying the premises, even if such occupiers exercised reasonable care. Motor repairers must provide good workmanship and are liable for defective work carried out by sub-contractors.

The reasonableness standard is similar to that used in negligence and essentially requires the consumer to show not that a service was defective, but rather that the provider was at fault in the way it provided the service. In *Wilson* v *Best Travel* (1993), a customer on holiday in Greece fell through a glass door. Because the glass complied with local standards, the court held that the service had been provided with reasonable care and skill.

Note that the service may not succeed in its purpose, for example to solve a damp problem, but still be done with care and skill.

Time

Section 14 creates the duty to carry out the service within a reasonable time. It is a question of fact as to what is a reasonable time. In *Charnock* v *Liverpool Corporation* (1968), damages were awarded for breach of the implied terms where a car should have been repaired in 5 weeks, but the work took 8 weeks.

Price

Section 15 implies a term that, where the price has not been provided for by the contract or by a course of dealing, the customer will pay the supplier a reasonable charge. It is again a question of fact as to what is reasonable.

The section would be relevant in situations where a builder is carrying out repair work and it is not clear at the outset how much work might be involved, or where a garage is investigating a fault on a car. The section applies irrespective of whether or not the supplier is in the course of business.

Questions

1 What is the effect of (a) sections 2 to 5 and (b) sections 7 to 10 of the 1982 Act?

2 How does the Act define 'supply of services'?

3 Give an example of something that would be treated as a service.

4 Give an example of a situation where it is not clear whether the contract is for goods or services.

5 What does s.13 cover and what is the standard applied?

6 Give examples of situations in which (a) s.14 and (b) s.15 might be applicable.

Exemption clauses

Exemption clauses are terms in a contract that seek to exclude or limit the liability of one of the parties:

* ❖ **Exclusion clauses** exclude all liability in certain events.
* ❖ **Limitation clauses** limit the liability of one party to a specific amount of money smaller than any reasonable pre-estimate of loss.

They can be part of a pre-written document, a separate notice or even be agreed by the parties orally. Such clauses may be a perfectly legitimate device in contracts between parties of equal bargaining power, but where the parties are unequal, it may result in injustice. This is particularly the case in **standard form contracts**, in which suppliers of goods and services seek to exclude or limit their possible legal liability by the insertion of these clauses in their standard contract terms. The widespread use of exemption clauses is associated with the growth of standard form contracts, which probably account for more than 90% of all contracts made. Contracts for travel, car parking, dry cleaning, theatre tickets, insurance and package holidays all regularly use standard printed terms, and most sellers and suppliers of goods have their own terms that are used in every transaction.

Common-law controls

Incorporation

Over the years, the common law has developed rules for determining whether particular exclusion clauses are valid. Essentially, these rules relate to whether or not the clause has been incorporated into the contract.

Incorporation implies that the clause has been agreed by the parties. In practice, the party disadvantaged by the clause may well argue that it did not agree to it, so the issue of incorporation becomes one of deciding whether it was drawn sufficiently to the party's notice. Even though exclusion clauses are now regulated by statute, it is still relevant to consider the issue of incorporation, because a clause that has not been incorporated cannot form part of the contract and therefore cannot be valid in the first place. The person seeking to rely on the exclusion clause must show that it formed part of the contract.

Signed documents

Where an exclusion clause is contained in a document that has been signed, it will automatically form part of the contract. The signer is presumed to have read and understood the significance of all the terms contained in the document. This is known as the **rule in *L'Estrange* v *Graucob*** (1934). In that case, Harriet L'Estrange, a café owner in Llandudno, signed a document without reading or understanding it, but she was held to be bound by it. In *Wilton* v *Farnworth* (1948), the court observed that, in the absence of fraud, a person should not be able to escape the consequences of signing a document by claiming he or she did not understand it. Any weakening of this principle 'would make chaos of everyday business transactions'.

Note that this rule will not be held to apply if the other party has misrepresented the terms of the agreement, as happened in *Curtis* v *Chemical Cleaning and Dyeing Co.* (1951).

For a signature to be effective in incorporating terms, the document signed must be regarded as contractual. A mere receipt or piece of paper for some other purpose is not enough. In *Grogan* v *Robin Meredith Plant Hire* (1996), it was held that a driver's time sheet was not the kind of document that a reasonable person would expect to contain relevant contractual conditions.

Unsigned documents

The exclusion clause may be contained in an unsigned document, such as a ticket or notice, but the burden of showing that the terms have been incorporated is on the party seeking to rely on them. The clause will only form part of the contract if certain conditions are met.

The document must be regarded by a reasonable person as contractual in nature, and as such likely to contain exclusion clauses. In *Chapelton* v *Barry UDC* (1940), it was held that a deckchair ticket would not be thought of as a contractual document. In *Parker* v *SE Railway* (1877), a cloakroom ticket was regarded as a contractual document giving reasonable notice, but in *Sugar* v *LMS Railway* (1941) the words on a train ticket 'for conditions see back' were hidden by the date stamp, and therefore no notice had been given.

Note that even if the document may be regarded as contractual, the person seeking to rely on the exclusion clause must show that reasonable steps have been taken to give notice of the clause to the other contracting party. As Denning LJ commented in *Spurling* v *Bradshaw* (1956):

> *...the more unreasonable a clause is, the greater the notice which must be given of it. Some clauses would need to be printed in red ink with a red hand pointing to it before the notice could be held to be sufficient.*

The 'red hand' rule was also referred to in *Thornton* v *Shoe Lane Parking* (1971), where the exclusion clause was wide, covering injury as well as damage to property, and should therefore have been brought to Thornton's attention in a most specific way. In fact, the clause in question was among other terms and not likely to be seen.

Notice of the exclusion clause must have been given before the contract was made or at the time the contract was made. Attempts to give notice after the contract has been concluded will be ineffective. This was the outcome in *Chapelton* v *Barry UDC* (1940), where a deckchair ticket was brought round after the money hade been paid and therefore after the contract had been formed. In *Olley* v *Marlborough Court Ltd* (1949), a notice on the hotel bedroom door was ineffective because the contract had already been made when checking in at reception; and in *Thornton* v *Shoe Lane Car Parking Ltd* (1971), a notice was situated inside a car park, but the contract was formed at the entrance to the car park, when money was paid into a machine that activated a barrier to allow entry.

If notice has not been given by display, as in a contractual document, it may have been given by a '**course of dealing**', i.e. if a previous course of dealing between the parties on the basis of such terms can be established. In *Hardwick Game Farm* v *Suffolk Agricultural Poultry Producers Association* (1969), the parties had dealt with each other three or four times a month for 3 years and a 'sold note' was sent to the buyer containing terms. This was sufficient to incorporate the terms, even though the buyer had never actually read them. Note that this principle has been accepted more readily in commercial rather than in consumer transactions. In *Hollier* v *Rambler Motors Ltd* (1972), a garage tried to rely on an exclusion clause in a notice displayed inside the garage. However, the court decided that Mr Hollier did not go to the garage frequently enough to have established a course of dealings within which he would have had the opportunity to read the terms. There was a similar outcome in *McCutcheon* v *David MacBrayne Ltd* (1964).

Interpretation

Where a clause is duly incorporated into a contract, the courts will proceed to examine the words used to see if the clause covers the breach and the loss that has occurred. The main rules of interpretation are:

* **Strict interpretation:** an exclusion clause will be effective only if it expressly covers the kind of liability that has, in fact, arisen. A clause, for example, which excludes liability for a breach of warranty will not provide protection against liability for a breach of condition.
* **The *contra proferentem* rule:** if there is any ambiguity or doubt as to the meaning of an exemption clause, the court will interpret it *contra proferentem* — that is, against the interests of the person seeking to rely on it. For example, in *Houghton* v *Trafalgar Insurance Co.* (1954), the word 'load' in a car insurance policy was held not to extend to an excess of passengers.

Fundamental breach

During the 1950s and 1960s, the courts developed the principle that as a matter of law, no exclusion clause could protect a party from liability for a serious breach of contract, even if the wording of the clause clearly covered that breach. However, this idea of 'fundamental breach' was rejected by the House of Lords in *Suisse Atlantique* v *NV Rotterdamsche Kolen Centrale* (1967), and this decision was confirmed in *Photo Productions Ltd* v *Securicor Transport Ltd* (1980).

Questions

1 Explain what is meant by (a) exemption clauses, (b) exclusion clauses and (c) limitation clauses.

2 Why is the issue of incorporation still relevant?

3 What does the rule in *L'Estrange* v *Graucob* (1934) say?

4 When will the rule not apply?

5 What are the conditions that determine whether a clause in an unsigned document will be treated as incorporated?

6 What are the main rules for determining whether the clause covers the breach that has occurred?

7 Explain the principles of law illustrated by each of the following cases:

❖ *Chapelton* v *Barry* (1940)

❖ *Sugar* v *LMS Railway* (1941)

❖ *Spurling* v *Bradshaw* (1956)

❖ *Olley* v *Marlborough Court* (1949)

The Unfair Contract Terms Act 1977

The **Unfair Contract Terms Act 1977** is the most important piece of legislation affecting exclusion clauses: it applies to contract terms and to notices that are non-contractual and purport to exclude or restrict liability in tort. It seeks to limit the circumstances in which terms and notices restricting/limiting liability may apply. Before the Act was passed, the Sale of Goods Act implied terms could be excluded by unscrupulous retailers, and one of the purposes of the Act was to prevent this from happening. In some ways, the name of the Act is misleading, because it deals only with exclusion clauses and not other terms, it does not impose a fairness standard and it is not restricted to contract law but deals with liability for negligence as well. Most of the provisions of the Act apply only to 'business liability', i.e. liability for things done in the course of business or from the occupation of premises used for business purposes. It should be noted that this term includes the professions, government, and local and public authorities. In *Stevenson* v *Rogers* (1999), the sale of a fishing boat by a fisherman satisfied the statutory test of 'in the course of business', even though fishing, not selling boats, was the fisherman's trade.

Dealing as a consumer

The Act affords the greatest protection to consumers, and many of the provisions only apply where one of the parties is contracting as a consumer. Under s.12(1), a person 'deals as a consumer' if:

* he or she neither makes the contract in the course of business nor holds him- or herself out as doing so, and
* the other party does make the contract in the course of business, and
* any goods supplied under the contract are of a type ordinarily supplied for private use or consumption

In practice, judicial interpretation has widened the definition of 'consumer', for example in *Peter Symmons and Co.* v *Cook* (1981) it was widened to include the sale of a Rolls Royce to a partner in a firm of surveyors.

Regulation of exclusion clauses

Exclusion clauses are regulated by the Act in two ways. They are either:

* rendered void and completely ineffective, or
* made subject to a test of reasonableness
  There are guiding principles of 'reasonableness':
* In the case of a contractual term, it must be judged in the light of circumstances at the time the contract was made.
* The Act also makes clear that it is up to the person who claims that a term/notice is reasonable to show that it is.

Clauses that are always void

* Under s.6 and s.7, any clause in a consumer sale that tries to exclude or limit the implied terms in the **Sale of Goods Act** is void. The implied term relating to title (SOGA s.12) cannot be excluded or limited in any contract. The implied terms in SOGA relating to description (s.13), satisfactory quality (s.14(2)), fitness for purpose (s.14(3)) and sample (s.15) cannot be excluded or limited in any consumer contract. This is extended by s.7 to the **Supply of Goods and Services Act** to other contracts under which goods are supplied, e.g. contracts for hire of goods and those involving work and materials.
* Under s.2, any clause that seeks to exclude or limit liability for death or injury caused by negligence is void. This will particularly apply to situations involving the provision of a service where there is an attempt to exclude s.13 of the **Supply of Goods and Services Act**, which requires work to be done with reasonable care and skill.
* Under s.5, a manufacturer's guarantee cannot exclude liability for loss or damage caused by defects in the goods while they are in consumer use. This section is aimed at relations between manufacturer and consumer.

Clauses that are valid if reasonable

In certain situations, clauses are only valid if reasonable. This applies:

* under s.2, to clauses either with consumers or between businesses seeking to exclude or limit liability for negligent loss or damage

* under s.6, to clauses in contracts between businesses that seek to exclude or limit the implied terms
* under s.3, to clauses in consumer contracts or clauses between businesses where written standard terms are used that:
  – seek to exclude or limit liability for any term (other than for breach of implied terms — these will be void), e.g. a clause limiting compensation for delays to a holiday flight
  – permit one party to perform the contract in a different way to that agreed, e.g. a term in a holiday contract allowing the operator to alter flight dates/times or accommodation
  – allow one party not to perform at all, e.g. a clause allowing cancellation of a concert with compensation limited to the cost of the ticket
* under s.8, to clauses that seek to exclude or restrict liability for misrepresentation

What is reasonable?

The test of reasonableness is found in s.11 and schedule 2 of the **Unfair Contract Terms Act 1977**. Section 11(5) places the burden of proof on the party inserting the clause to show that it is reasonable in all the circumstances. In *Warren v Trueprint Ltd* (1986), a limitation clause made the defendants liable only for a replacement film if the original film were lost or damaged during processing. They were unable to show that this clause was reasonable when they lost a couple's silver wedding photographs.

There are tests to be applied in measuring reasonableness. Section 11(1) states that the court should ask whether the term is fair and reasonable when having regard to the circumstances that were, or ought reasonably to have been, known, or in the contemplation of the parties when the contract was made.

Schedule 2 of the Act refers to some potentially relevant issues:

* the relative strength of the parties' bargaining positions: a clause is more likely to be reasonable if the bargaining strength of the parties is comparable or equal and if the buyer could easily be supplied from another source
* whether the customer received an inducement to agree to the term, e.g. a cheaper price
* whether the goods were manufactured, processed or adapted to the buyer's specifications
* whether the customer ought to have expected such a term from customary practice or previous dealings

These guidelines show that common law is still relevant, and they follow many of the rules made by judges. The factors on reasonableness are not closed, and therefore new ones may emerge through judicial interpretation.

Clauses held to be unreasonable

In *Smith* v *Eric Bush* (1990), surveyors negligently conducted a building society valuation in a house purchase, and a defect was missed that resulted in substantial loss to the purchaser. The building society terms contained an exclusion of liability for the accuracy of the valuation report, even though the purchaser was obliged to pay for it. The court held that the exclusion was unreasonable since it should have been obvious that the purchaser would rely on the valuation.

In *Green* v *Cade* (1978), a consignment of potatoes was supplied to a farmer, with a clause requiring any complaint about the consignment to be reported within 3 days of delivery. The crop failed because of a virus within the potatoes that only became apparent when the crop was harvested. The clause was unreasonable because the defect could not have been discovered on inspection at the time of delivery. Similarly, in *George Mitchell* v *Finney Lock Seeds* (1983), cabbage seed supplied was defective. A clause in the contract limited compensation to the cost of the seed, which was about £200. The actual loss was £61,000, which was the whole year's crop. The Court of Appeal stated that the clause was unreasonable.

Reasonable clauses

Watford Electronics v *Sanderson* (2001) is an example of a clause found to be reasonable. In this case, the terms had been agreed by experienced businesspersons of equal bargaining power, and they had negotiated additional clauses to a standard form contract. The Court of Appeal concluded that in situations like this, unless satisfied that one party has in effect taken advantage of the other, or that a term is so unreasonable that it cannot properly have been understood or considered, the court should not interfere with what the parties agreed. A similar approach was taken in *Granville Oil and Chemicals Ltd* v *Davies Turner and Co.* (2003), in which the Court of Appeal indicated that it was concerned about the intrusion of the 1977 Act into contracts between commercial parties of equal bargaining strength.

Although, in general, exemption clauses in consumer contracts are less likely to satisfy the test of reasonableness, those that are well drafted and placed in the right context *can* be reasonable. For example, in *Woodman* v *Photo Trade Processing* (1981), a clause limiting compensation for photographic processing to the cost of replacing the film was held to be unreasonable when a film with wedding photos was lost. However, the court added that such a clause might have been reasonable if it had been made clear that a premium service was available, costing more but without the limitation. In *Waldron-Kelly* v *British Rail* (1981), there was a clause limiting compensation for loss of a suitcase to £27, but the actual value of the suitcase lost was £320, and this was held to be reasonable. In *Wright* v *British Railways Board* (1983), a suitcase was left subject to 'owner's risk' and to a limitation of liability based on the weight of the suitcase. The terms were displayed clearly on a coloured poster and the court held that the Board had done all it reasonably could to bring the conditions to the claimant's notice. It was not reasonable for it to have to bear the cost of insurance, and similar limitations based on weight were in common use among competitors.

Unfair terms in Consumer Contracts Regulations 1999

In 1993, the European Union passed the **Directive on Unfair Terms in Consumer Contracts**. This was initially incorporated into English law by the **Unfair Terms in Consumer Contracts Regulations 1994**, and these have now been replaced by the **Unfair Terms in Consumer Contracts Regulations 1999**. The 1999 Regulations follow the wording of the EU legislation more closely and permit more institutions to enforce the legislation.

They apply to any terms in contracts with consumers, and therefore cover not only exemption clauses, but also any other type of clause considered to be unfair. A consumer is defined as 'any natural person...acting for purposes outside his trade, business or profession'.

The Regulations apply to terms that have not been individually negotiated, but they do not apply to 'core terms', which are those defining the subject matter of the contract, or to the adequacy of the price or remuneration for goods or services provided. The House of Lords, in *Director-General of Fair Trading* v *First National Bank* (2001), held that the expression 'core terms' must be interpreted restrictively, otherwise virtually anything could be regarded as dealing either with the main subject matter of the contract or the price paid by the consumer, thus creating 'a gaping hole' in the protection provided under the Regulations.

The definition of 'unfairness'

Regulation 5 states that a term will be regarded as unfair if it causes a significant imbalance to the detriment of the consumer. Under regulation 6, the unfairness of a term is to be assessed by taking into account the nature of the goods or services, the circumstances under which the contract was made and any other contractual terms on which it is dependent. This replaces the list of factors included in the 1994 Regulations.

For a term to be unfair, the significant imbalance it creates must be 'contrary to good faith'. This means that the parties are required to deal with each other in an open and honest way, taking into account their relative bargaining strengths. Bingham LJ, in *Interfoto Picture Library* v *Stiletto Visual Programme Ltd* (1989), described it as 'playing fair', 'coming clean' or 'putting one's cards face up on the table': 'It is in essence a principle of fair and open dealing.' In *Bairstow Eves* v *Adrian Smith* (2004), a clause in an agreement with an estate agent doubling the commission payable if payment was not made within 10 days of the contract being completed was held to be unfair.

Enforcement

Enforcement is usually conducted by the Office of Fair Trading (OFT), which has wide powers to investigate terms in company standard contracts. In particular, it is required to consider any complaints made about specific terms. In most cases, companies challenged by the OFT have accepted the change suggested or negotiated a compromise, but there is also now the provision in the **Enterprise Act 2002** for the OFT and certain other enforcers to apply for an enforcement order.

Questions

1 Explain what is meant by 'business liability' under the Unfair Contract Terms Act 1977.

2 How does the Act define a consumer?

3 Illustrate how this definition has been widened.

4 List the clauses that will always be void under the Act.

5 What kind of clauses in contracts with consumers will be valid if reasonable?

6 How is reasonableness measured by s.11(1)?

7 Suggest two issues that might be relevant in determining whether the clause is reasonable.

8 Identify two cases in which clauses were held to be unreasonable and two in which clauses were held to be reasonable.

9 What is the origin of the 1999 Regulations?

10 How is 'consumer' defined in the Regulations?

11 Why has the House of Lords defined 'core terms' narrowly?

12 How is 'unfairness' defined in the Regulations?

13 How did Lord Bingham describe the requirement for fairness?

Sample exam questions

Past and specimen questions (and mark schemes) for this specification are available on the AQA website (www.aqa.org.uk). You are advised to look at these and to write answers to them.

The following questions will also provide practice in answering the kind of problem-solving questions that are likely to be asked.

1 Dave agrees to install a new kitchen in Peter's house. After Dave has removed the existing fittings and completed about half of the new installation, Peter discovers that the new fittings are of inferior quality and that Dave has misread the plans in fitting them. When Peter points out the mistakes, Dave tells him that he can make alterations but that he will need an extra £1,000 to install higher-quality fittings and to cover the extra work that would

be involved. At first, Peter agrees to pay the extra money, but he then decides to refuse to pay anything to Dave, stop him doing any further work, and ask someone else to complete the work.

Discuss the rights, duties and remedies of both Peter and Dave in connection with the new kitchen.

2 Harry buys some fireworks from 'Bangers', a specialist shop in the High Street. A notice in the shop warns customers that they use the fireworks at their own risk and that the shop will not be liable for any damage or injury caused by the fireworks. While he is letting them off at a family party, one them explodes prematurely and injures his hand and burns the clothes he is wearing.

Consider Harry's rights and remedies, if any, against 'Bangers' in connection with the sale of the fireworks and the damage and injury suffered.

3 Lesley hires a car from Supercars Ltd to take her to her wedding. The car is hired well in advance and she explains to Supercars what it is needed for. On the wedding day, the car does not arrive and she has to hire a taxi, which costs her £50. She has also arranged for photographs of the wedding to be taken, and she sends the films to be developed at 'ProcessMyPhotos'. When the photos are sent to her, she is told that one of the films was lost and the other damaged, so only five of the 70 photos have been printed. She is also referred to a clause on the outside of the envelope in which she sent the films, which says that in the event of loss or damage to films the liability of 'ProcessMyPhotos' is limited to the cost of replacement films. She is also told that for an extra 50% on top of the cost of developing she could have had the premier service, which carries a guarantee that the company would be liable for any financial loss arising from loss or damage to films.

Consider Lesley's rights and remedies arising out of both these situations.

4 Jamal is a wealthy businessman whose hobby is breeding thoroughbred horses. He buys some special high-protein horse feed mix from Animal Feeds Ltd. The product proves to be faulty because it has become contaminated while being stored in the warehouse owned by Animal Feeds Ltd. As a result of eating this horse feed mix, most of Jamal's horses become ill about 3 months later and three of them die. The contract of sale had a clause stating that the purchaser must inform the seller of any defects in the product within 1 week of purchase.

Consider Jamal's rights and remedies arising out of this situation. Would it have made any difference if Jamal's business had been breeding horses?

Further reading

Charman, M. (2007) *Contract Law*, chapters 6–8 and 16, Willan.
Elliott, C. and Quinn, F. (2007) *Contract Law*, chapters 7–8 and 16, Pearson Longman.
Smith, D. (2009) 'Unfair contact terms: proposals of the Law Commission', *A-Level Law Review*, Vol. 4, No. 2, pp. 28–29.
Treitel, G. H. (2007) *The Law of Contract*, chapters 6–7, Sweet & Maxwell.
Turner, C. (2006) 'Contract and consumer law: exemption clauses', *A-Level Law Review*, Vol. 1, No. 2, pp. 22–25.
Turner, C. (2006) 'Understanding terms in contract law', *A-Level Law Review*, Vol. 2, No. 1, pp. 7–9.

Chapter 9

Misrepresentation

Misrepresentation is a vitiating factor. Vitiating factors have the effect of invalidating consent. This means that although the agreement may appear to be valid because it meets the requirements of offer and acceptance, consideration and intention to create legal relations, something stops this consent being genuine. Besides misrepresentation, there are other vitiating factors. For example, in some circumstances, a mistake by the parties as to the subject matter of the contract will invalidate consent. More obviously, consent achieved by duress or as a result of undue influence will not be considered genuine.

The AQA specification only requires candidates to study misrepresentation.

Untrue statement of fact

Statements made prior to or during contractual negotiations are representations. A misrepresentation is an untrue statement of fact that induces a party to enter a contract, but which is not itself part of the contract.

A representation need not always be verbal. Conduct may amount to representation — for example, payment by cheque implies a representation that the bank will honour the cheque. Lord Campbell in *Walters* v *Morgan* (1861) referred to things such as 'a nod, a wink, a shake of the head or a smile' qualifying as statements.

Failure to disclose

The general rule is that silence does not amount to misrepresentation, and there is no liability for failing to disclose relevant facts to the other party. Lord Campbell in *Walters* v *Morgan* (1861) said: 'Simple reticence does not amount to legal fraud, however it may be viewed by moralists.' Similarly, in *Peek* v *Gurney* (1873), Lord Cairns stated: 'Mere non-disclosure of material facts, however morally censurable, would form no ground for an action for misrepresentation.' *Peek* was applied in *Hamilton* v *Allied Domecq PLC* (2007).

Exceptions

There are, however, some exceptions to this general rule.

First, if a party makes any representation on a particular matter, it must be full and frank, and silence may not be used to distort a positive representation. A half-true statement, which is accurate as far as it goes but which conveys a misleading impression by being incomplete, may give rise to a misrepresentation.

For example, in *Dimmock* v *Hallett* (1866), a seller of land stated that all the farms on the estate were let to tenants, but omitted to add that the tenants had all given notice to leave.

The same point is illustrated by *Spice Girls Ltd* v *Aprilia* (2000). This case concerned negotiations for a sponsorship deal, during which marketing material was made available by Spice Girls Ltd, emphasising the distinct and individual image, style and personality of each of the *five* Spice Girls, when it knew and did not disclose the fact that Geri Halliwell was about to leave the group.

The second exception is that where the contract requires *uberrima fides* (utmost good faith), the party is bound to disclose all material facts. For example, in insurance contracts, the insured party is required to disclose all material facts, whether or not he or she is asked about them.

A company is in a similar position in respect of the sale of shares. Also, in potential 'undue influence' cases, good faith is required of the party supposed to be in the stronger position. And where there is a fiduciary relationship (i.e. a relationship of trust) between the parties to a contract, a duty of disclosure will arise, for example solicitor and client, bank manager and client, trustee and beneficiary, and inter-family agreements.

In *Spice Girls Ltd* v *Aprilia* (2000), Spice Girls Ltd failed to disclose the fact that Geri Halliwell was about to leave the group

What is not a misrepresentation?

A misrepresentation must be distinguished from:

❖ **a mere commendation.** This may be a difficult distinction. An example is *Dimmock* v *Hallett* (1866), in which an estate agent's description of land as 'fertile and improvable' was a mere commendation.

❖ **a statement of opinion.** An example is *Bisset* v *Wilkinson* (1927), in which the seller of a farm that had never had sheep gave it as his opinion that it would support about 2,000 of them. In reality, this was not the case, and the purchaser sought the return of his purchase money. The Privy Council said the statement had not been a representation of fact but merely an expression of the seller's honestly held opinion.

However, a statement of opinion may be regarded as a statement of fact where one party possesses greater skill or knowledge than the other and by implication knows facts that justify the opinion.

In *Esso Petroleum* v *Mardon* (1976), Esso sold a new garage, forecasting that sales of petrol would be roughly 200,000 gallons per year. Actual sales turned out to be less than half of this and the court held that the experience and skill of its market analysts put it in a position where it should have known what the actual prospects were. Its expert forecast was to be treated as a statement of fact.

Misrepresentations must also be distinguished from:

❖ **a statement of future intention.** This could become a misrepresentation if it can be proved that there was no intention to do the promised act at the time the statement was made. For example, in *Edgington* v *Fitzmaurice* (1885), a prospectus inviting loans stated that the money would be used to improve the buildings and extend the business, but the person issuing the prospectus did not intend to use the money in this way.

❖ **a statement of law.** Statements of law are not regarded as statements of fact, and there is an assumption that everyone has equal access to the law. Lawyers or other professionals may, however, be liable for a breach of professional duty.

Inducement to enter a contract

For a claim for misrepresentation to succeed, there must be evidence that the untrue statement of fact induced a party to enter a contract because it relied on that statement.

The question of reliance is particularly important where the party to whom the statement is made is in a position to check its truth for him- or herself. In *Attwood* v *Small* (1838), buyers of a mine were not able to succeed in a claim for misrepresentation because they had relied on the results of their own private survey rather than the statements of the seller.

The misrepresentation does not have to be the only reason why the other party entered the contract. In *Edgington* v *Fitzmaurice* (1885), the claimant was induced to enter the contract partly because of the misrepresentation and partly because he mistakenly believed that it would give him some rights over the property.

Types of misrepresentation

A misrepresentation could arise in a number of different ways. It could be:

❖ a deliberate lie
❖ a statement made carelessly without checking its accuracy
❖ an entirely innocent statement of facts believed to be true

The law classifies these as three different types of misrepresentation. Since the passing of the **Misrepresentation Act 1967**, these distinctions are less important. Originally, only fraudulent misrepresentation was actionable. This is no longer the case, but there are still differences between fraudulent misinterpretation and what the law treats as negligent or innocent misrepresentation.

Fraudulent misrepresentation

Fraudulent misrepresentation occurs when a party makes a false statement without honestly believing it to be true. It may be a deliberate lie, or it may be a statement made recklessly.

The classic definition outlined by the House of Lords in Derry v Peek (1889) is a false statement made 'without belief in its truth, or recklessly as to whether it is true or false'. In that case, a company set up to run trams thought that obtaining Board of Trade consent was a mere formality. In fact, consent was refused, but the court decided that it was an honest mistake, and not fraudulent.

In such cases, there are two remedies available. The injured party may:

❖ affirm the contract and claim damages for consequential loss, suing for the tort of deceit, or
❖ repudiate the contract and claim damages and/or rescission (see pages 137–38)

Common law

In situations that are not fraudulent, it used to be the law that damages were not available, but this changed with the House of Lords judgement in *Hedley Byrne* v *Heller* (1964). Success depends upon proof of a special relationship existing between the parties.

The principle of liability is based on the duty of care in tort, and it seems clear from the case of *Esso Petroleum* v *Mardon* (1976) that such a relationship will be considered to exist where the person making the representation possesses relevant knowledge or skill and would expect the other party to rely on this.

The Misrepresentation Act 1967

Section 2(1) of the Misrepresentation Act 1967 provides that a non-fraudulent misrepresentation will be treated in the same way as a fraudulent one, unless the person making it can prove that he or she had reasonable grounds to believe and did believe up to the time the contract was made that the facts represented were true.

This provision reverses the burden of proof, so that the person to whom the misrepresentation was made does not have to establish a duty of care. Once a party has proved that a misrepresentation induced him or her to enter into the contract, the person making the misrepresentation will be liable in damages unless he or she proves he or she had reasonable grounds to believe and did believe that the facts represented were true.

This burden may be difficult to discharge, as was shown in *Howard Marine and Dredging Co.* v *Ogden and Sons* (1978), where the hirer of barges was told their carrying capacity by the owners, who looked up the information in the Lloyd's register. On this occasion, the register was wrong and the information obtained from the official register of ships was not checked with the barge owners' head office. The court held that the suppliers were negligent and there was a misrepresentation. They had an absolute obligation not to state facts that they could not prove they had reasonable grounds to believe.

In *Spice Girls Ltd* v *Aprilia* (2000), the defendants successfully argued that the failure to disclose the fact that one of the five girl-band members was about to leave the group amounted to a misrepresentation.

If it is established that the misrepresentation was negligently made, the claimant has the choice of whether to sue under the Act or on the basis of the common-law rule in *Hedley Byrne*. If the claim is brought under the Act, there is no need to prove that there is a relationship of proximity as required under *Hedley Byrne*.

Innocent misrepresentation

The emergence of the *Hedley Byrne* principle and the introduction of s.2(1) of the Misrepresentation Act 1967 mean that the only misrepresentations that can be claimed to have been made innocently are where someone makes a statement with an honest belief in its truth. For example, he or she might be repeating inaccurate information supplied by someone else. Even in this case, it may be possible to bring an action in equity for rescission. Also, under s.2(2) of the Act, the court has a discretion to award damages as an alternative to rescission.

1 What is misrepresentation? What are the two requirements for a statement to be a misrepresentation?

2 Under what circumstances might conduct amount to misrepresentation?

3 What is the general rule on whether silence can amount to a misrepresentation?

4 In which modern case was this rule confirmed?

5 What exceptions are there to this rule on whether silence can amount to misrepresentation?

6 Why was *Esso Petroleum* v *Mardon* (1976) decided differently to *Bisset* v *Wilkinson* (1927)?

7 How was fraudulent misrepresentation defined in *Derry* v *Peek* (1889)?

8 How is negligent misrepresentation treated under the common law?

9 Where does the burden of proof lie under s.1(2) of the Misrepresentation Act?

10 Explain the principles of law illustrated by the following cases:

❖ *Walters* v *Morgan* (1861)

❖ *Attwood* v *Small* (1838)

❖ *Spice Girls Ltd* v *Aprilia* (2000)

Remedies

The two main remedies for misrepresentation are rescission and damages, and the injured party makes a decision as to which is appropriate. This is now a genuine choice and is not dependent on the type of misrepresentation.

Rescission

This is an equitable remedy, which sets the contract aside and puts the parties back in the position they were in before the contract was made. It is available for all types of misrepresentation.

The injured party can rescind the contract by notifying the other party, or if this is not possible because of the behaviour of the defaulting party, by taking some reasonable action to indicate the intention to rescind. In *Car and Universal Finance* v *Caldwell* (1965), a person had sold a car but been paid with a dishonoured cheque. The buyer subsequently sold the car on to a third party and disappeared. The original seller was held to have made his intention to rescind clear when he contacted the police and the AA.

Bars to rescission

First, rescission will not be ordered where it is impossible to return the parties to their original pre-contract positions. This would most obviously be where the subject matter of the contract has been used up or destroyed. This was the case in *Vigers* v *Pike* (1842), where restitution of a mine was not possible because considerable extraction had already taken place. Precise restoration is not required and the remedy is still available if substantial restoration is possible.

Second, rescission cannot be ordered where a third party has acquired rights under the contract. In *White* v *Garden* (1851), iron bars had already been sold to a third party and rescission was therefore not possible.

Third, affirmation of the contract (saying or doing something that indicates an intention to continue with the contract) is an important bar to rescission. In both *Leaf* v *International Galleries* (1950) and *Zanzibar* v *British Aerospace* (2000), bringing the action several years after the contract had been made, rather than at a much earlier stage, was held to amount to affirmation. Where the misrepresentation is fraudulent, time runs from the point when the fraud was discovered, or with reasonable diligence could have been. In the case of non-fraudulent misrepresentation, time runs from the date of the contract, not the date of discovery of the misrepresentation.

In *Long* v *Lloyd* (1958), claims were made by the seller of a lorry that were not true. When the lorry developed problems, the buyer telephoned the seller and agreed to share the cost of repair. The court held that this willingness to share the cost of repair amounted to affirmation.

Damages

There are circumstances in which rescission is not an adequate remedy. This is probably the case whenever some kind of consequential loss has occurred, for example the failure of a cooling system with the resulting loss of foodstuffs in storage.

Damages for misrepresentation are calculated on the same basis as they are in tort (see pages 237–39), so that the aim is to put the parties back in the position they were in before the misrepresentation was made. This allows claims for losses caused by the misrepresentation.

It was held in *Royscott Trust Ltd* v *Rogerson* (1991) that damages under s.2(1) of the 1967 Act will be assessed on the same basis as fraudulent misrepresentation.

The remoteness test for common-law negligent and innocent misrepresentation is less generous and is restricted to losses reasonably foreseeable at the date of the misrepresentation.

Where the misrepresentation is innocent, an award of damages is an alternative to rescission and under s.2(2) is at the discretion of the court. Because the two remedies are alternatives, only one can be granted rather than both.

Exclusion of liability for misrepresentation

Section 3 of the Misrepresentation Act 1967, as amended by s.8 of the Unfair Contract Terms Act 1977 (UCTA), provides that:

If a contract contains a term which would exclude or restrict:

(a) any liability to which a party to a contract may be subject by reason of any misrepresentation made by him before the contract was made; or

(b) any remedy available to another party to the contract by reason of such a misrepresentation,

that term shall be of no effect except insofar as it satisfies the requirement of reasonableness as stated in s.11(1) of the Unfair Contract Terms Act 1977; and it is for those claiming that the term satisfies that requirement to show that it does.

Section 11(1) provides that:

...the term shall have been a fair and reasonable one to be included having regard to the circumstances which were, or ought reasonably to have been, known to or in the contemplation of the parties when the contract was made.

This was illustrated in *Walker* v *Boyle* (1982), where there was a clause excluding liability for errors, misstatements or omissions in answers given to preliminary enquiries in the sale of a property. The seller innocently but mistakenly stated that there were no boundary disputes and the court held that the exclusion clause was unreasonable.

Questions

1 What is meant by rescission?

2 Explain three circumstances in which rescission would not be available.

3 Under what circumstances will rescission not be an adequate remedy?

4 How are damages calculated for fraudulent misrepresentation?

5 On what basis are damages calculated under s.2(1) of the Misrepresentation Act 1967?

6 To what extent can liability for misrepresentation be excluded?

Sample exam question

Past and specimen questions (and mark schemes) for this specification are available on the AQA website (www.aqa.org.uk). You are advised to look at these and to write answers to them.

The following question will also provide practice in answering the kind of problem-solving questions that are likely to be asked.

George advertises a second-hand car for sale and Sally agrees to buy it over the telephone, having first asked what the fuel consumption is. George looks at the guide for new cars and tells her that it does 45 miles to the gallon. After using the car for a year, she discovers that it never does more than 30 mpg and she wants to take the car back.

When insuring the car, she says that it will be kept in a garage, but after about 6 months she has the garage converted into an office. Now Sally wants to make a claim because the car was damaged while left outside her house.

Having regard to the relevant rules on misrepresentation, consider Sally's rights and remedies arising out of these two situations.

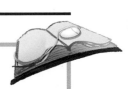

> ### *Further reading*
>
> Charman, M. (2007) *Contract Law*, chapter 11, Willan.
> Elliott, C. and Quinn, F. (2007) *Contract Law*, chapter 9, Pearson Longman.

Chapter 10

Discharge of contract

A contract can come to an end in a number of ways:
* performance
* agreement
* breach
* frustration

Performance

The law expects performance of the terms of a contract to be exact and complete, and each party must carry out its obligations under the contract. In *Re Moore and Landauer* (1921), tins of fruit were packed in wrong-sized cases; therefore, the contract had not been performed and the buyer could reject the whole consignment. A similar outcome occurred in *Arcos v Ronaasen* (1933), where a contract was made for the supply of barrel staves half an inch thick. The staves were about nine-sixteenths of an inch thick when delivered, and the House of Lords held that the purchaser was entitled to reject the consignment, even though the extra sixteenth would make no difference to the usefulness of the staves.

Another case where the courts decided that performance had not been completed was *Cutter v Powell* (1795), in which a seaman died en route and his widow sued for a proportion of his wages. Her claim was unsuccessful because he had failed to fulfil his part of the bargain, which was to complete the voyage.

Per Karlsson — BKWine.com/Alamy

In *Arcos v Ronaasen* (1933), the purchaser was entitled to reject the consignment of barrel staves

Substantial performance

However, the courts do recognise the idea of substantial performance, where the work is almost completed and any minor defects can easily be corrected. Substantial performance can only apply when there is a breach of warranty, because clearly a breach of condition would involve a significant and major failure to fulfil contractual obligations. In practice, therefore, it is a question of degree.

In *Hoenig* v *Isaacs* (1952), a flat was to be decorated and furnished; the customer claimed that the work was incomplete. The court found that although there were defects, they were minor, and that there was substantial performance. However, in *Bolton* v *Mahadeva* (1972), a central-heating system was installed in a house, but the work when completed was seriously defective and the system did not heat the house adequately. As the estimated cost of repairs was about a quarter of the total price, it was impossible to describe the contract as having been substantially performed. Also, the customer had not had a realistic opportunity of accepting or rejecting the incomplete performance offered.

Partial performance

Partial performance is where some work has been done, but it is insufficient to amount to substantial performance. To be valid, partial performance must be accepted by the other party, so that in effect it is entering into a new agreement to pay a lesser amount than the sum agreed under the contract, for a reduced amount of work. Payment would be made on a *quantum meruit* basis (literally, 'as much as is deserved'). The party not at fault must have a genuine choice about whether to accept partial performance. In *Sumpter* v *Hedges* (1898), a builder left construction of houses and stables half done, and the claimant had no choice but to have the work finished. This could not therefore amount to partial performance.

Sometimes an issue arises over the time allowed for completion. Late performance will always amount to a breach of contract, giving rise to a damages claim, but it will only give the right to terminate the contract if the delay constitutes a substantial failure to perform or if 'time is of the essence'. Where it *is* of the essence, any failure to perform on time will justify termination of the contract, even if little hardship is caused.

Time becomes of the essence if it is explicitly stated in the contract, or if it can be inferred from the nature of the agreement. An example would be a contract involving perishable goods or goods where the price fluctuates. Time may also become of the essence if, following a delay in performance, the injured party gives notice of a time limit on performance. This happened in *Charles Rickards* v *Oppenheim* (1950) where, having accepted a delay of 3 months in the delivery of a car, the customer gave

notice that a further delay would lead to him cancelling the order. Following this further delay, the court held that time had now been made of the essence and the customer was entitled to refuse to accept the car.

Vicarious performance

Another issue that may arise is completion by a third party, referred to as 'vicarious performance'. The rule here is that in situations that are not of a personal nature, providing that all the terms of the contract are met, vicarious performance is acceptable. In contracts where individual skills are involved, for example the painting of a portrait, vicarious performance is unlikely to be appropriate.

In *Edwards* v *Newland* (1950), the court held that the choice of a particular firm for the storage of goods was because of its specific skills, and that passing the goods to someone else was not acceptable.

Agreement

This occurs where a contract is abandoned or its terms are varied by agreement. Since both parties enter into a new agreement, both must provide consideration for it to be valid. For example, in a contract to decorate two rooms, the decorator might have other urgent work to do and the customer might change his or her mind about the second room. The agreement to release the decorator from the obligation to continue would be consideration for the decorator's agreeing not to charge part of the money originally agreed.

Breach

Whenever a party fails to perform an obligation under a contract, it is said to be in breach of contract.

Breach through failure to perform

Actual breach

An actual breach is when there is a failure to fulfil an obligation under the contract, or to fulfil it to the required standard. An example is the case of *Pilbrow* v *Pearless de Rougemont and Co.* (1999), where an appointment was made for an interview with a solicitor. The client was not told that the person conducting the interview was not a solicitor. Even though the standard of work provided was that of a competent solicitor, the court held that there was a failure to perform the contract because the firm had not supplied what the contract specified.

Anticipatory breach

An anticipatory breach occurs when one party shows by express words or by implications from his or her conduct at some time before performance is due that he or she does not intend to observe his or her obligations under the contract.

In cases of anticipatory breach, the injured party is not under any obligation to wait until the date fixed for performance before commencing his or her action, but may immediately treat the contract as at an end and sue for damages. This principle was established in *Hochster* v *De La Tour* (1853), where an employer told his employee (a travelling courier) before the time for performance arrived that he would not require his services. The courier sued for damages at once, and the court held that he was entitled to do so.

The injured party in an anticipatory breach of contract also has the option of waiting for the performance date to pass and then suing for breach. This is what happened in *Avery* v *Bowden* (1855), although in this case the delay was unwise because a war broke out and performance of the contract became illegal.

In cases of anticipatory breach, it is important to ascertain whether, once repudiation has been communicated to the injured party, that party chooses to accept it. In *Vitol SA* v *Norelf Ltd* (1996), the House of Lords held that silence or inaction can amount to acceptance of a wrongful repudiation of a contract.

The effects of breach of contract

The rights of the injured party depend on the nature of the term broken.

A **breach of condition** is a breach of an important term, giving the right to terminate the agreement and repudiate (cancel) the contract. Where the injured party elects to repudiate for a breach of condition, the general effect is to terminate the contract from the date of this election. Thus, all obligations accruing before that date remain to be performed, but all those accruing after it are avoided. So, in an appropriate case, the injured party that elects to repudiate may sue for damages for non-performance of those obligations that remain to be performed.

A **breach of warranty** is a breach of a minor term that does not go to the root of the contract. It only gives rise to a claim for damages.

What this means in practice is that the injured party is prevented from using a minor breach of contract as an excuse for cancelling the whole contract. If, for example, a new car is delivered that has a faulty interior light, it is reasonable to expect the supplier to put it right at his or her expense (damages), but unreasonable to allow the purchaser to cancel the contract and demand his or her money back. If, on the other hand, there is a series of technical failures, which are not easy to put right and which result in the car breaking down, you can see that these relate to the very purpose of the contract and understand why in this situation the law might allow the purchaser to cancel the contract and buy a different car elsewhere.

If there is a breach of an **innominate** term in a contract (i.e. a term that could be either a condition or a warranty), and if the results are so serious as to undermine the foundation of the contract, the injured party has the right to terminate the contract. The injured party may elect to affirm the contract, and if this is done, the contract remains in force and the injured party may sue for damages.

Repudiatory breach

Another circumstance in which the wronged party may choose to discharge the contract is where there has been a repudiatory breach by the other party. This is where that party makes it clear that it no longer intends to be bound by the contract.

The courts are reluctant to find that there has been a repudiatory breach. In *Woodar Investment Development Ltd* v *Wimpey Construction Ltd* (1980), Lord Wilberforce said repudiation was a drastic conclusion that 'should only be held to arise in clear cases of a refusal, in a matter going to the root of the contract, to perform contractual obligations'. The more recent cases of *Vaswani* v *Italian Motors* (1996) and *Martin-Smith* v *Williams* (1999) have confirmed this reluctance. The latter case concerned circumstances surrounding the break-up of the pop group Take That, and in particular the allegation by Robbie Williams that the manager of the group had committed a repudiatory breach. The court held that the conduct of the manager, though opposed to what Robbie Williams wanted, was not a repudiatory breach because he was offering advice in the best interests of all the members of the group.

How the injured party responds to a breach

A contract is not automatically ended by a breach, because the injured party has the choice of treating the contract as discharged or continuing with it.

If the injured party decides to treat the contract as discharged, that decision must be communicated in a clear and unequivocal manner. However, the House of Lords held in *Vitol SA* v *Norelf Ltd* (1996) that communicating this decision required no particular form, and that in some circumstances mere silence and a failure to carry out contractual obligations would be sufficient. In Lord Steyn's words: 'Sometimes in the practical world of businessmen, an omission to act may be as pregnant with meaning as a positive act.'

Mitigation of loss

Sometimes, the injured party may choose to continue by fulfilling its part of the contract. The injured party may not always be able to insist on affirming the contract, however, because (under the principle of mitigation of loss) it usually has a general duty to take reasonable steps to mitigate its loss.

In *White and Carter (Councils) Ltd* v *McGregor* (1962), the claimants opted to affirm the contract. The court upheld this, but added the conditions that it must be possible to carry out the contract without needing the other party's cooperation and there must be a 'legitimate interest' in pursuing the contract.

Because the injured party has an obligation to try to mitigate its loss, it is unlikely in practice that the decision in *White and Carter* will be applied frequently. The judgement in the *Clea Shipping Corp.* v *Bulk Oil International Ltd (The Alaskan Trader)* (1984) would seem to confirm that the courts are unlikely to be sympathetic when there is clearly no legitimate purpose in continuing with the contract (see Chapter 10).

Questions

1 What is the expectation of the law in terms of performance?
2 Explain what is meant by 'substantial performance'.
3 Under what circumstances might partial performance be valid?
4 Under what circumstances might vicarious performance be acceptable?
5 Explain the difference between actual breach and anticipatory breach.
6 What options are available for the claimant in cases of breach of condition?
7 Under what circumstances might the courts accept the idea of repudiatory breach?
8 Explain the principles of law illustrated by the following cases:
   * *Arcos* v *Ronaasen* (1933)
   * *Hoenig* v *Isaacs* (1952)
   * *Sumpter* v *Hedges* (1898)
   * *Hochster* v *De La Tour* (1853)
   * *Vitol SA* v *Norelf Ltd* (1996)

Frustration

The old common law, as illustrated in *Paradine* v *Jane* (1647), contained a doctrine of absolute contract, under which contractual obligations were binding no matter what might occur. In this case, the fact that land was occupied by a foreign army during the English Civil War did not excuse the tenant from his obligation to pay rent for it. The doctrine of frustration was developed as a way of easing the hardship this rule might cause in cases where the contract could not be properly fulfilled through no fault of either party.

The most widely accepted test of frustration is that set out by Lord Radcliffe in *Davis Contractors* v *Fareham UDC* (1956), namely that:

> *...frustration occurs whenever without default of either party a contractual obligation has become incapable of being performed because the circumstances in*

which performance is called for would render it a thing radically different from that which was undertaken by the contract.

Frustration therefore arises when an event occurs, during the lifetime of the contract, which is not the fault of either party and which makes completion of the contract impossible or illegal or radically different. It is important to notice that the substance of the agreement itself must be undermined and it is not sufficient that completion is only made more difficult or expensive. The example of frustration in *Taylor* v *Caldwell* was that a music hall was hired for a series of concerts on certain dates, but before those dates arrived the hall was destroyed by fire.

Usually the parties allow for such circumstances within the contract itself, where they are foreseeable. This is the case, for example, with tickets for watching sporting events that might be affected by the weather. Tickets for test match cricket have specific terms relating to how much cricket has to be played for the customer not to be entitled to a refund. In situations like this, the terms of the contract apply and there is no frustration.

Tickets for test match cricket have specific terms relating to how much cricket has to be played

Circumstances amounting to frustration

Impossibility

The example in *Taylor* v *Caldwell* (1863) is of destruction by fire. In *Morgan* v *Manser* (1948), a music hall compère was called up for war service, and as a result he would not be available to fulfil the contract.

Genuine incapacity through illness would also make completion impossible, as in *Condor* v *Barron Knights* (1966), in which a member of a pop group fell ill and was advised by his doctor to reduce his workload. The group replaced him with another performer, and the court held that the contract had been frustrated.

Illegality

The fulfilment of a contract might be rendered impossible due to the passing of a new statute or the outbreak of war making the provisions of the contract illegal.

Radical change in circumstances

Two cases concerning the postponement of the coronation of Edward VII illustrate that the change in circumstances must be such that the original contract no longer has any purpose.

In *Herne Bay Steamboat* v *Hutton* (1903), an agreement was made for the hire of a ship 'for the purpose of viewing the naval review and for a day's cruise around the fleet'. On the day in question, the fleet was assembled but the royal review was cancelled because of the king's illness. The Court of Appeal said the contract had not been frustrated, because the review was not the sole foundation of the agreement and the cruise around the fleet could still have taken place.

However, in *Krell* v *Henry* (1903), the contract was for the hire of a flat in Pall Mall to watch the coronation procession as it passed. The Court of Appeal said the contract had been frustrated; although the purpose of the hire had not been stipulated in the contract, the circumstances were such that both parties clearly knew it, and the sole foundation of the contract had been destroyed.

Limits to frustration

The courts have to determine whether there is genuine frustration or whether it is just being used as an excuse for breach of contract. The courts are wary of allowing claims too easily, for fear of opening the floodgates. Where a contract is merely more onerous, more expensive or takes longer to perform, it will not be frustrated. Often, such events could be foreseeable and the parties could frame the terms of their agreement accordingly. The following cases illustrate the way in which law has set limits to the application of the doctrine.

In *Maritime National Fish* v *Ocean Trawlers* (1935), the owners of a fishing operation signed a contract to hire a fifth trawler before applying for fishing licences. They applied for five licences and were granted three, which they allocated to three other vessels. The Privy Council said their claim that the contract had been frustrated could not succeed; the lack of a licence for the chartered boat was a matter of their own choice, and a party cannot rely on frustration that is wholly or partly self-induced.

In *Davis Contractors* v *Fareham UDC* (1956), the claimants agreed to build some houses for the council, within 8 months and at a predetermined price. Unfortunately, an unexpected national shortage of skilled labour meant that the contract took 22 months to complete and cost considerably more than had been envisaged. The builders claimed the original contract had been frustrated and sought a *quantum meruit* payment over and above the contract price. The House of Lords said there had been no frustration; the contract had not become impossible to perform, and the rise in costs was a risk that the builders must have accepted when making the contract.

The court also took the view that the events that caused the delays were within the range of things that could reasonably be expected to happen when building houses.

There was a similar outcome in *Tsakiroglou v Noblee and Thorl* (1961).

Legal effects of frustration

A contract that is frustrated comes to an end as soon as the frustrating event occurs, automatically and without further action by either party. All further obligations are then annulled, but the contract is not in itself void and past obligations generally remain in force. The common-law rule was that any losses lay where they fell, and that payments in advance were not generally recoverable.

This 'all or nothing' approach had the potential to cause unfairness, as was evident in *Fibrosa Spolka Akcyjna v Fairbairn Lawson Combe Barbour Ltd* (1943), a case that resulted from the German occupation of Poland during the Second World War.

This situation was changed by the **Law Reform (Frustrated Contracts) Act 1943**, which applies only to frustrated contracts and not to those terminated in other ways.

Section 1(2) gives a right to recover money already paid under such a contract and to withhold anything still payable, but allows the court (if it considers it just) to permit the payee to retain (or claim) an amount not exceeding any expenses he or she has incurred before termination in pursuance of his or her obligations. The court therefore has no discretion over the recovery of monies paid, only over whether to allow the other party to claim expenses.

Section 1(3) provides that where a party has received some valuable benefit (other than the payment of money) under the contract before its discharge, the court may order him or her to make an appropriate payment to the other party.

The effect of this is to return all money to the original position, allowing the court to apportion losses fairly between the parties so that either party can be reimbursed for expenses or for goods or services already obtained under the contract. One problem is deciding whether the valuable benefit is the work itself or the end product. For example, if a building is constructed that is then burned down so that the contract is frustrated, the owner of the building could not be said to have received a valuable benefit and presumably under s.1(3) would not be expected to pay for the work done.

In *Gamerco SA v ICM/Fair Warning (Agency) Ltd* (1995), the court concluded that its task was 'to do justice in a situation which the parties had neither contemplated nor provided for, and to mitigate the possible harshness of allowing loss to lie where it had fallen'.

On the whole, the statute seems to have been effective in apportioning losses fairly, and few cases have arisen under it.

Questions

1 What is the most widely accepted test for deciding when frustration occurs?

2 How can the parties allow for frustration within the contract itself?

3 What are the three circumstances that may amount to frustration? Illustrate each of these using case law (using your own research if necessary).

4 Identify two cases in which a claim of frustration was rejected.

5 What was the common-law rule on the effects of frustration on a contract?

6 What changes did the Law Reform (Frustrated Contracts) Act 1943 make?

7 What difficulties have arisen in determining whether a party has received a 'valuable benefit'?

Sample exam questions

Past and specimen questions (and mark schemes) for this specification are available on the AQA website (www.aqa.org.uk). You are advised to look at these and to write answers to them.

The following questions will also provide practice in answering the kind of problem-solving questions that are likely to be asked.

1 Y Ltd contracts to build 10 houses on land owned by Z Ltd for a total price of £2 million. It is prevented from starting the work because of a dispute with local residents over planning permission, which results in an unexpected delay and also in Y Ltd being told by the planning authority to make expensive alterations to its plans. A further delay is caused when unusually heavy rain causes a river to burst its banks and flood the area, leading to concerns from prospective purchasers that the site might be vulnerable to flooding in the future. By the time it is ready to start building work, house prices have fallen and Y Ltd says that it would be uneconomic to build the houses, claiming that the contract has been frustrated.

Taking into account the rules on breach and frustration of contract, consider the rights and remedies available to Z Ltd.

2 A school hires a coach and driver from Coaches Ltd to take students to a concert to be given by a well-known pianist. At the last minute, the concert is cancelled because the pianist is taken ill. The school has paid the full cost of the hire to Coaches Ltd, and Coaches Ltd has contracted to pay a driver.

Having regard to the relevant rules on termination of a contract by frustration and by breach, consider the rights and remedies that might be available to the school.

Further reading

Charman, M. (2007) *Contract Law*, chapter 14, Willan.
Elliott, C. and Quinn, F. (2007) *Contract Law*, chapter 14, Pearson Longman.
Treitel, G. H. (2007) *The Law of Contract*, chapters 19–20, Sweet & Maxwell.

Chapter 11

Remedies

There are three kinds of remedies you need to know about:

❖ remedies for breaches of statutory implied terms
❖ remedies for breach of contract
❖ remedies for misrepresentation

Remedies for misrepresentation are discussed in Chapter 9, and so will not be dealt with here. Remedies for breaches of statutory implied terms were discussed in Chapter 8; they are revised briefly here, but you should look again at the fuller explanation in that chapter. This chapter deals mainly with remedies for breach of contract.

Remedies for breaches of statutory implied terms

As an alternative to damages for breach of contract, the law provides the remedy of rejection of the contract for breach of the implied terms contained in the **Sale of Goods Act 1979** and the **Supply of Goods and Services Act 1982**.

Additional remedies are now available under the **Sale and Supply of Goods to Consumers Regulations 2002**, which implemented the 1999 EU **Directive on the Sale of Consumer Goods** and came into effect on 31 March 2003. Under the Regulations, consumers can request either repair of the goods or replacement. The retailer can decline either of these if he or she can show that they are disproportionately costly in comparison with the alternative. However, any remedy must also be completed without significant inconvenience to the consumer.

If neither repair nor replacement is realistically possible, consumers can request instead a partial or full refund, depending on what is reasonable in the circumstances. It may be the case that a full refund is not the reasonable option because the consumer will have enjoyed some benefit from the goods before the problem appeared. This needs to be taken into account before a reasonable partial refund can be assessed. A full refund is referred to as rescission, and unlike the remedy of

rejection of the contract is not affected by acceptance of the goods. It is therefore theoretically available for up to 6 years (the full limitation period).

Remedies for breach of contract

Repudiation of the contract

As you saw in Chapter 10, repudiation of the contract is only available when there has been a breach of condition. It is a far-reaching and drastic remedy, and will result in any goods supplied or money paid under the contract being returned.

Damages

This remedy is always available for all kinds of breach of contract, and may well be appropriate even in cases where the contract has been rescinded. It is an award of money that aims to compensate the injured party for the financial losses it has suffered as a result of the breach. It is the usual remedy, and damages are available as of right where a contract is breached.

The purpose of damages

The principle as stated in *Robinson* v *Harman* (1848) is that:

> *...when a party sustains loss by reason of a breach of contract he is, so far as money can do it, to be placed in the same situation with respect to damages as if the contract had been performed.*

Three factors are taken into account when determining whether an award of damages should be made:
* It must be clear that the defendant is the cause of the loss.
* The loss must be within the parties' contemplation and not be too remote.
* The claimant has a duty to mitigate the loss.

Causation

There must be a causal link between the breach of contract and the damage suffered. This is a question of fact in each case.

If the loss arises partly from the breach and partly as a result of intervening events, the party in breach may still be liable, providing the chain of causation has not been broken. For example, in *Stansbie* v *Troman* (1948), a decorator failed to lock the premises he had been working in and a thief entered and stole property. He was liable for the loss because it was the result of his failure to comply with his contractual duty to secure the premises on leaving.

In *The Monarch SS Co. Case* (1949), a ship owner was not liable to a charterer when, as a result of delay, the ship ran into a typhoon, because such an event could have occurred anywhere at any time.

Remoteness of damage

The courts have to decide how far the losses suffered by the injured party should be recoverable. The principle used is that losses are recoverable if they are reasonably within the contemplation of the parties as a probable result of the breach.

This principle is known as the **rule in *Hadley* v *Baxendale* (1854)**. In that case, a new mill shaft was ordered and the carrier was late in delivering it, with the result that the whole mill was out of action for several days. The carriers said that they had not been told that the existing shaft was broken and therefore they did not know that their delay would result in the mill being unable to function. It was held that they were not liable for the loss of profit. The court judgement was that damages should only be awarded for losses that could fairly and reasonably be considered to have arisen naturally, in the usual course of things, or those as may be supposed to have been 'in the contemplation' of the parties at the time they made the contract as the probable result of it.

The application of the principle can be illustrated by the case of *Victoria Laundry* v *Newman Industries* (1949), in which a boiler was not delivered on time. Damages for the loss of profits from the laundry business were recoverable, but losses from not being able to take up a lucrative dyeing contract for the Ministry of Supply were not recoverable because the defendant company had no knowledge of this contract and it could not be expected to have had it in contemplation.

Once it is established that a particular type of loss is within the contemplation of the parties, it does not matter if the actual loss turns out to be greater than could have been foreseen. In *Wroth* v *Tyler* (1974), the breach of contract resulted in the sale of a house being delayed. House prices rose rapidly during the period of the delay and the court held that the defendant could not escape liability just because he could not have contemplated the extent of the loss. This point was confirmed in *Brown* v *KMR Services* (1995).

Mitigation

It is the duty of every party claiming damages to mitigate loss. This means that it needs to ensure that as far as possible losses are kept to a minimum. There are three rules:

* The claimant cannot recover for loss that could have been avoided by taking reasonable steps.
* The claimant cannot recover for any loss that has actually been avoided, even if the claimant went further than was necessary in compliance with the above rule.
* The claimant may recover loss incurred in taking reasonable steps to mitigate loss unsuccessfully.

British Westinghouse v *Underground Electric Railway of London* (1912) concerned a contract for the supply of turbines. Those supplied were less efficient, and used more coal. The buyer accepted them and used them, before replacing them with turbines that were more efficient than those specified in the original contract.

It was held that there was no duty to mitigate by buying new turbines, but since this had been done, the financial advantages gained from new turbines had to be taken into account. Because the new turbines were so efficient, they more than covered the additional costs involved in replacing the original turbines, and so the buyer was not entitled to damages. However, if the buyer had claimed damages before purchasing the new turbines, it would have been successful.

Claimants are only expected to do what is reasonable. In the *British Westinghouse* case, it was said that they would not be expected to 'take any step which a reasonable and prudent man would not ordinarily take in the course of his business'.

For example, in *Pilkington* v *Wood* (1953), the claimant bought a house with defective title because of his solicitor's negligence. The solicitor argued that the claimant should have mitigated his loss by suing the vendor. The court held that 'the duty to mitigate does not go so far as to oblige the injured party to embark on a complicated and difficult piece of litigation against a third party...in order to protect his solicitor from the consequences of his own carelessness'.

Liquidated damages

Sometimes the parties may agree in advance what would be reasonable compensation in the event of a breach, and this is referred to as 'liquidated damages'. However, the courts will only accept this sum if it represents an accurate and proper assessment of loss. If not, it will be treated as a 'penalty' and be unenforceable. A penalty clause, rather than seeking to give a genuine estimate of the likely loss in the event of a breach, threatens to penalise the party in breach. In *Bridge* v *Campbell Discount Co.* (1962), a depreciation clause in a hire-purchase contract for a car was treated as a penalty because it did not reflect the actual depreciation in value.

In *Dunlop Pneumatic Tyre Co.* v *New Garage and Motor Co.* (1914), the House of Lords set out the criteria for determining when a liquidated damages clause will be treated as genuine. It concluded that an extravagant sum will always be a penalty; payment of a large sum for failure to settle a small debt would also probably be treated as a penalty, as would a single sum being the fixed damages for a variety of different kinds of breach.

Unliquidated damages

These are damages that have not been agreed to in advance, and they are determined by the court.

Quantifying damages

The courts can award unliquidated damages on the basis of three different assessments:

* **Substantial damages** are designed to compensate for actual losses suffered. This is the usual basis on which damages are calculated.
* **Nominal damages** are where the court awards a very small amount, indicating that although technically the party has a claim, the court does not feel that compensation is appropriate. An example is *Staniforth* v *Lyall* (1830), in which a boat owner hired his boat out to someone else immediately after a breach of contract, and made a larger profit than he would have done if the original contract had been completed. The court held that he had suffered no loss and awarded nominal damages. Similarly, in *Charter* v *Sullivan* (1957), a buyer refused to take delivery of a car, but demand for the model in question outstripped supply and the seller was easily able to sell it to someone else. The seller was therefore awarded nominal damages.
* **Exemplary damages** are also possible, where the court uses its power to award a much larger sum than would be needed to compensate the injured party. This would demonstrate the court's disapproval of the party at fault.

Because the aim of damages is to put the injured party as far as possible in the position it would have been in if the contract had been performed properly, how damages are assessed depends on the circumstances of the case. We have already seen that where no loss is suffered, the court may order nominal damages. There are a number of other bases on which the calculation could be made. It could be based on the difference in value between the goods or services contracted for and the value of those actually delivered, or the difference between the contract price and the market price if goods have to be obtained or sold elsewhere. The basis might also be the loss of profit as a result of the contract not being completed, or even the loss of an opportunity as in *Chaplin* v *Hicks* (1911).

Another possibility is claiming for expenses incurred in advance of the contract. This is known as 'reliance loss' and is an alternative to loss of profit, where this is difficult to calculate. For example, in *Anglia Television* v *Reed* (1972), the television company spent large sums on scriptwriters, technical staff and other expenses in preparation for a film. When the main actor contracted to make the film pulled out, there was no appropriate substitute and the film project was abandoned. It was easier to calculate the expenses incurred than to estimate loss of profit from the film, and the claim was therefore made on the basis of reliance loss.

In certain circumstances, damages may be awarded for more intangible loss, such as mental distress. In *Cook* v *Spanish Holidays* (1960), damages for loss of enjoyment were paid to a honeymoon couple who were left without a room on their wedding night.

Equitable remedies

Equitable remedies, unlike damages, are discretionary. They are awarded by the court only if the circumstances of the case warrant their use, for example when the award of damages would be an inadequate remedy and justice would not be served.

❖ **Rescission** is a specific remedy applicable in cases of misrepresentation and is discussed in Chapter 9.

❖ An **injunction** may also be an appropriate remedy, for example to prevent someone from acting in breach of contract. It might be used to enforce a contract in restraint of trade or to enforce a provision protecting trade secrets or specialist information.

❖ '**Specific performance**' is an order of the court to make a party carry out its obligations under the contract. It would be appropriate only in situations where the subject matter of the contract is unique in some way, such as in *Falcke* v *Gray* (1859), where the contract concerned a valuable work of art.

Questions

1 What is the purpose of damages in contract cases?

2 What are the three factors a court will take into account when determining an award of damages?

3 Explain the rule in *Hadley* v *Baxendale* (1854) in your own words.

4 Which losses in *Victoria Laundry* v *Newman Industries* (1949) were not recoverable and why?

5 What are the three rules relating to mitigation of losses?

6 What are liquidated damages?

7 What is meant by nominal damages? Identify a case in which they were awarded.

8 Suggest three bases on which losses might be calculated.

9 Explain what equitable remedies are available and when their use might be ordered.

10 Explain the principles of law illustrated by the following cases:

   ❖ *Robinson* v *Harman* (1848)

   ❖ *Pilkington* v *Wood* (1953)

   ❖ *Chaplin* v *Hicks* (1911)

   ❖ *Anglia Television* v *Reed* (1972)

   ❖ *Cook* v *Spanish Holidays* (1960)

Exam hint

It is likely that any question on the contract law examination paper will ask you to comment on both rights and remedies. There is not likely to be an exam question on remedies alone, and certainly one has not been set by AQA in recent years. You should look at the relevant practice questions at the end of other chapters and on the AQA website (www.aqa.org.uk) to apply your knowledge of remedies.

Further reading

Charman, M. (2007) *Contract Law*, chapter 15, Willan.
Elliott, C. and Quinn, F. (2007) *Contract Law*, chapter 15, Pearson Longman.

Chapter **12**

Evaluation of contract law

This chapter provides guidance on answering part (c) questions, where you are expected to evaluate how effectively the law operates and comment critically on the rules of law outlined and applied in the problem-solving parts. It is crucial to be aware of the problems and issues that have been identified over the years, so that you can tailor your knowledge to fit the requirements of the exam question.

Formation of contract

It is likely that your exam paper will contain an evaluation question on some aspect of formation of contract. Evaluation of offer and acceptance is generally the most popular question for candidates, because of the wealth of material that can be discussed, but it is also important to prepare answers on consideration and intent to create legal relations.

Identifying offer and acceptance

It is essential to identify what constitutes offer and acceptance and decide when and where the contract was formed. On the whole, the rules on offer and acceptance are straightforward, once you have a sound understanding of:
* the difference between offers and invitations
* counter-offers
* what constitutes acceptance
* when acceptance occurs

However, be aware that there are some situations where the rules do not seem to operate clearly. The case of *Clarke* v *Dunraven* (1897), for example, does not seem to fit with conventional ideas of offer and acceptance. In that case, it seemed that when competitors entered a yachting competition, a contract was created between all the competitors, even though there was no specific offer and acceptance between individual competitors.

Sometimes, there are situations where it is difficult to determine what constitutes an offer. One approach, favoured by Lord Denning in *Gibson* v *Manchester City Council* (1979), is to look at negotiations as a whole rather than identify offer and acceptance specifically. It was often his approach to look for the right outcome and then adapt the legal rules to achieve that outcome. The same solution was adopted in *Butler Machine Tool Co. Ltd* v *Ex-Cell-O Corporation* (1979). The problem with this approach is that it leads to uncertainty.

Offers and invitations to treat

Are the rules that distinguish offers from invitations satisfactory? A good answer will briefly outline the relevant rules and comment on them. Are the cases decided appropriately? It is likely that most people will agree that the rules on self-service stores are sensible, but what about the outcome of *Fisher* v *Bell* (1961)?

There is still confusion in some areas when deciding whether something is an offer or an invitation to treat, for example with timetables and tickets for transport. A bus journey is clearly a contract, but when do offer and acceptance occur? What constitutes the offer? Is it the timetable, or running the bus, or perhaps allowing someone on the bus? Is the offer made by the person getting on the bus? One possible solution is to apply the approach in *Thornton* v *Shoe Lane Parking* (1971). Car park owners make the offer by having the machine ready for use, and acceptance occurs when the customer uses the machine. By analogy, the passenger accepts the offer by travelling on the bus.

A bus journey is clearly a contract, but when do offer and acceptance occur?

One consequence of the current law on offers and invitations is that in retail situations, the seller retains ultimate control over whom to sell to. It is based on the principle of freedom of contract and Winfield (*Law Quarterly Review* 1939) made the case for it, arguing that 'a shop is a place for bargaining and not compulsory sales'. He went on to say that if displaying goods constituted an offer, shopkeepers would be forced to sell to their worst enemy. But are we satisfied with the view that the seller should be entitled to sell to whom he or she wants?

Another issue is the difficulty in distinguishing between counter-offers and requests for information. Do you think the rules are sufficiently clear in this area?

Acceptance

What constitutes acceptance?

Because acceptance in unilateral contracts can be through conduct, it may not always be clear when performance constituting acceptance has started. In contracts with estate agents, the contract is only made when a buyer is found and the sale goes through. Any preparatory work by the estate agent in looking for buyers does not form part of the contract, but applying this rule to preparatory work in all contractual negotiations would be potentially unjust. The law is unclear on how to deal with this problem, although academics have suggested various solutions.

That the offer is accepted when work is started seems to be the clearest solution, but there is still the difficulty of determining when performance begins. Because the offeree has not promised to complete performance, he or she is free to stop at any time. It would therefore arguably be unfair in many situations to allow acceptance to be valid from the first act. Looking for a lost item but not finding it would not be performance, but perhaps once it is found, even if not yet returned, performance has begun. But equally it would be unfair in other circumstances, when a substantial amount of work has been done, for the offeror to revoke the offer.

The Law Commission in 1975 suggested that if the offeror has said that the offer will be open for a specific period, it should not be revocable within that period.

The postal rule

The main problem with the postal rule is that the offeror may not be aware of acceptance. Some decisions, such as in *Re London and Northern Bank* (1900) and *Holwell* v *Hughes* (1974), do address specific anomalies, but the broader issue is whether this rule is any longer appropriate in view of the other means of communication now available. The postal rule arose when there were few other means of communication, and without it, contracting parties who posted letters of acceptance would have been unsure whether their acceptances had been successful. In the twenty-first century, a person accepting an offer can easily check whether any e-mailed acceptance has been received, possibly using an instantaneous method of communication, such as the telephone or fax.

Fewer and fewer contracts are made by letter, so the postal rule is becoming less relevant, but there may still be situations where it would apply. Delivery by courier is similar to sending a letter, therefore it could be argued that the postal rule should apply in that situation.

Even when acceptance is delivered, there is still the issue that letters opened in the front office may not be seen by the intended recipient until much later.

The use of electronic communications

Because some modern methods of communication are considered to be instantaneous, other problems arise. How should we treat e-mails delivered when an office is closed? Lord Denning in *Entores* v *Miles Far East* (1955) suggested that the burden should rest with the person accepting an offer to make sure his or her communication has been received. For example, if the phone goes dead, there is a need to phone again. With telex, it is clear to the sender if it has not got through, and therefore he or she would need to make further contact. With e-mails it is easy to check whether the e-mail has been opened by means of read receipts or by phoning for confirmation. This approach was confirmed by the House of Lords in *Brinkibon* v *Stahag Stahl* (1983), and it does seem to be reasonable to put the onus on the person accepting to check that the acceptance has been received.

Messages left on answer phones pose further problems. Cheshire and Fifoot in *Law of Contract* (2006) argue that it is reasonable to assume that anything arriving during office hours has been received.

Another issue is whether a person can countermand acceptance by a faster method such as the phone. It seems reasonable that the person who has posted an acceptance should be able to countermand it by telephone or e-mail.

Problems caused by standard form contracts

The battle of the forms and the 'last shot' principle are discussed on page 92. The examples of cases there (such as *British Road Services* v *Crutchley*, 1968 and *Butler Machine Tool Co. Ltd* v *Ex-Cell-O*, 1979) demonstrate the problems the law has in deciding what constitutes offer and acceptance. In *Davies* v *William Old* (1969), for example, a building company's standard form contract with shopfitters said that it would not pay until it had itself been paid. It was held that this was accepted by shopfitters when they started the work.

However, sometimes situations arise that are impossible to resolve. In *BSC* v *Cleveland Bridge and Engineering Co.* (1984), the parties were never able to agree on a BSC disclaimer and a written agreement was never made. However, the work was carried out. The judge found that there was total disagreement over a major term, and therefore concluded that no contract was made.

Consideration

Adequacy and sufficiency

A number of questions might be considered here. For example, is it fair that something that is not of the same market value can be good consideration? Also, is it helpful to have a distinction between sufficiency and adequacy? The courts are not interested in whether it is a good or a bad bargain, but simply that a bargain exists.

What is adequate is the decision of the parties themselves, therefore is it necessary to say that there must be sufficiency: something real, tangible and with some actual value?

Past consideration rules

The outcome of cases involving the past consideration rule (for example *Re McArdle*, 1951) does not seem to be fair. *Re Casey's Patents* (1892) did allow payment for what appeared to be work done in the past, but this seemed to be because it was carried out on the understanding of payment. Look back at this case (pages 94–95) and reflect on whether you think the rule has worked fairly.

On the other hand, it could be argued that the past consideration rule is fair, because it prevents the unscrupulous from forcing people into contracts on the basis of providing goods or services that they have not ordered.

Existing duty rules

Williams v *Roffey* (1990) shows that the courts are making efforts to consider the business reality of the situations facing parties in commercial contracts. However, it seems unlikely from cases like *Re Selectmove* (1995) that this development will be taken any further.

Promissory estoppel seems a fair solution to the problem of promises to accept part-payment of debts. Applying the part-payment rule could create unfairness, but promissory estoppel is subject to many conditions. For example, Lord Birkett said that it should be 'a shield and not a sword', and also there is some uncertainty about aspects of it. It is clear, as Lord Roskill said in *Brikom Investments* v *Carr* (1979), that it would be wrong to extend it to the point of abolishing the doctrine of consideration.

Part-payment and consideration

The rule that without consideration a promise to accept part-payment is not binding was criticised by the Court of Appeal in *Couldery* v *Bartrum* (1881), to the effect that a creditor may accept anything in satisfaction of his or her debt, for example 'a horse, a canary, or a tom tit ' — anything, that is, 'except a lesser sum of money'. It could be argued in defence of the rule that it protects creditors who are in a weak bargaining position from being forced into accepting less than they are owed.

Perhaps one solution would be to extend the rule in *Williams* v *Roffey*, so that there has to be a practical benefit in order to accept part-payment. But is practical benefit sufficient to be consideration? The Privy Council accepted that it was in *R* v *Attorney General* (2003), where the consideration for an SAS soldier not to be able to publish his memoirs was the practical benefit of not being demoted to the rank of an ordinary soldier.

The future of consideration

Both *Williams* v *Roffey* and promissory estoppel seemed to be an attack on the doctrine of consideration, and Professor Atiyah suggested that if you have offer, acceptance and intention to create legal relations, there would be no need for consideration.

Lord Mansfield at the end of the eighteenth century argued that a moral obligation could amount to consideration, but this view was firmly overruled in *Eastwood* v *Kenyon* in 1840.

There are circumstances in which rigid adherence to the rule can arguably defeat the intentions of the parties. If there is obvious agreement between the parties, it seems unnecessary to add the further requirement of consideration.

In addition, it seems to make no sense that parties can agree to a gratuitous promise and rely on it and not have a legally binding agreement, whereas it would become binding if a peppercorn were provided in return. Putting the agreement in the form of a deed seems on the face of it a reasonable solution, though to take advantage of it the parties would probably need to have access to legal advice.

The Law Revision Committee in 1937 proposed reforms to the use of consideration. These included the suggestions that:

❖ a written promise should always be binding, with or without consideration
❖ past consideration should be valid
❖ performance of an existing duty should be good consideration
❖ a creditor should be bound by a promise to accept part-payment in full settlement of a debt

To date, none of these proposals has been adopted.

However, one reform has been made. The **Contracts (Rights of Third Parties) Act 1999** has corrected a number of unfair aspects of rules on third-party consideration. For example, cases like *Tweddle* v *Atkinson* (1861) would be likely to be decided differently today.

Intention to create legal relations

Relatively few problems come before the courts that are specifically related to intention to create legal relations. One reason for this is that many of the situations where it might be a relevant issue are domestic or social, and often there is no consideration. It could be argued that there is no need for a separate requirement of intention to create legal relations, and that providing there is valid offer and acceptance and consideration is present, there should be no reason in law why the agreement should not be valid. Feminists have argued that the requirement serves to reinforce the stereotype of the woman in the home not contributing anything of economic value.

Balfour v *Balfour* (1919) is an example of a case where there was offer, acceptance and consideration, and yet the agreement was not legally binding. The crucial element in this case was the intention of the parties, and there would seem to be a case for insisting that a contract must reflect what the parties genuinely intend.

Scrutton LJ in *Rose and Frank* v *Crompton* (1925) commented that he could 'see no reason why, even in business matters, the parties should not intend...to exclude all idea of settling disputes by an outside intervention'. The important point in business arrangements is that the parties have to make it clear that they do not intend the agreement to be legally binding, whereas in social and domestic agreements there is a presumption that legal relations are not intended.

A further point that could be made is that the 'binding in honour' exception for football pools agreements does not seem to be justified and can result in unfairness in cases like *Jones* v *Vernons Pools* (1938).

Contract terms

The following issues might be considered.

The conditions/warranties distinction is arguably fair because of the emphasis on how relatively important the term is. The contrast between the situations in *Bettini* v *Gye* (1876) and *Poussard* v *Spiers* (1876) would seem to warrant the terms being treated in different ways. Inevitably, there are situations where the law has difficult judgements to make. *Schuler* v *Wickham* (1974) demonstrates that it may not always be enough to rely on how the parties themselves describe the term.

Does the idea of having innominate terms create welcome flexibility or confusion? The idea certainly clouds the distinction between conditions and warranties, and yet it recognises the reality of what parties do in practice and gives flexibility. It enables the courts to deal with each case on its particular merits. On the other hand, there is the contrasting advantage of the certainty that would be provided by having terms that were fixed in their effect.

The value of statutory implied terms

The implied terms in the Sale of Goods Act 1979 and the Supply of Goods and Services Act 1982 provide important safeguards for consumers.

How effective do they seem to be? Look at pages 112–15. Do the provisions seem to work in a sensible way? Look particularly at the cases dealing with description. Have the courts applied the right balance when interpreting the statutes? Is the decision in *Reardon Smith* v *Hansen Tangen* (1976) an improvement on the position in *Re Moore and Landauer* (1921)? Think also about the recent decisions in *Clegg* v *Andersson* (2002) and *Bramhill* v *Edwards* (2004).

Note that the 1982 Act provided protection for those hiring goods and extended the Sale of Goods implied terms to goods supplied as part of a service, as well as introducing specific terms in respect of services. These are important additions to the rights of consumers.

Have changes in the 1994 Act improved consumer protection?

The change of wording from 'merchantable quality' in s.14(2) of the **Sale of Goods Act 1979** (SOGA) to 'satisfactory quality' in s.1 of the **Sale and Supply of Goods Act 1994** was an attempt to make the section clearer, although it could be argued that both terms are equally vague. Perhaps there is a change of emphasis: 'merchantable quality' implies that the goods are fit to be sold, while 'satisfactory quality' may suggest the state in which the customer is happy to receive the goods. It is closer in nature to what consumers would expect of the goods that they purchase. The 1994 Act also adds some clarification on the meaning of 'satisfactory'.

The **Sale and Supply of Goods Act 1994** further modifies the law in relation to acceptance of goods. Section 2(6) states that the buyer must have reasonable opportunity to examine goods, and that even having something repaired may not amount to acceptance. It seems that simply signing a receipt to acknowledge delivery also does not constitute acceptance.

Under the 1994 Act, there is also a right of partial rejection, where a defect only affects some of the goods and the buyer accepts the remainder. The Act also added the provision that in consumer sales the right to reject is lost when the breach is so slight that rejection would be unreasonable.

One problem is often that a product may have a latent defect, which does not emerge until some time after the consumer starts to use it. Because acceptance puts an end to the right to reject the goods, the remedy of rescission is only available for a short time.

The courts do not seem to have been entirely consistent in the way they have treated acceptance. In *Bernstein* v *Pamson Motors* (1987), the purchaser was deemed to have accepted a car when he had had it for 3 weeks and driven it for 140 miles. In *Rogers* v *Parish (Scarborough)* (1987), in contrast, the buyer had the car for several

The courts have not been entirely consistent in the way they have treated acceptance: compare *Bernstein* v *Pamson Motors* (1987) and *Rogers* v *Parish* (1987)

Shepic/Alamy

months and it had been replaced, but the Court of Appeal held that it had not been accepted.

Freedom of contract

Wider issues of freedom of contract could be considered. Is it right that the law should interfere with what the parties have freely contracted to do? Most commentators would accept that the protection afforded to consumers is necessary. The original Sale of Goods Act was passed in 1893, at a time when freedom of contract was regarded as a more sacred doctrine than it is today; and the provisions of that original statute were themselves based on rules that had been developed by the common law. Until the passing of the **Unfair Contract Terms Act 1977**, it was possible for one party to exclude the Sale of Goods Act provisions, and in terms of freedom of contract this is the more significant statute.

Note the distinction between business and private sales. Is the law right to treat these differently? It is arguably advantageous that weaker parties should be protected, for example in dealings with retailers. Think about the advantages that the retailer possesses in terms of knowledge about the product and access to advice and legal support.

The treatment of exemption clauses

Exemption clauses may be a perfectly legitimate device in contracts between parties of equal bargaining power, but where the parties are unequal, it may result in injustice; this is particularly the case in standard form contracts. Suppliers of goods and services have sought to exclude or limit their possible legal liability by the insertion of these clauses in their standard contract terms, which consumers have to accept and almost certainly will not understand.

Sometimes in the past, these exemption clauses have been far-reaching, and the courts have been hostile to them. Despite this, it is true to say that the common law ultimately proved unequal to the ingenuity of those who sought the protection of the exemption.

Look at the treatment of such clauses by the common law. The emphasis is on incorporation and interpretation, rather than on the actual merits of the clauses. However, note Lord Denning's efforts with the 'red hand' rule to address more fundamental concerns. How successful do you think these were?

The **Unfair Contract Terms Act 1977** (UCTA) does seem to have been successful in addressing the issues that the common law was not able to deal with. In particular, it introduced the idea of the consumer sale, allowing the law to offer specific protection to the most vulnerable. It also deals with standard form contracts.

Does the Act strike the right balance? Does it deal appropriately with exclusion clauses between businesses?

Overlap between UCTA and Unfair Terms in Consumer Contracts Regulations 1999

This is an important area to consider. Note that the Regulations originate from a European Union directive, and that although they overlap with UCTA provisions in some respects, they are wider than these because they do not just apply to exclusion/limitation clauses. However, also note that in some respects they are narrower, in that they only apply to consumer contracts where the terms are not individually negotiated.

Because the Regulations and the UCTA overlap, there is the danger of confusion, especially as the test of unfairness in the Regulations is quite different to the approach in the UCTA. The Law Commission was therefore asked in 2001 to investigate whether it would be possible to produce a single piece of legislation, which would make the law clearer for consumers. It was also asked to respond to the concerns of small businesses (i.e. those employing fewer than 9 people) that when negotiating with large commercial organisations, they were often in the same vulnerable position as consumers. For example, small businesses frequently signed contracts containing unfair terms, which the existing law did not allow them to challenge. This was especially true where a small farmer, manufacturer or builder supplied a much larger business. The small business might be required to indemnify the larger business for losses that are not its fault, or forfeit deposits, or accept variations of price after the contract has been agreed. They might also find that the larger business has reserved the right to terminate a contract at will, or for only a minor default, while the small business is bound more rigorously by the contract.

The resulting report, 'Unfair terms in contracts' (2005), recommended the introduction of a single Act, replacing the Regulations and the UCTA. The report also recommended the extension to small businesses, in certain circumstances, of the protection offered to consumers.

The report was accompanied by a draft bill, which covers all terms currently dealt with by the Regulations and not just the exemption terms covered by the Act. Whenever there were differences between the Regulations and the Act, the draft bill adopted the option that best protected the consumer. In respect of small businesses, the bill allowed them to challenge any standard term of the contract that had not been altered through negotiation and was not the main subject matter of the contract or the price. Excluded from this 'micro-business' protection were contracts for financial services, contracts over £500,000 and situations where the apparently

small business is associated with other businesses, so that overall the group has more than 9 employees.

In July 2006, the government accepted the report and undertook to introduce the recommendations 'as soon as is practicable'.

Enforcement

Enforcement in relation to exemption clauses is usually by the OFT, and it has wide powers to investigate terms in company standard contracts. In particular, it is required to consider any complaints made about specific terms. In most cases, companies challenged by the OFT have accepted the change suggested or negotiated a compromise, but there is also now the provision in the Enterprise Act 2002 for the OFT and certain other enforcers to apply for an enforcement order.

This approach can be contrasted with the traditional requirement for aggrieved parties to take action themselves through the courts. It is entirely in keeping with the modern emphasis on consumer rights, which has given the state a much more significant role in enforcement. Enforcement is now much less dependent on proving a contractual relationship and much more concerned with providing effective protection. The Consumer Protection Act 1987 and the Trade Descriptions Act 1968 are examples of measures that are not based on proving a contractual relationship.

The Law Commission report expressed some frustration about the difficulty small businesses faced with enforcing existing rights. The Commissioners commented that many small businesses had told them about unfair terms that could be challenged under the present law, but which were still used because the small business lacked the ability to bring court action. They added that in an ideal world, a well-resourced organisation would use preventive powers to protect small businesses generally, by challenging those that imposed unfair standard terms on them. However, they had not been able to find an organisation with the resources to take on this task.

The roles of common law and statute

This section provides material that could be used to illustrate the contrasting roles of common law and statute. It can be seen particularly in respect of common-law approaches to implied terms as compared with the statutory provisions, and in the way exemption clauses are dealt with.

Misrepresentation

The distinction between terms and representations has already been considered, and the provisions of the Misrepresentation Act 1967 are outlined in Chapter 9.

In the past, because of the lack of remedies for non-fraudulent misrepresentation, it was important to try to argue that a statement had been incorporated and become a term; incorporation in the contract meant that remedies for breach of contract became available. It is arguable that since the 1967 Act this is not an issue.

Types of misrepresentation

In the past, the definitions were more significant because damages were only available for fraudulent misrepresentation through the tort of deceit. The only remedy for other kinds of misrepresentation was rescission. The Misrepresentation Act is a significant improvement. All the remedies are now available for all types of misrepresentation and distinctions are less significant. The 1967 Act followed the recommendation of the Law Reform Committee that damages should be available for negligent misrepresentation. The effect of s.2(1) is particularly significant in allowing a claim without having to prove fraud or the special relationship under *Hedley Byrne*. Also under the 1967 Act, the burden of proof is reversed. The defendant must demonstrate that he or she held a reasonable belief in the truth of the statement.

The effect of all these measures is to make it easier to obtain redress for innocent or negligent misrepresentation.

An evaluation question on misrepresentation would require you to contrast the situation before the 1967 Act with the situation today and to draw attention to the improved remedies available for negligent and innocent misrepresentation. Further guidance is provided in the section on remedies below.

Remedies

The basic issue to consider is whether the remedies are adequate.

Remedies for breach of contract

Damages are always available for all kinds of breach of contract. It is the usual remedy, and damages are available as of right where a contract is breached. In many cases, it is possible for an award of damages to place the claimant in the same situation as if the contract had been performed. The requirements that the defendant must be the cause of the loss, that the loss must not be too remote and that the

claimant must mitigate his or her loss would appear to be reasonable and ensure fairness between the parties.

Equitable remedies, unlike damages, are discretionary. They are awarded by the court only if the circumstances of the case warrant their use, for example when the award of damages would be an inadequate remedy and justice would not be served. They are therefore a valuable tool in several unusual cases.

An injunction, for example, may be used to prevent someone from acting in breach of contract. It might be used to enforce a contract in restraint of trade or to enforce a provision protecting trade secrets or specialist information.

Specific performance would be appropriate only in situations where the subject matter of the contract is unique in some way, such as in *Falcke* v *Gray* (1859), where the contract concerned a valuable work of art.

Remedies for misrepresentation

The remedy of rescission is equitable and therefore discretionary, and it is available for all types of misrepresentation. However, there are a number of circumstances in which it is not available. These are considered on pages 137–38.

One problem is that it may not be the claimant's fault if any of these events have occurred, and it could therefore be argued that it is not fair that the remedy of rescission is lost.

Before 1964, the only remedy for non-fraudulent misrepresentation was rescission, and damages were not available unless fraud could be proved. This situation changed through *Hedley Byrne* (1964), a tort case, and the **Misrepresentation Act 1967**, which provides a specific remedy of damages where recission would have been available if the misrepresentation had been fraudulent. However, note that under s.2(2) there is no actual right to damages. It is discretionary, as an equitable remedy would be. Also, damages are an alternative to rescission, therefore the claimant cannot get both.

It could be argued, therefore, that remedies for fraudulent misrepresentation, non-fraudulent misrepresentation and breach of contract are now more or less equivalent.

Remedies for breaches of statutory implied terms

The remedies available for breach of these implied terms have been strengthened for consumers by the **Sale and Supply of Goods to Consumers Regulations 2002**, and the benefits to consumers brought by these Regulations are fully discussed in Chapter 8.

Damages are also available as a remedy. Refer back to the information on terms in Chapter 8, and look at the situations where damages would be a better remedy than rejection.

Sample exam questions

Past and specimen questions (and mark schemes) for this specification are available on the AQA website (www.aqa.org.uk). You are advised to look at these and to write answers to them. The specification indicates that evaluative questions could be asked on any part of the material except discharge of contract. Where appropriate, you will be expected to make some reference to proposals for reform.

The following questions will provide practice in answering the kind of questions that are likely to be asked.

1 **How satisfactory are the rules on offer and acceptance?**

2 **Critically evaluate the rules either on misrepresentation or on exclusion clauses.**

3 **What criticisms would you make of the rules on consideration and intention to create legal relations?**

4 **How effective are the remedies available in contract law?**

5 **Discuss the view that the rules on implied terms are satisfactory and not in need of reform.**

Further reading

Smith, D. (2009) 'Unfair contact terms: proposals of the Law Commission', *A-Level Law Review*, Vol. 4, No. 2, pp. 28–29.

Unit 4

A: Criminal law
(offences against property)
Chapters 13–17

Chapter **13**

Theft and robbery

Theft

It is crucial to have an excellent understanding of theft, as not only is it a stand-alone offence, it is also a part of robbery and burglary.

Theft is defined in s.1 of the **Theft Act 1968**:

> *A person is guilty of theft if he dishonestly appropriates property belonging to another with the intention of permanently depriving the other of it.*

This definition can be split into *actus reus* and *mens rea*, both of which must be present for the defendant to be found guilty. Each element should be explained and then applied in turn, starting with the *actus reus*.

Actus reus

The *actus reus* of theft consists of three elements:
* appropriation (s.3)
* property (s.4)
* belonging to another (s.5)

Appropriation

Appropriation is defined under s.3(1) as 'any assumption by a person of the rights of an owner'. Essentially, this means that the defendant must have taken the item and treated it as his or her own. The rights of an owner can include actions such as:
* selling
* destroying
* hiring
* lending

For example, if someone takes a book from a library and then sells it, he or she would be deemed to have treated it as his or her own and would be found to have appropriated that item. Only the owner has the right to sell the book.

It is worth noting that appropriation does not take place until the assumption is present. For example, if Josh borrows a DVD from Jasbinder but quite innocently forgets to return it to him, he has not appropriated the item. However, if Josh discovers the DVD and then decides to sell it at a carboot sale, it is at this point (the decision to sell) that he would be deemed to have 'appropriated' the DVD, and therefore treated it as his own.

Generally, this area of law is straightforward. However, the main problems that have arisen include issues of rights, consent and gifts.

Rights

In *R* v *Morris* (1983), the defendant switched the price labels on items in a super-market, giving a more expensive item the lower price. He then purchased the item with the lower price on it. The courts had to determine whether the assumption had to be of *all* the rights of the owner or whether it could be of *any* rights, including possession or control. The House of Lords stated that 'the assumption of *any* of the rights is sufficient to amount to appropriation'.

Consent

Following the case of *Lawrence* v *Metropolitan Police Commissioner* (1972), the House of Lords confirmed that a defendant can be deemed to have appropriated an item even when consent has been given by the owner. In this case, an Italian student, speaking little English, summoned a taxi from Victoria station and showed the driver (Lawrence) the address of his destination. Upon arrival, the driver told the student a price that exceeded the true fare. The student, not under-standing English monetary values, offered a pound, but the driver signalled that this was not enough. The student then offered the wallet and allowed Lawrence to help himself; he took the pound plus another six. It was held by both the Court of Appeal and the House of Lords that this amounted to appropriation.

Following the case of *Lawrence* v *Metropolitan Police Commissioner* (1972), the House of Lords confirmed that a defendant can be deemed to have appropriated an item even when consent has been given by the owner

This point of law was backed up by *R* v *Gomez* (1993) and *R* v *Hinks* (2000), which are both explained below. The courts commented that if the appropriation took place with consent, it must be looked at in conjunction with s.2 dishonesty. In *Hinks*, it was held that the defendant appropriated the item dishonestly, even though she had full consent from the owner.

A further widening of the concept of appropriation occurred in the consolidated appeals of *R* v *Morris* and *R* v *Anderton and Burnside* (1983). Both cases involved switching price labels in a supermarket and the defendants' convictions were upheld on appeal. The House of Lords (per Lord Roskill) held that:

> *...in the context of s.3(1), the concept of appropriation in my view involves not an act expressly or impliedly authorised by the owner but an act by way of adverse interference with or usurpation of those rights.*

This case also ruled that appropriation merely requires an assumption of *any* of the rights of the owner, not all of them. This was later confirmed in *R* v *Gomez* (1993).

This vexed question of consent was finally resolved in *R* v *Gomez* (1993). The defendant, the assistant manager of an electrical goods shop, was asked by an acquaintance to supply goods from the shop to the value of two building society cheques that were known by the defendant to be stolen. Having obtained his manager's approval, the defendant agreed to do this and supplied the goods. Later, both cheques were returned by the bank marked 'Orders not to pay. Stolen cheques'. The defendant, the acquaintance and another store employee were convicted of theft. Although their conviction was quashed by the Court of Appeal, that court certified the following point of law of general public importance for the House of Lords:

> *When theft is alleged and that which is alleged to be stolen passes to the D with the consent of the owner, but that has been obtained by a false representation, has (a) an appropriation taken place, or (b) must such a passing of property necessarily involve an element of adverse interference with or usurpation of some right of the owner?*

The House of Lords restored the defendants' convictions and stated that it chose to follow *Lawrence*. The answers to the certified questions were (a) 'yes', and (b) 'no'. The House of Lords thus accepted that an appropriation may involve an unauthorised act, but stated that it could equally involve an authorised act.

In *Criminal Law: The Fundamentals* (2007), Rebecca Huxley-Binns and Christina McAlhone argue that: 'the effect of allowing appropriation to include an act which is done with the consent of the owner is a considerable widening of the scope of appropriation'. They then quote Professor J. C. Smith, who wrote (in *The Law of Theft*, 8th edn) that 'an appropriation may now be committed by anyone doing anything to property belonging to another, with or without the authority or consent of the owner'.

Gifts

The law of appropriation was widened further by *R* v *Hinks* (2000). A 53-year-old man of limited intelligence transferred a large sum of money and a television set to a young female friend. He understood what it meant to make a gift, but there was some evidence of undue influence, though no deception. The House of Lords, in upholding her conviction for theft, held that where a defendant dishonestly acquires ownership of property belonging to another even by way of a valid gift, he or she will have appropriated and stolen it. Janet Loveless in *Complete Criminal Law* (2008) concludes that:

> *...the result of this decision is that appropriation as defined by s.3(1) has more or less vanished from sight. The only real question left for determination is one of dishonesty.*

Property

Property is defined under s.4(1) as 'money and all other property, real and personal, including things in action and other intangible property'. This suggests five different types of property:

❖ **Money** — this includes all coins and banknotes of any currency.
❖ **Real property** — this refers to land and buildings, but has limitations under s.4(2). Land or things forming part of the land cannot be stolen except in the following situations:
  – where a trustee or other authorised person disposes of land, going against the authority initially given to him or her, showing a breach in confidence
  – where someone severs something from land that is not in his or her control, e.g. taking turf from a front garden of another or the removal of a fixed concrete statue from a garden
  – where a tenant removes fixtures from premises or land without direct permission from the owner or person in control of the property at the time
❖ **Personal property** — property that is 'tangible', i.e. items that can be seen, touched and moved. These items are not attached to land. Examples are books, DVDs, watches and jewellery.
❖ **Things in action** — this refers to something that can be enforced against another person by an action in law, for example a bank account. If someone enforces a debit to be made from a bank account, this can be seen as appropriating a 'thing in action'. Tickets also fall into this category. A ticket has greater value than just a piece of paper, and it is clear that a purchaser who is deprived of his or her ticket to travel will be permanently deprived of both the ticket and the right to travel.
❖ **Intangible property** — something that cannot be seen or touched. Such items would include patents or quotas, as in the case of *Attorney General of Hong Kong* v *Chan Nai-Keung* (1987), where a director of a textile company sold a large quantity of the company's export quotas at well below their proper value, transferring them to another textile company.

Property not capable of being stolen

The courts have held that some things are not capable of being stolen and therefore do not amount to property under the **Theft Act 1968**:

❖ Section 4(3) states that flowers, foliage and fruit that have been picked from the wild cannot be stolen — unless they are then used to make a gain or are sold for commercial purposes. Anyone is able to pick wild flowers and fruit for his or her own purpose but cannot then sell them on to make profit.

❖ Section 4(4) states that wild creatures cannot be stolen, unless they have been tamed or are being kept in captivity. In effect, you are able to take a creature such as a rabbit from the wild, but would not be permitted to take such a creature from a zoo.

There are also exclusions under the common law. Whereas gas and water may be stolen, electricity cannot (*Low* v *Blease*, 1975), although there is an offence under s.13 of the 1968 Act of abstracting electricity. Neither can heat be appropriated; however, in *Clinton* v *Cahill* (1998), the defendant diverted the victim's hot water pipes to heat his own property, and this was held to be theft.

Confidential information is also excluded under the common law. Following the case of *Oxford* v *Moss* (1979), where the defendant obtained a copy of an exam paper, read the questions and then replaced it, it is deemed that intangible property in the form of knowledge is not capable of being stolen. If the student concerned had kept the actual question paper, he would have been deemed to have appropriated personal property. However, it was never his intention to take the paper away or deprive the university of it.

Belonging to another

This is defined under s.5(1): 'property shall be regarded as belonging to any person having possession or control of it.' Having 'possession or control' at the time the property is appropriated is sufficient, and means that this section does not necessarily refer to the legal *owner* of the property. For example, if A has hired a cement mixer for the day, he would not be the legal owner of it, as it would be the property of the hire company. He would, however, be in possession and control of it. If the mixer were to be taken from him without his permission, this would be seen as appropriating property belonging to another. A, although not the legal owner, was clearly in possession and control at the time of appropriation.

Appropriating your own property

Following the case of *R* v *Turner (No. 2)* (1971), a legal owner may be found guilty of appropriating his or her own property in certain circumstances. The defendant took his car to a garage to be repaired, and had agreed to pay for the repairs when he collected the vehicle. The garage parked the car on the road outside the premises at the end of the day. During the night, the defendant used a spare key to remove the car without paying for the repairs. It was held by the Court of Appeal that the garage was in possession and control of the car by reason of their proprietary right over the car until the bill was paid, and as a result the defendant could be found guilty of stealing his own property.

A contrasting case, however, is *R* v *Meredith* (1973), where it was held that a car owner who removed his car from a police yard without paying the fine was not guilty of theft, because the statutory regulations gave the police no power to prevent the vehicle being repossessed by its owner.

Property obtained by mistake

If someone receives property because of a mistake, he or she could be under a legal obligation to return such property. Section 5(4) states:

> *Where a person gets property by another's mistake, and is under an obligation to make restoration (in whole or in part) of the property... an intention not to make restoration shall be regarded accordingly as an intention to deprive that person of the property...*

An example is being given too much change by a shopkeeper. If you fail to return the excess money, you are liable under s.5(4), and would be deemed to have appropriated property that belonged to another. This also covers situations where money is paid into the wrong bank account by mistake.

In *Attorney General's Reference No. 1 of 1983*, an employee was paid more than she was entitled to in her wages. The court held that she had a legal obligation to return the money, even though as a matter of civil law she became the owner of the money as soon as it was paid into her bank account. The money belonged to her employer, and she was obliged to rectify the mistake that had been made.

Note that if money is received by mistake in a gambling situation, as in *R* v *Gilks* (1972), the ownership of the money would be deemed to have passed, and the mistake does not have to be rectified. Betting transactions are *not*, as a matter of contract law, legally enforceable.

Mens rea

Once the *actus reus* is established, the prosecution must prove that the defendant had the necessary *mens rea*: being dishonest and having the intention of permanently depriving the other of something, as defined under sections 2 and 6 of the Theft Act 1968 respectively.

Dishonesty

Despite the greater significance placed on dishonesty in theft following the decision by the House of Lords in *R* v *Gomez*, the 1968 Act does not contain a definition of it.

The Criminal Law Revision Committee, whose report was the basis of the Act, deliberately omitted to provide such a definition because 'dishonesty is something which laymen can easily recognise when they see it'.

However, s.2(1) of the Act outlines situations that would be classed as *not* dishonest in the eyes of the law:

❖ Where a person believes that he or she has in law the right to deprive the other of it, on behalf of himself or herself or of a third person. This may be applicable if the person believes that the item concerned is in fact his or her own property.

❖ Where the person believes he or she would have the other's consent if the other knew of the appropriation and circumstances of it. This would be where the person is of the honest belief that the owner of the item would not mind if he or she appropriated it, for example borrowing a friend's iPod.

❖ Where the person believes that the owner of the property cannot be traced by taking reasonable steps. For example, if you found a stray dog and you put up poster stating 'dog found', this would be taking reasonable steps. If no one came forward as owner, you could legally keep the dog.

Only explain the situations that are not dishonest if they are relevant to scenario in the exam question.

Belief in a legal right

This section is phrased in subjective terms and is known as the 'claim of right' defence. The belief must be honest but need not be correct or even reasonable (note: this echoes the issue of mistaken belief in self-defence). In *R* v *Small* (1988), the defendant was charged with stealing a car he genuinely thought had been abandoned. The Court of Appeal ruled that the trial judge had been mistaken when he directed the jury to consider whether or not the defendant *reasonably* believed that the car had been abandoned.

A distinction must be made between a legal and a moral right. Janet Loveless in *Complete Criminal Law* (2008) provides an example where the defendant's aunt promised her that when she died she would leave her a diamond ring. After the aunt's death, the defendant discovered that the ring had in fact been bequeathed in the will to her cousin. If the defendant were then to take the ring, she could not argue that she had a legal right to it, and the 'claim of right' defence would not apply.

In *R* v *Forrester* (1992), the defendant entered his former flat by force and locked the landlord in a room, as he had refused to repay the defendant's £200 deposit. He then took goods to the value of the deposit, intending to keep them for a few days to see if the landlord would return the money. At the appeal against his conviction for robbery, the Court of Appeal held that the defendant might believe himself to be entitled to act unlawfully, but there was little substance in his argument that he was honest.

Belief in consent

As above, the belief must be honest and genuine, but it need not be reasonable. Whether this defence is available depends, therefore, on the circumstances of the relationship between the defendant and the victim. The defendant must believe not only that the owner would have consented to the appropriation, but also that the owner would have consented to it in the particular circumstances. Smith and Hogan (*Criminal Law*, 7th edition) give the following example. The defendant, having forgotten to order milk, may believe that his neighbour would consent to his appropriating a pint of milk from the neighbour's doorstep, but may believe that the neighbour would *not* consent to his appropriation of the milk to sell at a profit to a thirsty hiker passing by.

Note that under s.2(2), a person's appropriation may be dishonest even if he or she is willing to pay for the property.

Belief that property is lost

The general rule is that lost property still belongs to the owner, and it is possible for someone to be charged with theft in respect of appropriation of property from 'persons unknown'. The issue here is what constitutes taking 'reasonable' steps to find the owner. This depends on the individual circumstances of each case, with relevant factors including the value of the property and the place where it is found.

Two-stage test

If none of the situations described above fits the scenario, a two-stage test to determine dishonesty must be applied. This test originated in *R* v *Ghosh* (1982), where the defendant was convicted of offences under the Theft Act of attempting to obtain money by deception and obtaining money by deception. When working as a locum consultant in a hospital, he falsely represented that he had carried out an operation that had been performed by another surgeon. His defence was that there was no deception: the sums paid to him were due from consultation fees, which were legitimate under NHS regulations, or were the balance of fees properly due. In other words, there was nothing dishonest about his behaviour on any of the separate counts against him. After the jury members were directed to apply their own standards to decide if what the defendant did was dishonest, he was convicted.

At his appeal, the Court of Appeal decided that the correct test for determining dishonesty should be based on both an objective and subjective element. Lord Lane CJ stated that a jury must be asked the following questions:

❖ Was the action dishonest according to the standards of a 'reasonable and honest man'? This is an objective test, and, in most cases, the answer is easy to establish. If the answer is 'yes', the following question is asked.

❖ Did the defendant realise that what he or she was doing was dishonest by those standards? This is a subjective test, and is determined by trying to understand what the defendant was thinking at the time of the *actus reus*.

It is dishonest for a defendant to act in a way which he or she knows ordinary people consider to be dishonest, even if he or she asserts or genuinely believes that he or she is morally justified in acting as he or she did.

Only if both questions from the Ghosh test return the answer 'yes' will the defendant be held to have been dishonest and therefore guilty of theft under the 1968 Act.

Note that a Ghosh direction on dishonesty is not required in every theft case. If the defendant claims that the appropriation of property was not dishonest because of the exceptions in s.2(1), the only issue for a jury or for magistrates is whether he or she had genuine belief. Alternatively, the defendant may claim that he or she took the goods absent-mindedly and had no intention to steal. In such cases, a Ghosh direction would be inappropriate.

Intention to permanently deprive

Section 6(1) states that:

> *A person appropriating property belonging to another without meaning the other permanently to lose the thing itself is nevertheless to be regarded as having the intention of permanently depriving the other of it if his intention is to treat the thing as his own to dispose of regardless of the other's rights...*

This may include selling the item, destroying it, or, in the case of money, spending it. The defendant must intend not to return the item but to deprive the person of it permanently, clearly treating it as his or her own. This is the final element that has to be proved to find the defendant guilty of theft.

Following *R* v *Velumyl* (1989), it is held that someone may be found guilty of theft if he or she borrows cash — even with the honest intention of replacing it

Following *R* v *Velumyl* (1989), it is held that someone may be found guilty of theft if he or she borrows cash — even with the honest intention of replacing it. Velumyl was owed £1,050 by a friend and took the same amount of money from the office safe, intending to replace the money when the friend had repaid him. The Court of Appeal held that he had the intention of permanently depriving the company of the money because the money he would use to replace the banknotes taken from the safe would not be the same original notes.

Borrowing property

Under normal circumstances, if an item is borrowed, this does not give rise to an intention to permanently deprive, as the intention is to return it. However, following

R v *Lloyd* (1985), if the goodness, virtue and practical value have gone out of the article, this would amount to an intention to permanently deprive for the purposes of s.6.

In this case, the defendant took a film from a cinema, copied it and then replaced it. This did not amount to theft, as no goodness or practical value had gone. In contrast, if a defendant took a ticket to a football match, went to see the match and then returned the ticket, this would clearly reduce the value of the ticket and would therefore show the intention to permanently deprive.

Conditional intent

Following *R* v *Easom* (1971), if the defendant has the intention to deprive based on a condition, for example that something is actually worth taking, this is not sufficient to fulfil s.6. The defendant in this case picked up a handbag while in a cinema, looked inside and then replaced it without taking anything. He was not guilty of theft.

Robbery

Robbery, often referred to as 'theft with force', is defined in s.8(1) of the **Theft Act 1968**:

> *A person is guilty of robbery if he steals, and immediately before or at the time of doing so, and in order to do so, he uses force on any person or puts or seeks to put any person in fear of being then and there subjected to force.*

To find the defendant guilty of robbery, it must be shown that force was used in order to steal, so the offence of theft must also be fulfilled. Robberies include muggings, car-jackings and bag-snatching, as well as armed bank robberies.

The definition can be split into the *actus reus* and *mens rea*, and both elements must be present for the defendant to be guilty of the offence.

Actus reus

In addition to the requirements for theft, the *actus reus* consists of the use or threat of force on any person immediately before or at the time of the theft in order to steal.

Theft

To find a defendant guilty of robbery, the theft must be complete. If any elements of theft are missing, for example if the defendant did not have the intention to permanently deprive, there would be no offence of robbery. Similarly, if the defendant took a wheelbarrow by force from his or her neighbour in the belief that he or she had a legal right to do so, the offence could not be robbery. Thus, any defence to theft is also a defence to robbery.

In *R* v *Robinson* (1977), the defendant ran a clothing club to which the victim's wife owed £7. The defendant met the victim and threatened him. In the fight, a £5 note slipped out of the victim's pocket and the defendant took it, claiming he was still owed £2. His conviction for robbery was quashed on appeal because of his honest belief that he was entitled to take the money.

The theft, however, will be deemed complete where force is used to steal. In *Corcoran* v *Anderton* (1980), it was held that a robbery was committed where a woman was hit in the back and her handbag was wrestled from her grasp, even though it then fell to the ground and was not taken. The woman screamed and the defendant ran off. This was deemed to be a completed theft. As the tugging was force, and as it was at the time of the theft, the defendants were guilty of robbery. The theft would not have been complete if the woman had not let go of the bag, but there would have been an attempted theft, and as force was used this would have amounted to attempted robbery.

Force or threat of force

The defendant must have used force or threatened to do so. This is a question of fact for the jury to determine. It is not necessary that the intended victim actually fears force — the offence only requires that the defendant seeks to put his victim in fear of force, not that the victim is afraid.

This rule was clearly illustrated in *B and R* v *DPP* (2007). A 16-year-old schoolboy was surrounded in a street by a group of teenage males who demanded that he hand over his mobile phone and wallet. When the victim refused to do so, the teenagers went into his pockets and took his wallet, his watch and his travel card. The victim admitted that he did not feel 'particularly threatened or scared' and he had not been physically assaulted. On an appeal to the Divisional Court for the defendants' robbery convictions, it was argued that, in the absence of actual force, where the victim was not frightened, there could be no robbery. Lady Justice Smith, however, ruled that:

> ...as a matter of common sense, the victim was subjected to some force and the threat of force by an intimidating group of boys... He did not stand there allowing his pockets to be searched with his arms held, simply as an act of generosity... Applying the wording of the statute and in cases where property is in fact stolen, it is the intention of the perpetrator rather than the fortitude of the victim which is the touchstone of whether the offence is robbery or theft. A threat of force can be express or implied — that is implied from other words or conduct or both. Here, on the facts set out in the case, there was every reason to conclude that there was an implied threat of force.

Any use or threat of force is sufficient; actual physical force does not need to be applied (but no jury could reasonably find that the slight physical contact which a pickpocket makes with his victim would amount to use of force). An example would be where someone is threatened with being beaten up if he or she does not hand over a bag. This amounts to threat of force; if the theft is then completed, the charge of robbery would be successful. As well as words, the threat could also be made through the use of weapons or even silence.

The word 'force' is given its ordinary meaning by the courts. *R* v *Dawson and James* (1976) shows that force could be mere jostling or the slightest push. In this case, one of the defendants nudged the victim and he stumbled; the other defendant then took the victim's wallet.

Force must be used against a person, not property, but not necessarily against the person in possession. In *Smith* v *Desmond* (1965), the House of Lords confirmed the convictions of two men who had robbed a night-watchman and a maintenance engineer in a bakery. Force was used against the watchman and engineer in order to steal from an office under their care but some distance away.

It is also important to remember that the theft does not need to be from the person who is being threatened. For example:

* A man enters a bank. He holds a customer at gunpoint while demanding money from the cashier. The money is handed over and the man leaves. The force in this case is used on the customer, while the theft is from the bank.
* Similarly, a man in a shop points a gun at a mother and child, insisting that the shopkeeper hands over cigarettes; this amounts to putting a person in fear of being subjected to force. It does not matter that it is not the customer's property being stolen.

Note the extension of the definition of force in *R* v *Clouden* (1987), where the Court of Appeal held that the force applied to a bag when the property was snatched was force applied to the victim's hand, even though this was indirect when wrenching the bag.

In *R* v *Clouden* (1987), the Court of Appeal held that the force applied to a bag when it was snatched was force applied to the victim's hand

Immediately before or at the time of the theft

If the force is separate from the theft, there is no robbery. For example, if two men were fighting and one was pushed to the ground unconscious, and the other then decided to take the injured man's wallet, this would not amount to robbery. It would be classed as an offence against the person and theft — two separate offences.

Following the case of *R* v *Hale* (1978), theft can be classed as a continuing act, and the force can be used at any time during this continuing act. In this case, the defendants entered a house, and one tied up the occupant while the other went upstairs and took jewellery from the bedroom. The pair then left, leaving the victim tied up. This appropriation was deemed to be continuing and therefore the force was seen as being 'at the time of the theft'. A similar conclusion was reached in *R v Lockley* (1995), where the defendant took cans of beer from an off-licence and, when challenged by the shop owner, used violence. He appealed against his conviction for robbery, arguing that the theft had been completed *before* he used force. It was held that *Gomez* did not preclude the conclusion that appropriation was a continuing act and that therefore the force was used in order to steal.

Mens rea

The *mens rea* for theft must be present (dishonesty, s.2, and an intention to permanently deprive, s.3), otherwise there is no offence of robbery. There must also be an intention to use force or a threat of force on the victim in order to steal.

Questions

1 What is the definition of theft in s.1 of the Theft Act 1968?

2 Define what is meant by 'appropriation', and give examples of what conduct or actions could constitute appropriation.

3 What is the significance of the decision in *Lawrence v Metropolitan Police Commissioner* (1972)?

4 Explain the importance of the decision in *R v Hinks* (2000).

5 What types of property are not capable of being stolen?

6 What is the significance of *R v Turner (No. 2)* (1971)?

7 What is the significance of *Attorney General's Reference No.1 of 1983*?

8 What are the three situations in s.(2)(1) that would not be classified as dishonest?

9 What legal rule was confirmed in *R v Small* (1988)?

10 Describe the Ghosh test of dishonesty.

11 Why was Lloyd's conviction quashed by the Court of Appeal?

12 What is the definition of robbery in s.8 of the Theft Act 1968?

13 What is the significance of the decision in *B and R v DPP* (2007)?

14 Why were the convictions in *Smith v Desmond* (1965) confirmed by the House of Lords?

15 What legal rule is illustrated by *R v Lockley* (1995)?

Further reading

Huxley-Binns, R. and McAlhone, C. (2007) *Criminal Law: The Fundamentals*, chapters 7–8, Sweet & Maxwell.

Loveless, J. (2008) *Complete Criminal Law*, chapter 12, Oxford University Press.

Smith, J. C. and Hogan, B. (1999), *Criminal Law*, chapter 16, Butterworths.

Storey, T. and Lidbury, A. (2007) *Criminal Law*, chapters 10–11, Willan.

Chapter 14

Burglary and blackmail

Burglary

Burglary is defined in s.9 of the Theft Act 1968. It can be divided into two separate offences, both of which involve the defendant trespassing onto premises:

❖ Under s.9(1)(a), the defendant enters any building or part of a building as a trespasser and with intent to commit one of three ulterior offences: to steal; to inflict grievous bodily harm to any person in the building; or to cause criminal damage to the building or anything in it.

❖ Under s.9(1)(b), the defendant, having entered any building or part of a building as a trespasser, commits one of two offences: stealing (or attempting to do so) or inflicting (or attempting to inflict) grievous bodily harm on any person in the building.

Note that there is a considerable overlap between the two offences of burglary. Therefore it is possible that a person who commits an offence under s.9(1)(a) may also commit an offence under s.9(1)(b).

Both burglary offences state that the defendant must have entered a building (or part of a building) as a trespasser

Actus reus

Both burglary offences state that the defendant must have:

❖ entered
❖ a building or part of a building
❖ as a trespasser

Entry

The definition of 'entry' is not given in s.9 and, despite a series of Court of Appeal cases, it is still not entirely clear.

R v *Collins* (1973) stated that the entry has to be both 'effective and substantial'. In this case, the alleged female victim, following an evening's drinking, had gone to bed. The defendant had gone to her house, taken off his clothes and climbed a ladder, in order to enter her bedroom and have sex with her. He claimed that while balanced on the window sill, the girl had invited him in, assuming he was her boyfriend. However, during their sexual encounter, she realised he was not her boyfriend and demanded that he leave. When charged with burglary under s.9(1)(a), he argued that he had not entered the building as a trespasser, as he was still outside the building when the girl pulled him in. The Court of Appeal quashed his conviction, holding that, before a conviction was possible, the jury had to be 'entirely satisfied' that the defendant had made an 'effective and substantial' entry into the building (per Edmund-Davies LJ).

In *R* v *Brown* (1985), it was held that entry only had to be effective. Here, the defendant was standing outside the building in question and leaned through an open window to take goods. *R* v *Ryan* (1996) ruled that being part-way through a window, and actually being stuck and unable to reach anything, was also 'effective'. This means that effective entry can involve only part of the defendant's body and does not even require that enough of his or her body is inside the property to enable him or her to commit the relevant crime.

Prior to the 1968 Act, if a tool was used to gain access to carry out the ulterior offence before the defendant physically entered a building, this was sufficient for entry. However, following the Act, this is now an unresolved issue — for example, it is not clear if using a hook through a letter box to steal letters on the mat would be an 'entry'. This is a matter of fact to be determined by a jury.

Building or part of a building

Before the **Theft Act 1968**, burglary was restricted to dwelling houses. There is no definition under the Act other than under s.9(4), which states that:

> *References…to a building…shall apply also to an inhabited vehicle or vessel, and shall apply to any such vehicle or vessel at times when the person having a habitation in it is not there as well as at times when he is.*

The courts have helped to interpret the definition through case law, stating that a 'building' must possess a degree of permanence. Thus offices, barns, garages, shops and outbuildings attached to a dwelling have been ruled to be buildings. Caravans, houseboats, camper vans and mobile homes are also included, even if they are not occupied at the time of the burglary. So a shed that can be easily dismantled would appear *not* to be a building for the purposes of burglary. The more mobile the building in question, the less likely it is to be classed as a building.

In *Norfolk Constabulary* v *Seekings and Gould* (1986), a lorry trailer with wheels was held not to be a building, even though it was not in working order and was connected to electricity. In *B and S* v *Leathley* (1979), on the other hand, a free-standing freezer unit was held to be a building; it had been in a farmyard for a number of years, was no longer attached to the lorry and was connected to electricity. The greater the degree of permanence, the greater the chance the structure will be classed as a building.

'Part of a building' refers to situations where the defendant may have permission to be in a certain area of a building but not in other restricted areas. For example, the general public has permission to be in a supermarket, but the storage rooms at the back would be restricted to members of staff only, and any member of the public entering them would become a trespasser.

R v *Walkington* (1979) extends this example to shop counters. The defendant was found to have gone behind a shop counter to look into the cash till (a restricted area he did not have permission to go into). He was deemed to have trespassed into part of a building.

As a trespasser

A person will be classed as a trespasser if he or she enters a building (or part of a building) without permission. People are not classed as trespassers if they have permission to enter.

Following *R* v *Jones and Smith* (1976), someone will, however, become a trespasser when he or she goes beyond the permission given to him or her. In this case, the defendants took two television sets from the house of the father of one of the defendants, without the father's knowledge or consent. Although they had permission to be in the building while the father was away, they did not have permission to take the televisions and sell them. This is an example of going beyond the permission originally given, and resulted in them becoming trespassers.

Note that entering a public area such as a cinema requires the purchase of a ticket. This ticket is classed as a licence, which gives permission to the purchaser to enter the premises and watch the film. If, however, he or she enters the building and then goes beyond this permission, for example causing criminal damage, he or she will be classed as a trespasser.

The law is clear where a defendant gains entry through fraud. The defendant might, for example, claim to be working for the gas board and enter the premises to steal. In such circumstances, he or she has no genuine permission to be there and is therefore regarded as a trespasser.

A further point to be noted is that if a defendant is ruled to have entered as a lawful visitor, he or she cannot have committed burglary, even if any of the offences specified in s.9 have been committed.

Mens rea

The *mens rea* of burglary depends on whether the defendant is charged with s.9(1)(a) or (b).

Section 9(1)(a)

There are two main parts to the *mens rea* of burglary under s.9(1)(a).

Trespass: intention or subjective recklessness

The defendant must either intend to trespass or be subjectively reckless (*Cunningham* recklessness) as to whether he or she is trespassing. In *Collins*, it was held that no trespass could become a burglary unless it was either intentional or reckless at the point of entry. That is to say, the defendant must actually know he or she has no right to enter or know that he or she might not have such a right. In that case, Edmund-Davies LJ stated:

> ...there cannot be a conviction for entering premises [as a trespasser] unless the person entering does so knowing that he is a trespasser, and nevertheless enters, or, at the very least, is reckless as to whether or not he is entering the premises of another without the other party's consent.

Note that such intention or recklessness may be negated by the defendant's honest mistake or an honest belief in a right of entry.

Ulterior offence

The defendant must have the intention to commit one of the following offences:
* theft
* criminal damage
* grievous bodily harm — here, it is s.18 GBH which is to be considered and *not* s.20

These ulterior offences do not need to have been committed, provided there is proof of the defendant's intention to commit them.

Note that conditional intent is sufficient here — it makes no difference whether the defendant completes the ulterior offence. *Attorney General's References Nos 1 and 2 of 1979* involved two separate cases. In the first, the defendant was caught inside a house; in the second, the defendant was caught tampering with a set of French windows. Both claimed they planned to steal whatever they could find 'lying around'. The first defendant was charged with burglary, and the second with attempted burglary. The trial judge in each case directed that they be acquitted. However, the Court of Appeal held that the judges had misunderstood the law. It is no defence to burglary for a defendant to claim that he or she did not intend to steal any specific objects — an intention to steal whatever there is worth stealing is sufficient. In *Criminal Law* (2007), Tony Story and Alan Lidbury argue further that:

> ...presumably...the D also commits burglary if he enters a building with intent to inflict GBH on anyone he finds sitting around inside. As far as guilt is concerned it would not matter that no one was, in fact, inside; it is D's intent that defines the offence.

Section 9(1)(b)

There are two main parts to the *mens rea* for burglary under s.9(1)(b):

- ❖ As for s.(9)(1)(a) above, the *mens rea* for trespass must be established.
- ❖ The defendant must also have the *mens rea* for theft or GBH when committing or attempting to commit the *actus reus* of one of these offences.

As this is not a crime of ulterior intent, the *mens rea* for theft or GBH *does not* have to be present at the point of entry. Note that for s.9(1)(b), s.20 GBH is envisaged. Note also that GBH could be committed as the defendant escapes, as in *R v Jenkins* (2002).

Summary

Burglary is not complicated if you consider it as two different offences. First, establish that the defendant has (1) entered (2) a building (3) as a trespasser. Once this has been ascertained, determine what the defendant wanted to do before he or she entered. Did he or she want to commit one of the ulterior offences under s.9(1)(a)? If so, define that offence and then apply it. Then decide whether, once the defendant had entered the building, he or she then committed any offence under s.9(1)(b). Again, if so, define the offence and apply it.

Do not get confused if the defendant enters a building to steal, finds nothing but then causes criminal damage. Here the defendant is guilty under s.9(1)(a), remembering that conditional intent is sufficient. He or she is, however, guilty of the basic offence of criminal damage. Section 9(1)(b) would not apply, as the offence of criminal damage is not included under this section.

Blackmail

Blackmail is defined under s.21 of the Theft Act 1968:

> *A person is guilty of blackmail if, with a view to gain for himself or another or with intent to cause loss to another, he makes an unwarranted demand with menaces.*

Actus reus

Demand

The demand must be to make the victim do or stop doing something. This can take any form — words, writing or conduct — and can be either express or implied. In *Collister* v *Warhurst* (1955), where two police officers told the victim falsely that he would be prosecuted for an offence but that this could be avoided if he paid them, it was held that this was an implied demand.

With menaces

The word 'menaces' has no statutory definition. It has therefore been given its common-law meaning, which includes threats of violence but also threats of anything 'detrimental or unpleasant', as in *Thorne* v *Motor Trade Association* (1937).

In *R* v *Clear* (1968), it was held that the test of what constituted 'menaces' was that the threat had to be:

> *...of such a nature and extent that the mind of an ordinary person of normal stability and courage might be influenced or made apprehensive so as to accede unwillingly to the demand.*

Thus, the test is objective; it is accordingly irrelevant that the victim is not affected by the threat if the ordinary person would have been.

Note, however, that if the victim is affected by the threat because he or she is particularly cowardly, but the ordinary person would be unaffected by the same threat, menaces can still be established if the defendant was aware of the likely effect of his or her actions on that particular victim, as in *R* v *Garwood* (1987).

Mens rea

The demand must have been (a) unwarranted and (b) made with a view to gain or an intent to cause loss.

Unwarranted

Section 21(1)(a) states that a demand will *not* be unwarranted where the defendant has a belief:

❖ that he or she has reasonable grounds for making the demand, and
❖ that the use of menaces is a proper means of reinforcing the demand

Accordingly, a demand is unwarranted unless the defendant believes that not only is he or she entitled to make the demand, but also that the means adopted are a proper method to enforce that demand. An example would be where A demands that B repays an unpaid debt.

Whether the defendant had reasonable grounds for making the demand is a subjective test, which means that the defendant's state of mind can provide a defence. What matters is whether the belief was genuinely held *and* whether the defendant believed that the use of a threat was a proper means of enforcing that demand.

In *R* v *Harvey* (1980), the defendant and others paid £20,000 to the victim for what was believed to be a supply of cannabis, but it was not. They then kidnapped the victim's wife and child and told him they would kill them unless he returned the money. On the issue of the meaning of 'proper', Bingham J stated:

> *'Proper' is an unusual expression to find in a criminal statute. It is not defined in the Act and no definition needs to be attempted here. It is, however, plainly a word of wide meaning, certainly wider than 'lawful'. But the greater includes the less and no act which was not believed to be lawful could be believed to be proper within the meaning of the subsection. Thus no assistance is given to any D...who knows or suspects that his threat...is criminal, but believes it to be justified by his end or his peculiar circumstances. The test is not what he regards as justified, but what he believes to be proper.*

14

This obviously has the effect of making any threat involving the use of violence an 'improper' means of reinforcing the demand.

With a view to gain or an intent to cause loss

The words 'gain' and 'loss' refer 'only to gain or loss in money or other property...whether temporary or permanent' (s.34(2)).

Therefore, a demand with menaces will cover all sorts of gains and losses. In *R* v *Parkes* (1973), it was held that the fact that the defendant only wanted repayment of a debt did not mean that it was not 'with a view to gain'. It was thus capable of being blackmail because 'getting hard cash as opposed to a mere right of action is getting more than one already has'. In *R* v *Bevans* (1988), the meaning of 'gain in property' was even more widely drawn, when an arthritis sufferer was convicted of blackmail after threatening to shoot his doctor unless he gave him a pain-killing injection.

Questions

1 What is the definition of blackmail in s.21 of the Theft Act 1968?

2 What rule is illustrated in *Collister* v *Warhurst* (1955)?

3 How is 'menaces' defined?

4 What legal rule regarding 'menaces' was confirmed in *R* v *Clear* (1968)?

5 In what circumstances (under s.21(1)(a)) will a demand be held not to be unwarranted?

6 In *R* v *Harvey* (1981) how did Mr Justice Bingham explain the meaning of 'proper'?

7 What types of 'gain' feature in *R* v *Parkes* (1973) and *R* v *Bevans* (1988)?

Further reading

Huxley-Binns, R. and McAlhone, C. (2007) *Criminal Law: The Fundamentals*, chapter 8, Sweet & Maxwell.

Loveless, J. (2008) *Complete Criminal Law*, chapter 14, Oxford University Press.

Story, T. and Lidbury, A. (2007) *Criminal Law*, chapter 12, Willan.

Chapter 15

Fraud and making off without payment

This chapter covers the following offences:

❖ fraud by false representation (s.2 Fraud Act 2006)

❖ obtaining services dishonestly (s.11 Fraud Act 2006)

❖ making off without payment (s.3(1) Theft Act 1978)

Definitions

Dictionary definitions of fraud include 'wrongful or criminal deception intended to result in financial or personal gain' (*Compact Oxford English Dictionary*) and 'the use of false representation to gain an unjust advantage' (*Concise Oxford English Dictionary*). It is important to distinguish between taking another person's property *without* his or her consent and taking it *with* his or her consent but by a trick or deception. The Theft Act 1968 deals with the former situation in the offences of theft, burglary and robbery, all of which are usually committed without any fraud. Fraud-based offences, including obtaining property by deception and obtaining a pecuniary advantage by deception, were included in the 1968 Act, but there were problems in applying this Act. As Denis Lanser states in 'Reform of fraud offences in criminal law' (*A-Level Law Review*, Vol. 3, No. 3):

> ...the idea of 'deception' made proof of some obvious instances of fraud difficult or impossible, such as where a machine rather than a person was 'tricked', or where the V did not really care whether statements being made were true or false...

According to the 1968 Act, deception offences were crimes which required the victim actually to believe in a false representation.

Case law created further confusion where, as in *Lawrence v Metropolitan Police Commissioner* (1972), *R v Gomez* (1993) and *R v Hinks* (2000) (see Chapter 13), the House of Lords ruled that a defendant could be guilty of theft where, rather than simply taking the victim's property without his or her consent, the defendant deceived the victim into handing over the property. As Lanser observed in his article: 'there was a considerable overlap between theft and obtaining property by deception. Consequently, the offence of theft was also a mechanism for dealing with some aspects of fraud.'

For all these reasons, and following a Law Commission report in 2002 into fraud offences, the Fraud Act 2006 was passed, which came into effect on 1 January 2007. This Act abolished all eight deception offences in the Theft Act 1968 and instead created one offence of fraud, which can be committed in three different ways:

❖ s.2 — fraud by false representation
❖ s.3 — fraud by failing to disclose information
❖ s.4 — fraud by abuse of position

There is also the offence of obtaining services dishonestly under s.11.

Fraud is not defined within the Act and appears to be based more on the issue of dishonesty. It is now a conduct crime, which does not require the victim to be induced to believe in the fraud.

The AQA specification deals with offences under sections 2 and 11.

Fraud by false representation

According to s.2(1) of the Fraud Act 2006, this offence is committed where a person:

(a) dishonestly makes a false representation, and (b) intends, by making the representation (i) to make a gain for himself or another, or (ii) to cause loss to another or to expose another to a risk of loss.

Actus reus

Section 2(2) of the Act states that a representation is false if it is untrue or misleading, and the person making it knows that it is, or might be, untrue or misleading. More simply, a false representation is a false statement, a trick or a lie. In its response to the Law Commission consultation, the government stated that 'misleading' means 'less than wholly true and capable of an interpretation to the detriment of the victim'.

Under s.2(4), the representation may be express or implied. It does not need to be believed or relied upon by the victim for the offence to be committed. There is also no requirement that the defendant should actually make a gain as a result of the false representation, nor that the victim should suffer a loss or be exposed to the risk of a loss. Therefore, this offence can be committed in the absence of any actual loss made by the victim or even any threat to his or her economic interests. This has led to the criticism that this offence effectively criminalises lying.

Denis Lanser writes:

> ...in fact, the law goes rather further than this, because not only does it deal with lies as such, it also deals with misleading statements...it now appears that advertisers and salespeople may commit this offence if they knowingly mislead without actually telling lies.

Mens rea

Three requirements must be met for *mens rea* to be proved:

❖ **Dishonesty:** the three 'beliefs' (or defences) under s.2 of the Theft Act 1968 do *not* apply. Accordingly, the only test for dishonesty is the Ghosh test: whether the jury believes the defendant acted contrary to the standards of ordinary decent people and whether the defendant knew he or she was doing so. As in the offence of theft, where the decisions in *Gomez* and *Hinks* 'have forced dishonesty to bear a large burden in establishing the offence, so in fraud by false representation much will depend on the view taken by a jury of the D's conduct' (Denis Lanser).

❖ **Knowing that the representation might be false:** this is more demanding than belief or suspicion, which the previous law required. 'Closing one's mind to the obvious' could amount to knowledge; but, given the Ghosh test, this could well be encompassed within dishonesty. If the defendant argued that he or she did not know the representation might be false, in circumstances where it was obvious that he or she would have, this test is satisfied, although alternatively, he or she would still be found liable under the Ghosh test.

❖ **Intent to gain or cause loss to another or to expose another to the risk of loss:** there must be a causal link between the false representation and the intention of gaining or causing loss. Gain and loss are defined in s.5 as 'money or other property' and can be temporary or permanent.

Relevant cases

Janet Loveless in *Complete Criminal Law* (2008) provides a number of cases which, although decided under the previous law in the Theft Act 1968, could illustrate the new s.2 offence.

R v Firth (1990)

A consultant obstetrician referred private clients to an NHS hospital for treatment, omitting to declare that they were private. His silence was taken as an implied representation.

R v Rai (2000)

The defendant's mother obtained a local authority grant to install a bathroom and make adaptations to her house. She died before the work began but the defendant did not inform the authority until after the work had been carried out. He was convicted under s.1 of the Theft Act 1978 and his conviction was upheld by the Court of Appeal. The court decided that the defendant's conduct amounted to a continuing representation that his mother was still alive.

R v Silverman (1988)

This case illustrated silence being the setting for a criminal deception. The defendant charged two elderly sisters an excessive price for electrical work he had carried out. He was known and trusted by them and there was no evidence that he had applied pressure to have his high quotes accepted. The work was done satisfactorily. However, he was convicted of obtaining money by deception (under s.15) and appealed. It was conceded that he had been dishonest but it was argued that he had made no positive representations that the price charged was reasonable. He had merely provided a quote, which the sisters were free to accept or reject. The Court of Appeal held that his silence amounted to a false representation — the sisters were gullible and the defendant had taken dishonest advantage of the mutual trust between them.

Obtaining services dishonestly

This section replaces the similar offence of obtaining services by deception under s.1 of the Theft Act 1978. The crucial difference between the new and the former offence is that under s.11 of the Fraud Act 2006, the defendant must acquire the service by a dishonest act rather than by any deception or false representation. The services must be provided on the basis that payment has been, is being, or will be made, and the defendant must receive the service without such payment being made, or made in full.

Actus reus

The key element is the 'service'. Although this is not defined in s.11, it would appear to include all services for which payment is due. This means that all professional, financial and commercial services are covered, including banking, building society or credit card services (as in R v Sofroniou, 2003).

Denis Lanser's article in *A-Level Law Review* gives the following typical examples:

❖ sneaking into a cinema without paying

❖ pretending to be a young person or senior citizen to get reduced-price entry to an event

❖ using another person's membership card to get into a gym for free or at a reduced price

An example of obtaining services dishonestly would be using another person's credit card (without permission) to book tickets over the internet

❖ using another person's credit card (without permission) to book tickets over the internet

Mens rea

Three requirements need to be met:

❖ The defendant must act dishonestly (apply the Ghosh test). In *Criminal Law: The Fundamentals* (2007), Christina McAlhone and Rebecca Huxley-Binns write: 'the D may argue that, even though the *actus reus* is complete, he lacks *mens rea*, where, say, he walked out of a restaurant without paying in protest at poor service or poor food. If he thought he had acted reasonably and honestly, and though that ordinary honest people would agree, then he would be entitled to be acquitted.'

❖ The defendant must know the services are to be paid for, or know that they might have to be paid for.

❖ The defendant must intend to avoid payment in whole or in part at the time of obtaining the service.

Making off without payment

This offence, commonly referred to as 'bilking', is defined under s.3(1) of the **Theft Act 1978**:

> *...a person who, knowing that payment on the spot for any goods supplied or service done is required or expected from him, dishonestly makes off without*

having paid as required or expected and with intent to avoid payment of the amount due shall be guilty of an offence.

Janet Loveless describes it in *Complete Criminal Law* (2008):

This offence was designed to deal with the person who makes off from a restaurant or petrol garage without paying and against whom a dishonest intention to permanently deprive (theft) or a false representation (fraud/deception) cannot be proved at the time of the obtaining. It was designed to fill a gap in the law.

Note that there is a large overlap between this offence and others, such as theft under s.1 of the **Theft Act 1968** and obtaining services dishonestly under s.11 of the **Fraud Act 2006** (above). Since bilking does not require proof of any deception or false representation, it is easier to prove than these offences.

Actus reus

The defendant must make off — this involves the dishonest departure from the spot at which immediate payment is expected. The defendant does not have to 'run, sneak out or stealthily disappear' (C. McAlhone and R. Huxley-Binns, *Criminal Law: The Fundamentals*). In *R v Brooks and Brooks* (1982), it was held that the term 'making off' means simply what it says. In that case, it was also held that in restaurants, the 'spot' is the cash point, not the restaurant, so if a customer heads for the door, he or she 'makes off'. Leaving a worthless cheque on the reception counter in a hotel or on the restaurant table would also constitute making off.

An interesting case on the issue of what is meant by 'on the spot' is *R v Aziz* (1993). Here, the defendant refused to pay for a lengthy taxi ride (over 13 miles), whereupon the taxi driver said he would take the defendant back, but instead stopped at a police station. In upholding the conviction under s.3(1), the Court of Appeal ruled that, although the usual 'spot' for payment is at the end of a taxi ride, in this case the defendant made off when he got out of the taxi during its journey to the police station. 'On the spot' was not necessarily the final destination of the journey

Note that if a restaurant owner or hotel receptionist has given the defendant permission to leave because the defendant has deceived him or her by saying that he or she will pay later, then the defendant has *not* committed this offence, but will have obtained services dishonestly under s.11 of the **Fraud Act 2006**.

Goods supplied or service done

This includes any service or supply of goods where immediate payment is expected, as provided for example by taxis, filling stations, restaurants, hotels and emergency plumbers. The offence is only committed when the service or goods are actually supplied and when payment is expected.

Without having paid as required or expected

The payment must be lawfully enforceable. This means that if a supplier commits a breach of contract whereby he or she does not provide the service or supply the goods in question, there would be no liability to pay. This can be seen in *Troughton* v *Metropolitan Police* (1987), where a taxi driver deviated from his route to take a drunken passenger to a police station, and then demanded the full fare. The defendant left without paying, and his appeal against conviction was successful, as the change of route entitled him not to pay.

Mens rea

Dishonesty under the Ghosh test

If the defendant walked out of a restaurant without paying for his or her food as a protest against poor service or bad food, and if he or she thought this was both reasonable and honest and believed that ordinary, honest people would agree, then he or she would be acquitted.

Knowledge that payment on the spot was required or expected

If the defendant honestly believed that goods were supplied on credit and that he or she would be invoiced later, he or she would be acquitted, as would a foreign visitor who travelled on a bus without paying if in his or her own country bus travel was free. In *R* v *Aziz*, the defendant argued that when the driver said he was returning, this meant that his obligation to pay had ended. This was rejected by the Court of Appeal, which upheld his conviction.

Intent to avoid payment of the amount due

In *R* v *Allen* (1985), it was held that the prosecution must prove that the defendant intended to avoid payment permanently. Therefore, if the defendant made off but intended to pay later, or knew he or she would have to pay because the creditor knew where he or she lived, he or she would not be guilty. This is illustrated in *R* v *Vincent* (2001), where the defendant, who had stayed at two hotels, left without paying his bills, having first obtained agreements with the hotels to pay later when he could afford to. His conviction was quashed on appeal.

Table 15.1 Summary of fraud offences

	Fraud by false representation (s.2 Fraud Act 2006)	**Obtaining services dishonestly (s.11 Fraud Act 2006)**	**Making off without payment (s.3(1) Theft Act 1978)**
Definition	Dishonestly making a false representation to make a gain for oneself or cause a loss to another.	Obtaining services dishonestly where these services are provided on the basis that payment has been, is being or will be made for them, and the defendant obtains them without paying and intends not to pay.	The defendant who, knowing payment on the spot for goods supplied or services done is required or expected, dishonestly makes off without having paid, and with intent to avoid payment.
Actus reus	False representation: a trick, con or lie that does not need to be believed or relied on by the victim. Representation can be express or implied.	Services include all professional, financial and commercial services, including credit cards. No deception is required.	Making off from the spot where immediate payment is expected. Any service or supply of goods where immediate payment is expected — service or goods must have been supplied and be those which the defendant is permitted to use.
Mens rea	• Dishonesty does *not* include beliefs in s.2(1) Theft Act 1968, therefore the only test is the Ghosh test. • Knowing that the representation is or might be false. • With intent to gain or cause loss or to expose another to the risk of loss — representation must be made with intent to cause gain or loss.	• Dishonesty — Ghosh test applies. • Defendant must *know* the services are to be paid for or know they *might* have to be paid for. • Defendant must *intend* to avoid payment in whole or in part *at the time of the obtaining*.	• Defendant must have been dishonest when he or she makes off — Ghosh test. • A genuine mistaken belief that payment was not required will negate dishonesty. • Intent to avoid payment means intent to delay payment is not enough — intent must be never to pay.

Questions

1 What is the *actus reus* of s.2 fraud by false representation?

2 What criticism does Denis Lanser make of this new offence?

3 What are the three separate *mens rea* elements of this offence?

4 What legal rule is illustrated by *R* v *Silverman* (1988)?

5 What are the three *mens rea* elements of s.11 obtaining services dishonestly?

6 Explain the *actus reus* elements of making off without payment under s.3 of the Theft Act 1978.

7 What rule is illustrated by *R* v *Allen* (1985)?

Further reading

Lanser, D. (2008) 'Reform of fraud offences in criminal law', *A-Level Law Review*, Vol. 3, No. 3.

Loveless, J. (2008) *Complete Criminal Law*, chapter 13, Oxford University Press.

McAlhone, C. and Huxley-Binns, R. (2007) *Criminal Law: The Fundamentals*, chapter 9, Sweet and Maxwell.

Storey, T. and Lidbury, A. (2007) *Criminal Law*, chapter 10, Willan.

Chapter 16

Criminal damage

Basic offence

The basic offence of criminal damage is defined under s.1(1) of the **Criminal Damage Act 1971**:

> *A person who without lawful excuse destroys or damages any property belonging to another intending to destroy or damage any such property or being reckless as to whether any such property would be destroyed or damaged shall be guilty of an offence.*

Actus reus

The *actus reus* is destroying or damaging property belonging to another without lawful excuse.

Destroy or damage

The words 'destroy' and 'damage' are not defined in the Act itself. Property will be deemed to be destroyed if it is no longer 'fit for purpose', i.e. made useless. It does not have to be completely destroyed — television sets or computers would only need to be so broken that they could no longer be used.

Damage has occurred if 'time, money and effort' are required to return the property to its original state. It refers to both permanent and temporary damage:

❖ In *Roe* v *Kingerlee* (1986), mud smeared on a police cell wall was found to be damage; although not permanent, it cost money to clean off. If the damage can be removed without any expense or effort, then no damage has occurred. In *A (a juvenile)* v *R* (1978), the defendant spat at a policeman, who was able to remove the

PhotoDreams/Alamy

In *Hardman* v *Chief Constable of Avon and Somerset Constabulary* (1986), pavement paintings drawn with water-soluble paint constituted damage because the council had to incur expense and effort in using water jets to clean the pavement

damage by wiping it off his uniform. This did not incur any expense or effort and so was not deemed to be 'damage'.

❖ In *Hardman* v *Chief Constable of Avon and Somerset Constabulary* (1986), it was held that pavement paintings drawn with water-soluble paint constituted 'damage'. Although the defendant claimed that the paintings would be easily washed away by the rain, the council had to use water jets to clean the pavements, thus incurring expense and effort.

❖ In *R* v *Fiak* (2005), the defendant pushed a blanket into the toilet in his police cell and then repeatedly flushed the toilet, causing the floor to be flooded. It was held that he had caused criminal damage to both the blanket and the floor, as the cell was unusable for some time.

❖ In *Blake* v *DPP* (1993; see page 208), the defendant had written on concrete pillars, which incurred expense and effort to remove and was held to be 'damage'. This case clearly shows that graffiti can amount to criminal damage, as the majority of graffiti needs effort and expense to remove.

❖ It was decided in *R* v *Fisher* (1865) (a pre-Act case) that the removal of parts necessary for a machine to operate constituted damage to that machine.

It is also important to look at the *purpose* for which the property is used. In *Morphitis* v *Salmon* (1990), it was held that a scratch on a scaffolding pole did not take away the usefulness of the scaffolding, and scaffolding is liable to scratching when it is used. The same would apply if a tin of paint is thrown into a skip and the lid comes off, causing the paint to spill. This would not take away the usefulness of the skip, and skips are liable to become dirty and stained. However, if a car were to be scratched, this *would* amount to damage.

Property

For the offence of criminal damage, the definition of 'property' is basically the same as that under s.4 of the Theft Act 1968. The only difference is that you cannot damage wild flowers or mushrooms, so s.4(3) is not applicable. Section 4(4), however, is: property for the purposes of criminal damage does cover wild creatures that have been tamed or that are kept in captivity. You are also able to damage land, although, of course, this is property that cannot be stolen.

Belonging to another

The property that has been damaged must belong to another, so you cannot be guilty if you destroy or damage your own property. The definition is found in s.10(2) and states that the property will be treated as belonging to any person who:

❖ has the custody or control of it, or
❖ has any proprietary right or interest in it

Without lawful excuse

The defendant could be justified in damaging property in circumstances where either self-defence/prevention of crime or duress could be pleaded. Under s.5(2), there are two specific defences under this head.

Belief in the owner's consent: s.5(2)(a)

If the defendant is of the honest belief that the owner would have consented to the damage, he or she may raise this as a lawful excuse for his or her actions. In *R* v *Denton* (1982), a cotton mill worker used this defence successfully. He had overheard a conversation between his employer and another who were of the opinion that Denton would be the ideal person to burn down the mill, enabling them to make an insurance claim on the property. Denton, who was of low intelligence, was under the impression that they *wanted* him to set fire to the mill and so argued that he had the honest belief the owner was consenting.

Note that this defence can also be used if the defendant is intoxicated. An example is the case of *Jaggard* v *Dickinson* (1980). The defendant caused criminal damage to what she thought was her friend's house by breaking a window, and was of the honest belief that her friend, the owner, would have consented. However, the house in question was in fact another house, and she had made a mistake while intoxicated. The 'lawful excuse' was allowed to stand, despite the intoxication.

Belief that the property was in immediate need of protection: s.5(2)(b)

For this defence to succeed, the defendant must have believed that the property needing protection was in *immediate* danger of being destroyed, and so the action he or she took was to try to prevent this. The property might be the defendant's or belong to someone else.

An example is where a river is about to burst its banks, and the demolition of a brick wall might protect a house. A defendant would be able to raise the lawful excuse under s.5(2)(b), as he or she would have the honest belief that the house was in immediate need of protection from the flood water. If the danger was not immediate, the defence will fail. This defence is available subject to the objective requirements of immediacy and of causation (i.e. the link between the actual damage caused by the defendant and the prevention of harm to the other property was not too remote).

In *R v Hill and Hall* (1989), the defendant was arrested outside a US naval base in possession of a hacksaw blade, and she admitted intending to use the blade to cut through the perimeter fence. She was convicted of having the blade with intent to use it to cause criminal damage, and appealed arguing lawful excuse — an honest belief in the need for immediate protection of her nearby house because the presence of the base would, at some future time, be likely to result in a Russian nuclear strike. Unsurprisingly perhaps, her appeal was dismissed on the basis that 'the proposed act on her part was far too remote from the eventual aim at which she was targeting her actions to satisfy the test' (per Lord Lane CJ).

Blake v *DPP* (1993) raised both defences under sections 5(2)(a) and 5(2)(b). The defendant, a vicar, wrote biblical quotations on large concrete pillars outside the Houses of Parliament in London. He claimed that the government should not be sending troops to Iraq, and was opposed to the Gulf War. As part of his defence he claimed that:

* God consented to his writing the quotations on the pillars expressing his concerns and thus causing criminal damage — 5(2)(a).
* The damage he caused was going to protect property in the Gulf — 5(2)(b).

The courts, however, held that the defences could not stand, stating that:

* God could not consent to the damage.
* The damage he caused was not capable of protecting property in the Gulf at that immediate time.

Blake was convicted of criminal damage to the pillars. Note, however, that in the case described on page 209, the defence of lawful excuse was successfully pleaded.

Environment protesters cleared of power station criminal damage

Six environmental protesters accused of causing £30,000 worth of damage when they scaled a power station last year were cleared today.

The protesters climbed the 200-metre stack of Kingsnorth power station last October, painting 'Gordon' on its face to protest against the development of new coal-fired electricity plants.

The six, some of whom were Greenpeace volunteers, succeeded in temporarily shutting down the station, near Hoo in Kent, but abandoned their positions on the chimney after being threatened with a High Court injunction.

The jury at Maidstone Crown Court found the five men and one woman not guilty by majority verdict. All had pleaded not guilty to charges of criminal damage.

The defendants claimed that they had 'lawful excuse' because they were acting to protect property around the world 'in immediate need of protection' from the impacts of climate change.

Eon, the owners of the plant, are planning to replace the existing unit with two new coal-fired plants which, if built, would be the first new coal build power plants built for over 20 years. Eon say that the units would produce enough electricity to supply around 1.5 million homes.

Summing up, Judge David Caddick said that the case centred on whether or not the protesters had a lawful excuse for their actions. He told the jury that for a lawful excuse to be used it must be proved that the action was due to an immediate need to protect property belonging to another.

Environmental campaigners have fought against the development of new coal-fired power stations as part of the fight against climate change.

Ben Stewart, one of the defendants, said: 'This verdict marks a tipping point for the climate change movement. If jurors from the heart of Middle England say it's legitimate for a direct action group to shut down a coal-fired power station because of the harm it does to our planet, then where does that leave government energy policy?'

Laura Dixon, *Times Online*, 10 September 2008

These 'lawful excuse' defences can only be used when protecting property and will fail if the defendant is acting to protect a person. The defence did not succeed in *R* v *Baker and Wilkins* (1997), as the two defendants caused criminal damage to a door when they gained access to rescue Baker's daughter.

Mens rea

To satisfy the *mens rea*, it must be shown that the defendant either intended to damage or destroy the property or was reckless as to whether the property would be damaged or destroyed.

If the defendant had intent, that intent had to be to damage (or destroy) the property. In *R* v *Pembliton* (1874), the defendant wanted to break up a fight and threw a stone at the fighters to stop them. He missed, and the stone hit a window. He did not intend to damage the window and was not guilty.

Recklessness is sufficient *mens rea* for criminal damage, and the test from the case of *Cunningham* would be applied. The previous Caldwell test of objective recklessness was overturned by *R* v *G* (2003). The defendant must have foreseen, from his or her actions, the risk of the damage occurring. This is referred to as the conscious taking of an unjustified risk, and is a subjective test based on what the defendant was thinking at the time of the guilty act. In *R* v *G*, Lord Bingham applied the Draft Criminal Code definition of recklessness to criminal damage:

> *A person acts recklessly within the meaning of s.1 Criminal Damage Act 1971 with respect to:*
>
> *(i) a circumstance when he is aware of a risk that it exists or will exist;*
> *(ii) a result when he is aware of a risk that it will occur;*
>
> *and it is, in the circumstances known to him, unreasonable to take that risk.*
>
> *Therefore, recklessness is satisfied by:*
>
> *(i) awareness on the part of the D that property might belong to another (a circumstance), and*
> *(ii) awareness that damage or destruction might occur to that property.*

Aggravated offence

Section 1(2) of the **Criminal Damage Act 1971** states that:

> *A person who without lawful excuse destroys or damages any property, whether belonging to himself or another —*
>
> *(a) intending to destroy or damage any property or being reckless as to whether any property would be destroyed or damaged; and*
> *(b) intending by the destruction or damage to endanger the life of another or being reckless as to whether the life of another would be thereby endangered;*
>
> *shall be guilty of an offence.*

Actus reus

The *actus reus* for this offence is destroying or damaging any property and endangering life by that destruction or damage.

Destroy or damage any property

The same definition for 'destroy or damage' can be applied from s.1(1). The main difference is that the destruction or damage can be to *any* property. This means that the defendant can still be guilty if the damage or destruction is to his or her own property. Thus, if the defendant were to break a bottle of whisky over the victim's head, he or she would be guilty of a s.1(2) offence.

Endanger life by the destruction or damage

It must be the actual destruction or damage to the property that endangers the life of another. In *R* v *Steer* (1987), the defendant fired three shots from an automatic rifle at a house, causing damage to the door. Following an appeal to the House of Lords, it was held that for the defendant to be found guilty of s.1(2) it had to be shown that the damage endangered life. In this case, it was held that the damage to the door did *not* endanger life and the defendant was not guilty. Lord Bridge stated:

> ...to be guilty under s.1(1), the defendant must have intended or been reckless as to the damage to property which he caused. To be guilty under s.1(2) he must additionally have intended to endanger life or been reckless whether life would be endangered 'by the damage' to property which he caused.

Note that life does not have to be endangered — it is sufficient that the act was *capable of endangering life*. In *R* v *Sangha* (1988), the defendant set fire to furniture in a neighbour's flat. The flat was empty and, because of the construction of the block of flats, the fire could not spread to the other flats. However, as the defendant was unaware of this, he was still found guilty. If the defendant realised that life might be endangered, he or she would be guilty, even though no one actually was at risk.

Mens rea

The defendant must have the intention to damage or destroy the property or be reckless as to whether the property would be damaged or destroyed — the same as for the basic offence under s.1(1). The defendant must also have the intention or be reckless that the damage would endanger life.

Recklessness means applying the Cunningham test — the defendant must have realised the risk of the damage endangering the life of another. If he or she did not realise this, he or she would not be guilty. This means that if the defendant only intended to cause some minor damage, but unexpectedly the actual damage caused was far greater than that intended and this in turn threatened life, he or she would not be liable under s.1(2).

Arson

Under s.1(3) of the **Criminal Damage Act 1971**, this offence consists of the basic offence under s.1(1) with the addition that the damage or destruction is caused by fire. The *actus reus* and *mens rea* are the same as for the basic offence, except that the defendant must intend damage by fire or be reckless as to it. The offence can become aggravated where the damage caused also endangers life. This would be the same *actus reus* and *mens rea* as s.1(2), with the use of fire.

Under s.1(3) of the Criminal Damage Act 1971, arson consists of the basic offence under s.1(1) with the addition that the damage or destruction is caused by fire

Note that if the criminal damage is caused by the defendant setting fire to something, he or she would be liable for both s.1(1) and s.1(3). If life is endangered (which could be quite likely), the defendant would be liable for both s.1(2) and s.1(3).

Following the case of *R* v *Miller* (1983), arson can be committed by an omission. In this case, the defendant accidentally started a fire but failed to summon any help and simply left the building. The fire spread, causing damage to warehouses. He was found guilty of arson under s.1(3) of the **Criminal Damage Act 1971**.

Questions

1 Identify each of the *actus reus* elements required for the s.1(1) offence of criminal damage.

2 What test is applied to decide if property has been damaged?

3 In which case was it held that removal of parts necessary to operate a machine constituted criminal damage?

4 Explain the decision in *Morphitis* v *Salmon* (1990).

5 What are the two specific defences under s.5(2) (without lawful excuse)?

6 Explain why in *Jaggard* v *Dickinson* (1980) the defence was pleaded successfully.

7 Why was Hill's conviction upheld on appeal?

8 Explain the defence argument in the Kingsnorth case.

9 What is the *mens rea* for s.1(1) criminal damage?

10 How did Lord Bingham define 'recklessness' in *R* v *G* (2003)?

11 Explain the decision in *R* v *Steer* (1987) (s.1(2) offence).

12 What legal rule is illustrated by *R* v *Sangha* (1988)?

Further reading

Ashworth, A. (2006) *Principles of Criminal Law*, chapter 7, Oxford University Press.

Huxley-Binns, R. and McAlhone, C. (2007) *Criminal Law: The Fundamentals*, chapter 8, Sweet & Maxwell.

Loveless, J. (2008) *Complete Criminal Law*, chapter 14, Oxford University Press.

Smith, J. C. and Hogan, B. (1999), *Criminal Law*, chapter 18, Butterworths.

Storey, T. and Lidbury, A. (2001) *Criminal Law*, chapter 13, Willan.

Chapter 17

Duress and other general defences

Duress is the only separate defence applicable to offences against property — all other general defences, such as self-defence, intoxication and insanity, are explained in Chapter 5.

It has been a long-established principle that where a defendant commits a crime under threat of death or serious injury, or finds himself or herself in a situation which could cause fear of death or serious injury, he or she can plead the defence of duress. This defence has been called a 'concession to human frailty', but cannot provide a defence to murder or attempted murder charges.

There are two types of duress: duress by threats and duress of circumstances. However, they have the same rules.

Duress by threats

The typical case where this defence could operate is where the defendant is threatened that unless he or she robs a bank, he or she will be killed.

As Gavin Murray noted in his article 'The defence of duress by threats' (*A-Level Law Review,* Vol. 3, No. 2):

> *...duress operates in a slightly different way from other defences. Successfully pleading duress does not remove* mens rea, *nor does it prove that the* actus reus *was not voluntary; anyone pleading duress is simply saying: 'Yes, I committed the crime, but I should be excused from liability because I was unable to resist the threats that were made against me.'*

Lord Wilberforce explained duress in *DPP for Northern Ireland* v *Lynch* (1975) as 'something which is superimposed on the other elements of the offence so as to prevent the law from treating what she or he has done as a crime'.

In order for this defence to be successfully pleaded, the jury will have to be satisfied that a person of reasonable firmness would have no choice but to commit the offence.

The current rules for duress by threats were laid down in *R* v *Hasan* (2005) by Lord Bingham in a House of Lords judgement. In this case, the defendant worked as a driver for T, who was involved in prostitution. T's boyfriend, S, was involved in supplying drugs and had a reputation for violence: it was alleged that S had boasted about killing three people. The defendant said he had been 'ambushed' by S and another man and ordered to commit a burglary; the two men had threatened to kill him and his family unless he carried out the crime. They drove him to a house and gave him a knife. The defendant did break into the house but ran away when he saw the occupier. At his trial for aggravated burglary he pleaded duress, but was convicted. The Court of Appeal quashed his conviction and the Crown appealed to the House of Lords. In a wide-ranging judgement, Lord Bingham both clarified and tightened up the rules on duress.

Nature of the threat

The threat must be of death or serious physical injury and be directed against the defendant or his or her immediate family, or a person for whose safety the defendant would reasonably regard himself or herself as responsible. Threats involving damage to property or blackmail are therefore insufficient.

In *R* v *Baker and Wilkins* (1997), the defence was disallowed to the defendant who had tried to rescue her child whom she believed had been kidnapped by the child's father and his new partner. She broke through the front door of her former partner's house. It was argued that the defence of duress should be available because she believed that her action was necessary to avoid her having a nervous breakdown, but this was rejected both by the trial court and the Court of Appeal.

In *R* v *Conway* (1989), although the defendant and the passenger in his car were in no way related, it was clearly reasonable for the driver to hold himself responsible for the passenger's safety.

Immediate harm

The threat must be of immediate harm. In *R* v *Abdul-Hussain* (1999), the Court of Appeal preferred the use of 'imminent' to 'immediate', thus widening the scope of this defence. In a graphic illustration to support this, the court ruled (per Lord Rose) that:

> *If Anne Frank had stolen a car to escape from Amsterdam and had been charged with theft, the tenets of English law would not, in our judgement, have denied her a defence of duress on the ground that she should have waited for the Gestapo's knock on the door.*

However, in *Hasan*, Lord Bingham made it clear he preferred 'immediate' to 'imminent'. If there is any delay between the threat itself and it being carried out if the defendant does not comply with it, there is an obvious argument that the defendant could take evasive action to avoid committing the crime, for example by going to the police.

Connection between the threat and the crime

There must be some connection between the threat and the crime the defendant was compelled to commit. As Gavin Murray writes, 'a defendant cannot simply claim cover from a threat to justify whatever criminal endeavour he or she chooses to pursue'. This was affirmed in *R* v *Cole* (1994), where the defendant robbed two building societies because he owed money to money lenders who had threatened him and his girlfriend with violence if the money was not repaid. However, the money lenders had not ordered him specifically to carry out these robberies, and because of this, the defence was rejected.

Belief in the existence of the threat

The actual threat need not exist, provided the defendant reasonably believes that it does. This is a subjective test, as confirmed in *R* v *Safi* (2003), where the defendants hijacked an aircraft in order to escape from Afghanistan, where they feared being tortured or killed by the Taliban. The Court of Appeal ruled that the threat need not exist in reality, provided the defendant acted under the belief of an imminent threat.

The objective question

A sober person of reasonable firmness, sharing the defendant's characteristics, must have responded to the defendant's belief in the same way. As with provocation, this rule is designed to set limits to the availability of the defence. In *R* v *Horne* (1994), this 'sober person' was defined as 'an average member of the public; not a hero, not a coward, just an average person'.

However, in *R* v *Bowen* (1996), the Court of Appeal extended this definition. This case involved a defendant with a low IQ who claimed to have been threatened by two men to obtain goods. At his trial, he pleaded duress and led evidence that suggested he was abnormally vulnerable. The judge refused to allow these

characteristics to be put before the jury and he was convicted of obtaining services by deception. On appeal, his conviction was quashed. Stuart-Smith LJ ruled that, while mere personality traits are to be excluded, any characteristic which makes the defendant less able to resist the threats than persons without that characteristic is to be attributed to the reasonable person. He stated:

> Psychiatric evidence may be admissible to show the accused is suffering from some mental illness…provided persons generally suffering from such a condition may be more susceptible to pressure and threats and thus to assist the jury in deciding whether a reasonable person suffering from such a condition might have been impelled to act as the defendant did.

Voluntary association with criminals

The defence of duress is not available to a defendant who has voluntarily placed himself or herself in such a situation that he or she risks being threatened with violence to commit a crime. In *R* v *Fitzpatrick* (1977), the defendant had voluntarily joined the IRA and was therefore unable to plead duress as a defence based on threats from that organisation.

In *R* v *Sharp* (1987), Lord Lane CJ laid down four conditions that must be satisfied if this defence is to be ruled inadmissible:

❖ The membership of the criminal gang must be voluntary.
❖ The defendant must have knowledge of its nature.
❖ He or she must have known that gang members 'might bring pressure…to commit an offence'.
❖ He or she must have been an active member when put under such pressure.

In his judgement in *Hasan*, the key issue examined by Lord Bingham was whether the defendant should lose the benefit of this defence only if he or she foresaw the risk of coercion, or if he or she ought reasonably to have foreseen said risk — whether he or she foresaw the risk or not. He came down firmly on the side of this test being objective, reliant on whether the defendant *ought* reasonably to have foreseen. He stated:

> …policy in my view points towards an objective test of what the defendant, placed as he was and knowing what he did, ought reasonably to have foreseen. The policy of the law must be to discourage association with known criminals, and it should be slow to excuse the criminal conduct of those who do so. If a person voluntarily becomes or remains associated with others engaged in criminal activity in a situation where he knows or ought reasonably to know that he may be the subject of compulsion by them or their associates, he cannot rely on the defence of duress to excuse any act which he is thereafter compelled to do by them.

Duress of circumstances

In duress of circumstances, the threat does not come from a person but from circumstances that give rise to a fear of violence or death. The rationale for this extension to the 'basic' defence of duress is that it would be wrong to allow a defence to someone whose will was overborne by a personal threat but to deny a similar defence because the threat was 'circumstantial'.

Most cases here relate to driving offences. In *R* v *Martin* (1989), for example, the defendant drove his car while disqualified from driving. His wife had become hysterical and threatened to commit suicide if he did not drive her son to his work, as he was running late. In *R* v *Conway* (1989), the defendant, charged with reckless driving, argued that his driving was caused by his belief that two men were trying to kill his passenger.

The case of *R* v *Pommell* (1995) made it clear that this defence is one of general application to all offences, except murder and attempted murder. In that case, the defendant was charged with possession of a sub-machine gun without a firearm certificate. He claimed he had taken the gun from another person, in order to prevent that other from using it. He removed the bullets and decided to wait until the following morning to give the gun to his brother to take to the police. The defendant was convicted, despite his defence of duress. However, the Court of Appeal ruled to quash his conviction because the delay ought not to have denied him the defence, which should have been put to the jury at his trial.

The rules governing duress of circumstances are the same as those explained above for duress by threats.

Other defences

Intoxication

It is crucial to distinguish between specific and basic intent offences, and in the case of the latter to explain the rule derived from *R* v *Majewski* (see Chapter 5).

Remember that both basic and aggravated criminal damage offences are the *only* property offences of basic intent, whereas theft, burglary, robbery and making off without payment all contain specific intent requirements.

Self-defence

Self-defence is explained in Chapter 5 (pages 53–56). The main issue of self-defence or prevention of crime under s.3 of the **Criminal Law Act 1967**, when being applied to a property offence, is the rule that the use of force is not so highly regarded, thus limiting the defence. Professor Ashworth comments in *Principles of Criminal Law* (2006):

> *What is crucial is that it should rule out the infliction or risk of considerable physical harm merely to apprehend a fleeing thief, to stop minor property loss or damage, etc... The proper approach is to compare the relative value of the rights involved, and not to give special weight to the rights of the property owner simply because the other party is in the wrong (i.e. committing a crime).*

Sample exam question

Des, who has a violent and unpredictable personality, sees Eddie in the street and calls him over. Eddie, who is 16 years old and who knows Des, is very frightened when Des shows him a knife and tells him to 'get some money for me from a few old ladies'. Des also says that he will be watching Eddie all the time. Eddie manages to get some money from a few old people in the street, either by telling them that he is homeless and needs money for food, or if they refuse this request, by persistently asking in an increasingly aggressive manner. Des takes the money with him to a bar where he drinks a large amount of beer. He manages to get his last pint of beer without paying by allowing the barman to believe he is part of a larger crowd that has ordered a lot of drinks.

Des leaves the bar to visit a female friend. However, he has only been to her house once before and he becomes confused between a number of houses. Finally, though he is wrong, he is certain that he has found his friend's house. No one seems to be in, but he manages to go through an unlocked door from the garage into the house. Inside, he begins to play about lighting paper with his cigarette lighter. Eventually, the carpet is set alight, and he hastily smothers it with a cushion. The cushion is badly damaged.

When Des wakes up in the house next morning, he is confronted by the owner, Fred, who is returning from work. Des runs out, barging into Fred on the way. Fred is knocked down and suffers a broken arm.

Adapted from AQA Unit 4 paper, January 2008

1 **Discuss the possible criminal liability of Eddie for property offences arising out of his collection of money from the old people, and of Des arising out of the way in which he got his last pint of beer without paying.**
2 **Discuss the possible criminal liability of Des arising out of the incidents at the house.**

Further reading

Huxley-Binns, R. and McAlhone, C. (2007) *Criminal Law: The Fundamentals*, chapter 13, Sweet & Maxwell.

Loveless, J. (2008) *Complete Criminal Law*, chapter 9, Oxford University Press.

Murray, G. (2008) 'The defence of duress by threats', *A-Level Law Review*, Vol. 3, No. 2.

Smith, J. C. and Hogan, B. (1999) *Criminal Law*, chapter 10, Butterworths.

Storey, T. and Lidbury, A. (2001) *Criminal Law*, chapters 18–19, Willan.

Unit 4

B: Law of tort
Chapters 18–23

Chapter **18**

Introduction to negligence

'Negligence' is defined by the *Shorter Oxford Dictionary* as 'want of attention to what ought to be done or looked after; lack of proper care in doing something'. In law, negligence is more tightly defined as an actionable wrong flowing from a breach of duty of care that causes a victim foreseeable harm or loss. However, it is not the law that anyone who suffers harm as a result of another's carelessness can sue in tort — negligence requires more than 'heedless or careless conduct' (*Lochgelly Iron and Coal Co.* v *McMullan*, 1934, per Lord Wright). The key elements that the claimant needs to prove are:

❖ he or she was owed a duty of care by the defendant
❖ the defendant breached that duty
❖ the breach caused the claimant foreseeable harm or loss

Another way of putting this is to say that someone is negligent if he or she acts carelessly towards another person, to whom there is a legal obligation to act carefully, and the carelessness causes the other person to suffer some harm or loss.

Duty of care

The tort of negligence owes its origins to the tale of a decomposing snail found in a ginger-beer bottle — *Donoghue* v *Stevenson* (1932). The claimant, Mary Donoghue, went with a friend to a café, where her friend bought her a bottle of ginger beer. Donoghue opened it and poured some of the contents into a glass. When she finished the glass, she then poured the remainder of the ginger beer into the glass, and at this point the remains of a snail floated to the surface. This caused Donoghue to develop gastroenteritis and nervous shock, and she sought compensation from the ginger-beer manufacturer. The case eventually reached the House of Lords, where Lord Atkin decided the case in her favour with his famous **neighbour principle**:

> You must take reasonable care to avoid acts or omissions which you can reasonably foresee would be likely to injure your neighbour. Who, then, in law is my neighbour? The answer seems to be persons who are so closely and directly affected by my act that I ought reasonably to have them in contemplation as being so affected when I am directing my mind to the acts or omissions which are called in question.

In this case, the ginger-beer manufacturer should reasonably have had the claimant in mind when manufacturing and bottling the ginger beer.

This test clearly established that in order for a duty of care to be owed, there must be reasonable foresight of harm to persons whom it is reasonable to foresee may be harmed by one's actions or omissions. In many instances, determining whether a duty exists is straightforward, for example:

❖ manufacturers or repairers of goods owe a duty to those who use the goods
❖ doctors owe a duty to patients
❖ an occupier of land owes a duty to visitors
❖ drivers on public roads owe a duty to other road users

However, this neighbour test has been used to create a duty of care in many less obvious situations, and the courts therefore have had to develop further guidelines to impose some limits on the scope of the principle.

The modern approach comes from *Caparo Industries plc* v *Dickman* (1990), which laid down the 'incremental approach'. The claimant company, Caparo, when initiating a takeover bid on a second company, relied on accounts and a report that had been prepared carelessly. Caparo sued the auditors, but the House of Lords ruled that they did not owe Caparo a duty of care when conducting the audit. The accounts and the audit had been produced for the purpose laid down in the **Companies Act 1985** — that of ensuring that existing shareholders could exercise responsible control over the company. They were not created to guide potential new investors seeking to take over the company.

This case asks three questions to decide whether a duty of care exists:

❖ Was the damage or loss foreseeable?
❖ Is there sufficient proximity between the wrongdoer and the victim?
❖ Is it just and reasonable to impose a duty of care?

If the answer to all these questions is 'yes', a duty of care is established. The claimant then needs to ascertain that the defendant breached that duty of care, that the claimant's loss or injury was caused by the breach and that such a loss was reasonably foreseeable (i.e. not too remote).

Foreseeability

The issue of foreseeability simply means that a reasonable person would have foreseen some damage or harm to the claimant at the time of the alleged negligence. A doctor's failure to diagnose a common medical problem will foreseeably lead to complications; a car driver's mistake will foreseeably cause a road accident.

The case of *Langley* v *Dray* (1998) provides a clear illustration of this rule. The claimant was a police officer who was injured in a crash while pursuing a defendant driving a stolen car. The Court of Appeal ruled that the defendant knew he was being pursued and therefore that by increasing his speed he would cause the police officer to drive faster and risk being injured.

Another helpful case is *Kent* v *Griffiths* (2000), where a doctor called for an ambulance to take a patient suffering from a severe asthma attack to hospital immediately. The control centre replied 'Okay, doctor', but the ambulance failed to arrive within a reasonable time, and there was no good reason for this delay. The patient suffered a heart attack, which could have been avoided if the ambulance had arrived in time. It was held that it was reasonably foreseeable that the claimant would suffer some harm from this failure.

Foreseeability is an objective test — the question is whether a reasonable person would foresee the possibility of some harm or loss occurring, not whether the actual defendant actually foresaw loss or harm. Further, the test is whether *some* harm or loss is foreseeable, not the particular type of loss or harm that occurred.

Proximity

Proximity means closeness in terms of time, space or relationship, and in many cases the issues of proximity and foreseeability are similar. For example, in a car accident the fact that the injured party could foreseeably be harmed will itself be proof of proximity.

However, the case of *Bourhill* v *Young* (1943) is interesting in this context. The claimant was descending from a tram when she heard a motor accident. She did not actually see it but later saw blood on the road and suffered nervous shock and a miscarriage. Although it was reasonably foreseeable that some people would suffer harm as a result of the defendant's negligent driving, injury to the specific claimant was not foreseeable as she was not in the immediate vicinity of the accident — only hearing but not seeing it. Her action therefore failed.

In *Watson* v *British Boxing Board of Control* (2000), a professional boxer suffered severe brain damage after being injured in a boxing match. The Court of Appeal held there was sufficient proximity between the boxer and the Board to give rise to a duty of care, because the Board was the only body that could license professional boxing.

It therefore had complete control over and responsibility for a situation that could result in harm to the boxer if it did not exercise reasonable care.

Just and reasonable test

The 'just and reasonable' test is usually referred to as the 'policy test', under which judges are able to limit the extent of this tort. The principal reason for this judicial discretion is that the floodgates would be opened if claims of liability were determined simply by reference to foreseeability. American judge Cardozo CJ referred to this danger when he warned of 'liability in an indeterminate amount for an indeterminate time to an indeterminate class'.

A good case to illustrate the use of this discretion is *Mulcahy* v *Ministry of Defence* (1996). The defendant was a soldier who had served in the Gulf War, where he had suffered damage to his hearing when a fellow soldier fired a howitzer shell. The Court of Appeal held that, although both factors of foreseeability and proximity were present, the facts of the case required them to consider this policy issue — whether it was fair, just and reasonable to impose a duty of care on the Ministry of Defence in battlefield situations. Unsurprisingly, it was decided that no such duty of care could be imposed. The application of this test can also be seen in the following types of cases:

❖ nervous shock — *Alcock* v *Chief Constable of South Yorkshire* (1992), where the House of Lords created various 'control tests' to restrict liability to secondary victims in psychiatric injury cases
❖ pure economic loss — *Hedley Byrne* v *Heller* (1964), where the House of Lords created a 'special relationship' test to restrict liability where the claimant has suffered a direct financial loss
❖ public organisations exercising a statutory duty — *X* v *Bedfordshire County Council* (1995), where local authorities exercising a statutory power were not held to be liable

Breach of duty

Once the claimant has shown that the defendant owed him or her a duty of care, it is necessary to prove that the defendant breached this duty — in other words, that he or she acted carelessly. For example, in *Donoghue* v *Stevenson* (1932), it had to be proved that the defendant allowed the snail to get into the ginger-beer bottle. The key question that the court asks in order to determine whether this duty has been breached is: 'Did the defendant behave as the reasonable person would have in these circumstances?' This test was described by Alderson B in *Blythe* v *Birmingham Waterworks* (1856): 'Negligence [meaning breach of duty] is the omission to do something which a reasonable man…would do, or doing something which a prudent and reasonable man would not do.'

The standard is therefore objective — any personal difficulties or disabilities that might be encountered by the specific defendant cannot be taken into account. This is made clear in *Nettleship* v *Weston* (1971), where the claimant gave the defendant driving lessons. On the third lesson, the car struck a lamp post and the claimant was injured. It was decided that the defendant, although a learner driver, would be judged by the standard of the average competent driver:

The learner driver may be doing his best, but his incompetent best is not good enough. He must drive in as good a manner as a driver of skill, experience and care.

Children

The conduct of a child defendant is assessed by reference to the standard of conduct that can be expected of a reasonable child of the defendant's age. This was decided in *Mullins* v *Richards* (1998). The defendant and the claimant were 15-year-old schoolgirls who were 'fencing' with plastic rulers during the course of a lesson, when one of the rulers snapped and a piece of plastic flew into the claimant's eye, causing blindness. It was held that the proper test to apply was whether an ordinary, careful and reasonable 15-year-old would have foreseen that this game carried a risk of injury.

Professional persons

Where a defendant has a professional skill and the case involves the exercise of that skill, the court will expect the defendant to show that he or she has the degree of competence usually to be expected of an ordinary skilled member of that profession. The leading cases here are both medical — *Bolam* v *Friern Barnet Hospital Management* (1957) and *Bolitho* v *City and Hackney Health Authority* (1957).

In *Bolam*, it was held that:

...a doctor is not guilty of negligence if he has acted in accordance with a practice accepted as proper by a responsible body of medical opinion skilled in that particular art.

McNair J stated in that case:

Where you get a situation which involves the use of some special skill or competence, then the test as to whether there has been negligence or not is not the test of the man on the top of a Clapham omnibus, because he has not got this special skill. The test is the standard of the ordinary skilled man exercising and professing to have that special skill.

This means that a general practitioner is only expected to exercise the normal level of skill of a GP, not that of a senior consultant heart surgeon. This particular principle was followed in *Djemal* v *Bexley Heath Health Authority* (1995), where it was held the relevant standard was that of a reasonably senior houseman acting as a casualty officer — the defendant's position at the time — regardless of how long the defendant had actually been in that job.

Tests to determine breach of duty

To assist the court in deciding whether the defendant has breached his or her duty of care, straightforward tests have been established. You should be familiar with the structure of each test and be able to discuss accompanying case examples.

These tests must always be considered when asking if the defendant behaved as the reasonable person would have done in the circumstances. The trial judge is required to 'balance' on the one hand the probability and magnitude of harm, and on the other the cost and practicality of taking precautions.

Degree of probability that harm will be done

Care must be taken in respect of a risk where it is reasonably foreseeable that harm or injury may occur. Nearly all human actions or omissions involve the possibility of harm, but not every risky act will be regarded as negligent.

In *Bolton* v *Stone* (1951), the claimant was injured while standing on the road by a cricket ball struck over the defendant's ground. Evidence showed that a ball had only been hit out of the ground on six occasions in the previous 30 years, and on no previous occasion had anyone been injured. Here, the defendant was found not to have been negligent, as a reasonable person would have been justified in disregarding the risk.

Compare this case with *Haley* v *London Electricity Board* (1965). Here, the defendants left a hammer on the pavement to warn people of excavations. The claimant, who was blind, tripped over it and was injured. It was held that although the warning was sufficient for sighted people, it was not adequate for a blind person. The number of blind people was sufficiently large to make them a group that the defendants ought reasonably to have had in contemplation.

Magnitude of likely harm

The court considers not only the risk of harm, but also how serious the injury could potentially be.

In *Paris* v *Stepney Borough Council* (1951), the claimant, who had one eye, was employed as a mechanic in the defendants' garage, where his job included welding. It was not usual practice to supply goggles. When a piece of metal flew into the claimant's good eye, he became completely blind. The defendants were held to be liable, although they would not have been liable to a person with normal sight. The greater risk to the claimant meant that greater precautions than normal should have been taken.

Cost and practicality of preventing the risk

Once the court has identified a risk as reasonably foreseeable, the next issue is whether the defendant should have taken precautions against that risk. If the cost of taking precautions to eliminate the risk is completely disproportionate to the extent of the risk itself, the defendant will not be held liable.

In *Latimer* v *AEC Ltd* (1952), a factory was flooded, and the owner used sawdust to reduce the effects of the flooding. However, some areas of the factory floor remained slippery and, as a result, an employee was injured when he fell. The owner was held not to have breached his duty of care because the only way to have avoided that risk was to have closed the factory. In the circumstances, this was out of proportion to the level of risk involved.

Note that *Bolton* v *Stone* (page 227) also illustrates this test effectively.

Potential benefits of the risk

In some cases, the court has to weigh up whether there are some risks that have potential benefits for society. In *Daborn* v *Bath Tramways* (1946), it was held that:

> *If all trains were restricted to a speed of 5 mph, there would be fewer rail accidents, but our national life would be intolerably slowed down. The purpose to be served, if sufficiently important, justifies the assumption of abnormal risk.*

In *Watt* v *Hertfordshire County Council* (1954), the claimant fireman had been injured by a heavy jack that had been loaded quickly (but not secured) in the fire engine in order to respond to an emergency call involving a road accident victim. It was held that in these circumstances the risk involved was not so great as to prohibit an attempt to save life.

Res ipsa loquitur

This means literally 'the thing speaks for itself' and refers to situations where the judge is entitled to infer that the defendant's negligence caused the event, in the absence of any explanation from the defendant. In *Scott* v *London and St Katherine's Docks* (1865), the claimant, a customs officer, was injured by some bags of sugar falling on him while standing near the door of the defendant's warehouse. At the first trial, the judge directed the jury to find for the defendant on the grounds that no evidence of negligence had been led by the claimant. A retrial was ordered in which this 'doctrine' was first made:

...there must be reasonable evidence of negligence. But where the thing is shown to be under the management of the defendant or his servants, and the accident is such as in the ordinary course of things does not happen if those who have the management use proper care, it affords reasonable evidence, in the absence of explanation by the defendant, that the accident arose from want of care.

In *Lloyde* v *West Midlands Gas Board* (1971), there was an argument that *res ipsa loquitur* was not actually a rule of law but, as per Megaw LJ, a:

...convenient...phrase to describe what is in essence no more than a common-sense approach...to the assessment of the effect of evidence in certain circumstances. It means that a claimant prima facie *establishes negligence where: (i) it is not possible for him to prove precisely what was the relevant act or omission which set in train the events leading to the accident, but (ii) on the evidence as it stands at the relevant time it is more likely than not that the effective cause of the accident was some act or omission of the defendant...which act or omission constitutes a failure to take proper care for the claimant's safety.*

Three separate requirements must be satisfied for *res ipsa loquitur* to be accepted.

The doctrine is dependent on the absence of explanation

If the court finds from the evidence how and why the occurrence took place, the rule will not apply. In *Barkway* v *South Wales Transport Co. Ltd* (1948), the tyre of a bus burst and the bus mounted the pavement and fell down an embankment. *Res ipsa loquitur* did not apply because the court had evidence of the circumstances of the accident and was satisfied that the system of tyre inspection in the defendant's garage was negligent. The courts have applied the doctrine to things falling from buildings and to accidents resulting from defective machines, apparatus or vehicles.

The harm must be of such a kind that it does not ordinarily happen if proper care is taken

In *Ratcliffe* v *Plymouth and Torbay Health Authority* (1998), the claimant had gone into hospital for an ankle operation but sustained a serious neurological condition, which it was agreed had been triggered by the injection of a spinal anaesthetic. He argued this was a case of *res ipsa loquitur* because the injection must have been given negligently or it would not have caused the problem. The defendant health authority produced expert evidence stating that this condition might have been caused by the claimant's susceptibility to spinal cord damage, which could have occurred even if the injection was not administered negligently. The Court of Appeal restated the rule above from *Scott,* but further stated that the defendant could prevent the judge from inferring negligence under *res ipsa loquitur* either by showing that he or she took reasonable care, or by supplying another explanation for the events. The court emphasised that nothing in the application of *res ipsa* changed the rule that the burden of proof was on the claimant. The defendant's alternative explanation would have to be plausible, and not merely theoretically possible, but he or she would not be required to prove that it was more likely to be correct than any other. In this case, the defendant had provided such a plausible explanation, and therefore *res ipsa* did not apply.

What caused the accident must be within the exclusive control of the defendant

If the defendant is not in control, the doctrine does not apply. In *Turner v Mansfield Corporation* (1975), the claimant driver of the defendant's dustcart was injured when its back raised up as the claimant drove it under a bridge. It was held that since the claimant was in control, it was for him to explain the accident; since he could not provide any evidence from which negligence could be inferred, the action failed.

Two railway cases illustrate the degree of control essential for the doctrine to apply. In *Gee v Metropolitan Railway Co.* (1873), a few minutes after a local train had started its journey the claimant leaned against the carriage door, which flew open. This was held to be evidence of negligence, whereas in *Easson v LNER Co.* (1944), the claimant's action failed because it was held that 'it is impossible to say that the doors of an express train travelling from Edinburgh to London are continuously under the control of the railway company'.

Causing foreseeable loss or injury (damage)

The claimant must be able to prove both that his or her damage or injury was caused by the defendant's breach of duty and that the damage or injury was not remote (i.e. it was reasonably foreseeable).

'But for' question

The first question that needs to be asked is: 'but for' the defendant's breach of duty, would the damage or injury have occurred? The leading case is *Barnett v Chelsea and Kensington Hospital Management Committee* (1969). The claimant's husband attended the defendants' hospital complaining of severe stomach pain and vomiting. The doctor in the accident and emergency department refused to examine him and he was sent home. Five hours later, he died from arsenic poisoning. The defendants clearly owed the deceased a duty of care and equally clearly they were in breach by failing to examine him. However, they were not held liable because the facts established that, even if he had been examined, he would have died before diagnosis and treatment could have been carried out. As the deceased would have died regardless of the breach, the hospital's breach of duty of care was not the cause of his death.

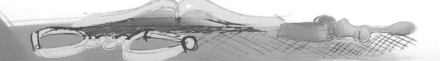

Sydney harbour — site of the oil leak in *The Wagon Mound* (1961)

Remoteness of damage

Damages may not be awarded even where the claimant has established that the defendant's breach of duty (negligence) caused the damage or injury. It must be established that the damage was not too remote.

The present rule of law was laid down in the Privy Council case of *Overseas Tankship (UK) Ltd* v *Morts Dock and Engineering Co.* (1961). This is better known as *The Wagon Mound No. 1* case, after the name of the ship concerned.

This case effectively overruled the case of *Re Polemis* (1921), where it had been held that the defendant was liable for all direct consequences of the breach. This test was held to be too wide and in the *Wagon Mound* case, the present rule of reasonable foreseeability was laid down.

The defendant negligently discharged fuel oil into Sydney harbour, and the oil spread to the claimant's wharf, where welding operations were taking place. The claimants were advised that there was no risk of this heavy oil catching fire on the water and as a result carried on welding. The oil did, however, ignite — sparks from a welder caused a pile of cotton waste floating on the water to catch fire, and this then set fire to the oil. As a result of this fire, damage was caused to two ships and fouling was caused to the wharf by the oil. On appeal, it was held that the defendants were only liable for the fouling to the wharf. The major damage to the ships caused by the ignition of the oil was too remote from the original discharge of the oil. The test for remoteness of damage was whether the kind of damage suffered by the claimant was reasonably foreseeable by the defendants at the time of the breach of duty.

The decision in this case was affirmed in *Doughty* v *Turner Engineering* (1964), which held that the defendant was not liable for the burns suffered by the claimant when an asbestos cover was accidentally dropped into some molten liquid. The resulting eruption of the liquid was too remote.

However, there are other rules that need to be learned. The first is that if the kind of damage suffered is reasonably foreseeable, it does not matter that the damage occurred in an unforeseeable way. This principle is illustrated by *Hughes* v *Lord Advocate* (1963), where the defendants had erected a tent over a manhole and surrounded the tent with paraffin lamps. The 10-year-old claimant dropped one of these lamps down the hole. Owing to an unusual combination of circumstances, there was an explosion and the claimant was badly burned. Despite the defendants' argument that the explosion of the lamp was too remote, the House of Lords held they were liable. The question was asked: 'What kind of injury was foreseeable as a result of the breach of duty?' (leaving the hole and the lamps unguarded). The answer was 'burns'. What kind of injury had occurred? Again the answer was 'burns'. The damage was therefore not too remote.

Another case to illustrate this rule is that of *Jolley* v *Sutton London Borough Council* (2000).

'Thin skull' test

As noted in Chapter 1 (page 6), when the possibility of damage is foreseeable, defendants must take their victims as they find them as regards physical characteristics. This means that the defendant will be liable even when the injuries to the claimant are more serious than might have been anticipated because of factors peculiar to the victim.

The leading case for this is *Smith* v *Leech Brain* (1962). The claimant's husband was employed by the defendants. His work required him to lower articles into a tank containing molten metal. An accident occurred and Mr Smith was struck on the lip by a piece of molten metal. He later died of cancer, which was triggered by the burn. Lord Parker CJ held:

> *The test is not whether these defendants could reasonably have foreseen that a burn would cause cancer and that Mr Smith would die. The question is whether these defendants could reasonably foresee the type of injury which he suffered, namely the burn. What, in the particular case, is the amount of damage which he suffers as a result of that burn, depends on the characteristics and constitution of the victim.*

Multiple causes

In some cases, it is possible for damage to have more than one cause. In *McGhee* v *NCB* (1972), the claimant's job brought him into contact with brick dust, which caused him to develop dermatitis. Although it was known that this condition could be caused by brick dust, it was not suggested that merely exposing workers to the dust was negligent, as this was an unavoidable risk of the job. However, it was also known that the risk of contracting dermatitis could be reduced if workers were able to shower after work. The defendants had not installed any showers, and the claimant argued that they had been negligent in not doing so. To succeed, the claimant had to prove that this negligence had caused the dermatitis, but since showers would only have reduced the risk, not removed it, the 'but for' test did not work. It was not possible to say that the damage would not have happened 'but for' the defendant's negligence, but equally impossible to say it would definitely still have happened without the negligence.

As a result, in cases where there is more than one possible cause of damage, the courts have modified the 'but for' test. In *McGhee*, they said that where there was more than one possible cause, causation could still be proved if the claimant could show that the defendant's negligence had materially increased the risk of the injury occurring, and it was not necessary to show that it was the sole cause.

However, in *Wilsher* v *Essex Area Health Authority* (1987), where doctors wrongly administered excess oxygen to a premature infant who later developed retrolental fibroplasia, it was held that because there were five other possible causes of this condition, the claimants' case had to fail. The claimant had not established that it was more probable than not that the excess oxygen was the cause of the condition.

General defences

In this textbook, defences specific to particular torts are considered in context. However, there are also general defences that are applicable to most torts. The AQA specification requires candidates to consider the general defences of contributory negligence and *volenti non fit injuria*.

Contributory negligence

Until 1945, contributory negligence was a complete defence. A negligent defendant could avoid paying any compensation if he or she could show that the victim had in some way contributed to his or her loss. The injustice caused to such victims prompted Parliament to remedy the situation by passing the **Law Reform (Contributory Negligence) Act 1945**. Section 1(1) provides:

> *Where any person suffers damage as the result of his own fault and partly of the fault of any other person or persons, a claim in respect of that damage shall not be defeated by reason of the fault of the person suffering the damage, but the damages recoverable in respect thereof shall be reduced to such extent as the court thinks*

just and equitable having regard to the claimant's share in the responsibility for the damage.

The effect of the Act is that contributory negligence is a partial defence which, if proved, results in the claimant's damages being reduced according to his or her responsibility for the loss suffered. While the wording of s.1 appears to be clear on this issue, there has nevertheless been uncertainty in the Court of Appeal on the question of whether damages can be reduced by 100%.

In *Jayes* v *IMI Kynock* (1984), the claimant was injured while checking an unfenced machine. He succeeded in an action for statutory duty, as the machine should have been fenced. The Court of Appeal upheld the decision of the first instance court and reduced damages by 100%, due to the claimant's admission that he had behaved foolishly. However, in *Anderson* v *Newham College* (2002), the Court of Appeal disapproved its decision in *Jayes* and held that the defence of contributory negligence is only relevant in circumstances where the defendant is partly to blame. In such circumstances, damages should not be reduced by 100%. The *Anderson* case would appear to be more in line with the wording of s.1 of the 1945 Act.

The wording of s.1 focuses on the damage suffered by the claimant. Lord Denning, in *Froom* v *Butcher* (1976), said: 'The question is not what was the cause of the accident. It is rather what was the cause of the damage.' This point is clearly illustrated by some of the road traffic accident cases in which the defence has been successfully raised. In *O'Connell* v *Jackson* (1972), a moped driver was injured while not wearing a crash helmet. Damages were reduced by 15%. The accident was not caused by the negligence of the claimant, but his injuries were more serious due to his failure to take reasonable care for his own safety. This rule was reinforced in *Capps* v *Miller* (1989), where the claimant suffered permanent brain injury when he was knocked off his moped by a drunken driver. He had not fastened the chinstrap of his helmet and the helmet came off before he hit the road. Although the trial judge held that the defendant was 100% to blame for the accident, and that no reduction should be made for contributory negligence, the Court of Appeal reversed that ruling, stating that the judge had made the mistake of focusing on responsibility for the accident rather than for the injury.

Emergencies

The requirement placed on the claimant to take reasonable care for his or her safety is important in the context of emergency situations. Any action taken by the claimant that is reasonable in the agony of the moment and results in injury to himself or herself will not amount to contributory negligence. In *Jones* v *Boyce* (1816), the claimant jumped from a coach when he saw that it was in imminent danger of overturning due to the breaking of a coupling rein. He broke his leg. The coach then halted safely. The court held that the claimant had acted reasonably in the agony of the moment and could therefore recover damages in full.

Children

There is no clear indication in the 1945 Act as to the age at which children can be guilty of contributory negligence. However, while no set guidelines on specific age limits can be gleaned from case law, the decisions do give some indication of future outcomes. For example, in *Snelling* v *Whitehead* (1975), the House of Lords was clear that contributory negligence would have been irrelevant as the claimant was only 7 years old. In *Morales* v *Eccleston* (1991), however, the Court of Appeal held the 11-year-old claimant to be 75% responsible for his injuries. In *Gough* v *Thorns* (1966), Lord Denning, taking a more lenient approach, held that the 13-year-old claimant was not contributorily negligent on similar facts, on the basis that a child does not have the same road sense as an adult.

Volenti non fit injuria

The Latin maxim *volenti non fit injuria* is usually expressed as 'voluntary assumption of risk'. Unlike contributory negligence, *volenti non fit injuria* is a complete defence which, if established, results in the victim receiving no compensation.

The essential elements of *volenti non fit injuria* are that the victim:
- knows of the risk of injury
- voluntarily decides to take that risk
- expressly or impliedly agrees to waive any claim in respect of such injury

Knowledge of the risk

A person cannot be *volenti* to a risk of which he or she has no knowledge, even if it can be shown that the reasonable person would have been aware of the risk.

The requirement of knowledge is illustrated by *Vine* v *Waltham Forest LBC* (2000). The claimant had become ill while driving and needed to vomit. She left her car in a private car park for a short while and returned to find it clamped. The defence did not apply because the claimant had no knowledge of the risk of the car being clamped. In her distressed condition, she had not seen the warning notices.

Mere knowledge of the risk does not constitute consent

It cannot necessarily be said that a person consents to a risk of injury merely because he or she is aware of it. This aspect of the defence was emphasised by the House of Lords in *Smith* v *Charles Baker* (1891). The claimant and other employees were aware that a crane often swung heavy stones above them as they worked, although no warning was given to the employees of particular times the crane would be operating. The claimant was injured when a stone from the crane fell on him. The

House of Lords held that the defence of *volenti* did not apply. Lord Herschell said mere continuance in service with knowledge of the risk did not constitute consent.

Consent must be given voluntarily

Voluntary consent requires a person to be in a position to choose freely. He or she must have full knowledge of the relevant circumstances, and there must be an absence of any constraints that might interfere with freedom of will.

In *Morris* v *Murray* (1991), the claimant was a passenger in a light aircraft being flown by his friend. Both men had been drinking heavily for many hours before they boarded the plane. The aircraft crashed, killing the pilot and seriously injuring the claimant. The defence of *volenti* was successful. The claimant had knowingly and willingly embarked on a flight with a drunken pilot and there had been no compulsion to do so.

It is clear that in the workplace, an employee's perception of the likely effect on employment prospects may constitute a feeling of constraint that interferes with his or her freedom of choice. One case in which there was said to be no such interference was *Imperial Chemical Industries Ltd* v *Shatwell* (1965). The claimant and his brother were shot firers employed by the defendants. They decided to test a circuit of detonators, ignoring the employer's usual safety procedures and warnings, and were both injured. The dangers of not taking precautions had been highlighted to the employees by the employers, and employees who continued to disobey instructions had been sacked. The House of Lords allowed the defence of *volenti* to succeed. The defence is, however, unlikely to succeed where the claimant is employed to do work that necessarily involves danger, as in *Bowater* v *Rowley Regis Corp.* (1944). Here, the claimant carter was ordered by his employers, despite his protests, to take out a horse known to be unsafe. He did so and was thrown off his cart when the horse bolted. The Court of Appeal rejected the *volenti* defence, holding (per Lord Goddard LJ) that this defence 'can hardly ever be applicable where the act to which the servant is said to 'volens' arises out of his duty'.

Claimants may also be said to voluntarily assume the risk of injury in sporting cases. The principle applied by the courts is that the claimant, whether a spectator or a participant, only consents to the risks ordinarily incidental to the particular sport. In *Wooldridge* v *Sumner* (1963), the claimant, a photographer, was struck by a horse competing at an equestrian event. The rider had, in an error of judgement, taken a corner too fast. The defence of *volenti* applied. However, in *Condon* v *Basi* (1985), the defence did not apply. The claimant sustained a broken leg as a result of a tackle by the defendant, which was said by the referee to constitute foul play. The defendant was liable on the basis that a footballer only consents to tackles permitted by the rules of the game.

Rescue cases

The courts take a more sympathetic approach to rescuers, as the law should not discourage people from coming to the aid of those in danger.

In *Haynes* v *Harwood* (1935), a policeman was injured while attempting to stop a horse bolting along a busy street. The Court of Appeal rejected the *volenti* defence. The claimant had taken a personal risk in order to eliminate the danger to others in the street.

The same approach was adopted by the Court of Appeal in *Baker* v *Hopkins* (1959), where a doctor, knowing the risk he was taking, insisted on going down a well to try to help two workmen who had been overcome by carbon monoxide fumes. The doctor was also overcome by the fumes and died. The *volenti* defence was rejected and the doctor's widow succeeded in her claim.

Damages

In Unit 4 tort questions, you need to explain the rights and remedies available to the claimant in the scenario. Although this does not need to be as detailed as a specific Unit 2 question on damages, you should still explain the purpose of damages — to compensate the victim by putting him or her in the position he or she would have been in if the tort had not occurred. You should refer to the special and general damages that are relevant to the particular situation.

Special damages

These comprise quantifiable financial losses up to the date of trial and are assessed separately from other awards, because the exact amount to be claimed is known at the time of the trial. The major heads of damages are:

* **Loss of earnings.** This is calculated from the date of the tort to the trial.
* **Medical expenses.** These cover any services, treatment or medical appliances, or the unpaid services of relatives or friends. Only such expenses as are considered reasonable by the court are recoverable.
* **Expenses to cover special facilities.** These can cover the cost of special living accommodation. The measure of damages here is the sum spent to obtain the special facility and its running costs.

General damages

This term covers all losses that are not capable of exact quantification, and they are further divided into **pecuniary** and **non-pecuniary** damages.

Pecuniary damages

Future loss of earnings

The courts calculate future loss of earnings using the multiplicand (an annual sum to represent the claimant's annual net lost earnings) and the multiplier (a notional figure representing a number of years by which the multiplicand is to be multiplied in order to calculate the future losses).

The multiplier is arbitrary — it can never be precise and is calculated by looking at previous cases. Even in the case of a young wage earner, the maximum multiplier used is 18, because it is intended to take into account the possibility that the claimant might lose his or her job or retire early.

The expectation is that the claimant will invest any money received as a lump sum and use the income, and possibly some of the capital, to cover living expenses during the years when he or she would have been earning, so that by the time of retirement the whole of the sum awarded will be exhausted.

As victims of accidents often receive financial support from several sources in addition to tort damages — such as social security benefits, sick pay and private insurance — amounts are deducted from the damages award to account for these.

Other future loss

The claimant is also entitled to an award to cover the cost of future care, such as nursing requirements and physiotherapy.

Non-pecuniary losses

Pain and suffering

Compensation for pain and suffering is subjective, as they are impossible to measure in terms of money. However, an award will be made to cover nervous shock and physical pain and suffering. It is important to achieve consistency between the awards made to different claimants who suffer similar injuries, so the Judicial Studies Board sets 'tariffs' to govern the fixing of the appropriate figure.

Loss of amenity

The claimant is entitled to damages for the inability to enjoy life in various ways, in particular regarding impairment of the senses. This includes, for example, inability to run or walk, or to play sport or a musical instrument. Such awards are assessed objectively and are thus independent of the victim's knowledge of his or her fate.

Damages for the injury itself

Injuries are itemised and particular sums are awarded for these on the basis of precedents.

Provisional damages

The general rule is that only one award of damages can be made. If an injury turns out to be more serious than was anticipated at the time of the award, no further action is available to the claimant, and this can cause obvious hardship in personal injury cases. Under s.32(a) of the **Supreme Court Act 1981**, the court has the power to make a provisional award allowing the claimant to return to court should further anticipated serious deterioration occur. However, this power is not commonly used.

Structured settlements

These are not the result of legislation but of practical moves by lawyers and insurers to circumvent the usual lump-sum payments and increase the benefit to the claimant. In essence, they involve the substitution of pensions for lump-sum payments, and, because of tax concessions by the Inland Revenue, the result is lower payments by insurers and higher incomes for claimants.

Sample exam question

As Edward drives round a roundabout in town, one of the ropes securing the load on his lorry snaps. As a result, the load shifts and the lorry begins to roll over. At that moment, Fred is passing Edward's lorry on his motorbike. In his haste to avoid being crushed, Fred accelerates and loses control of his motorbike, which mounts the kerb, narrowly missing Geri, and crashes through the large window of a shop. Fred suffers serious facial injuries and his right leg is severed below the knee.

Adapted from AQA Unit 5 paper, January 2006

Discuss the rights and remedies, if any, available to Fred against Edward.

Product liability

Product liability cases in tort are subject to the ordinary rules of negligence — as per *Donoghue v Stevenson*. A key issue is proving that the defendant's lack of reasonable care caused the defect that made the product dangerous, although the claimant does not need to prove exactly what the defendant did wrong.

In *Mason* v *Williams and Williams* (1955), the claimant was injured when using a chisel that

In *Mason v Williams and Williams* (1955), the fact that nothing had happened to the chisel since it left the defendant's factory was enough to establish liability

was too hard for its purpose. Although the claimant could not show any particular fault in its manufacture, he could prove that nothing had happened to it since it left the defendant's factory. This was enough to establish liability.

This reasoning was upheld in *Carroll* v *Fearon* (1998), which involved a car crash allegedly caused by faulty tyres. The tyre manufacturer was held to be liable, despite the fact that no particular negligent act or omission was identified in the manufacturing process. The Court of Appeal held it was not necessary to do so — it had been established overwhelmingly that the tyres were defective because of a fault in the manufacturing process, and since the manufacturer was unable to explain how the defects could have been caused without negligence, the judge was entitled to find it was negligent.

However, in the contrasting case of *Evans* v *Triplex Safety Glass* (1936), it was alleged by the claimant that the cause of a car crash was the shattering of the windscreen, in turn caused by a defect in its manufacture. The judge held that the claimant had not given sufficient evidence to satisfy the court that the manufacturers were at fault. The defect could have been caused by faulty fitting of the windscreen by the carmaker. In any case, the claimant had owned the car for a year before the accident happened, and either he or his supplier might reasonably have inspected the windscreen prior to the accident.

Limitations of common law

The above cases seem to indicate that the common law is broadly satisfactory in dealing with manufacturing defects, with courts being prepared to infer negligence and adopt a flexible approach towards liability. However, the thalidomide tragedy (where a drug believed to be safe for pregnant women caused their babies to be malformed) proved that the common law could not address problems in relation to *design* defects. This led to demands for law reform — in particular to demands to impose strict (no-fault) liability on manufacturers. These demands — and an EU Directive (85/374) — led to the enactment of the **Consumer Protection Act 1987**. Under this Act, if a claimant suffers harm as a result of a product being defective, he or she may be entitled to sue the manufacturer of that product for compensation without having to prove that it committed any kind of legal wrong in manufacturing that product.

What is a product?

In *Donoghue* v *Stevenson*, Lord Atkin restricted the term 'product' to consideration of articles of common household use, where it is known that they will be used by persons other than the purchaser. The courts, however, have been prepared to

interpret 'product' quite broadly to include hair dye, underwear, industrial chemicals and cars. An even broader definition exists under s.1(2) of the 1987 Act, which provides that 'product' means any goods or electricity and includes a product comprised in another product, whether by virtue of being a component part or raw material. So the term 'product' covers not only manufactured products, such as radios and computers, but also natural products, such as coal and flowers. In *A* v *National Blood Authority* (2001), it was even held that contaminated blood counted as a 'product' under the Act.

Who can be a producer?

Under s.1(2), the 'producer' can be:

❖ the actual manufacturer of the product; this could also be the manufacturer of a component, so if a product fails because of a faulty component, both the manufacturers of the final product and the component are liable
❖ someone who has 'won or abstracted' the product, e.g. a mining company
❖ an 'own brander' — liability is imposed on any person who brand-names a product or claims to be the producer in any way (however, retailers are only liable for defects in own-brand goods where it is proved that they 'hold themselves out' as being the producer, so a retailer who uses a label clearly stating the product is made *for* the store rather than *by* it will probably escape liability)
❖ the importer of the product into the EU from outside (if you bought a faulty Chinese food mixer, you could sue the firm that imported it into the EU)

Section 2(3) provides that any supplier of the product is liable unless he or she complies with a request to name, within a reasonable time, the person who supplied him or her with it. This means that distributors of the product — retailers and wholesalers — are liable under this section, unless they can and do name the actual manufacturer (in the EU) or the importer of the product into the EU.

Defining defect

According to the Act, the defendant will be liable for damage caused wholly or in part by a 'defect' in the product. Section 3 defines a defect as existing when 'the safety of the product is not such as persons generally are entitled to expect'.

Section 3(2) provides that in assessing whether a defect exists, the court should take all the circumstances into account, including:

❖ the manner in which and the purposes for which the product has been marketed, including any advertising claims
❖ the packaging of the product
❖ the use of any mark in relation to the product (e.g. the Kitemark of the British Standards Institution)

❖ the instructions for, or warning with respect to, doing or refraining from doing anything in relation to the product (this provision means that products which are inherently dangerous can be brought within the safety standard by their instructions or warnings, e.g. dosage instructions on drugs)
❖ what might reasonably be expected to be done with the product
❖ the time when the product was supplied by its producer to another

It is for the claimant to prove that, taking these factors into account, the product is defective. The test, given that no product can be entirely safe, is whether the risk to person and property posed by the product when in common use exceeds what is generally acceptable.

The following cases provide helpful illustration of how the issue of 'defect' is treated by the courts.

In *A* v *National Blood Authority* (2001), the claimants were infected with hepatitis C as a result of receiving a blood transfusion. At the time, no test existed to detect whether donated blood contained that virus. The claimants argued under the 1987 Act that the blood they had been given was defective. The defendants argued that, as no test was available, the most the public could legitimately expect was that all reasonable precautions would be carried out, not that the blood would be 100% clean. However, the judge ruled that the 'avoidability' of the harm suffered by a claimant in a product liability case was not to be taken into account in judging whether the product that harmed the claimant was defective or not under the Act. He held that the blood was defective, ruling that 'where, as here, there is a harmful characteristic in a non-standard product, a decision that it is defective is likely to be straightforward'.

In *Abouzaid* v *Mothercare (UK) Ltd* (2000), a 12-year-old boy was injured when trying to fasten a sleeping bag manufactured by the defendant to the back of a pushchair. The buckle on the elastic fastenings had sprung back, hitting him in the eye and damaging his sight. In considering the safety that the public is entitled to expect, Pill LJ found that, although this was a borderline case, the severe consequences of the injury indicated that the product was defective. It was irrelevant whether this defect should reasonably have come to the manufacturer's attention.

Defences

The following defences are specified under s.4(1) of the Act and confirm that liability under the Act is not strict:
❖ The product is defective because it had to comply with a legal requirement. However, this defence will only absolve a producer from liability if the defect was an inevitable result of such compliance.

❖ The defendants did not at any time supply the product to another person. This protects the defendants if the product has been stolen and then sold on to a customer who is injured because of a defect in the product.

❖ The supply by the defendants was not in the course of business and was not with a view to profit. So, if Mary bakes some cakes for a charity and Ian is poisoned by them, he cannot sue Mary under the Act. (He could possibly sue under negligence.)

❖ Scientific and technical knowledge at the time when the producer put the product into circulation was not capable of discovering the existence of the defect — the 'development risks' defence. This defence was led in *A* v *National Blood Authority* but failed. The judge ruled that even if there was no test to detect hepatitis C at the time, the authority was aware there was a risk that the blood they supplied might be contaminated with that virus.

Further reading

Elliott, C. and Quinn, F. (2007) *Tort Law*, Pearson Longman.
Murphy, J. (2007) *Street on Torts*, Oxford University Press.
Pitchfork, E. D. (ed) (2000) *The Law of Tort*, Old Bailey Press.

Chapter **19**

Psychiatric injury

Historically, the law did not extend to claims brought purely for psychiatric injury. The reason cited most often for the denial of such claims was that psychiatric injury is difficult to diagnose. This difficulty leads to the suspicion that victims may fake their symptoms and bring fictitious claims. There is also the fear of 'opening the floodgates' to numerous actions. Nevertheless, in recent years the law of negligence, in particular the duty of care element, has gradually evolved so that various categories of people may bring a claim, provided they satisfy the additional legal criteria. Once the claimant has satisfied specific duty of care requirements, the normal rules of breach of duty and causation apply.

Three categories of people can bring an action:
* **Primary victims** suffer psychiatric harm through fear for their own safety.
* **Secondary victims** suffer psychiatric harm through fear for someone else's safety.
* **Rescuers** suffer psychiatric harm as a result of coming to the aid of someone.

What is psychiatric injury?

All people who claim for psychiatric injury, whatever category they fall into, must show they are suffering from a recognised psychiatric illness, capable of resulting from the incident and recognised as having long-term effects. Mere distress, fright, grief and sorrow are insufficient.

Lord Steyn, in *White and others* v *Chief Constable of South Yorkshire* (1999), recognised the difficulty in distinguishing between two categories of claimants: those who suffer from extreme grief and those whose suffering amounts to a medically recognisable psychiatric illness. While the symptoms could be similar and equally severe, the law only provides redress to the claimants in the second category. The present position of the common law is that conditions such as post-traumatic stress disorder qualify as medically recognisable.

The outcomes of cases are somewhat unpredictable on this issue. In *Tredget* v *Bexley Health Authority* (1994), the claimants were held to have been caused psychiatric injury when, due to medical negligence, their child was born with serious injuries and died 2 days later. It had been argued that they suffered no more than profound grief. The decision of the Court of Appeal in *Vernon* v *Bosley* (1996) to hold that pathological grief disorder was medically recognisable blurred the distinction further. *Reilly* v *Merseyside RHA* (1994) held that apprehension, fear, discomfort and shortness of breath arising out of being trapped in a lift do *not* amount to psychiatric illness, whereas in *CJD Group B Plaintiffs* v *Medical Research Council* (2000), it was held that sleeplessness arising out of being told that one might in future contract CJD could amount to psychiatric illness.

In a problem-solving question involving psychiatric injury, you should first consider whether the defendant owed a duty of care to the claimant, whether that duty was breached, and whether that breach had caused the psychiatric injury. You can then go on to explain the special rules governing whether the claimant is a primary or secondary victim.

Primary victims

A primary victim suffers psychiatric injury as a result of being directly affected by a negligent act, or fears for his or her own safety. The early case law on psychiatric injury established that a person could claim if he or she was within the range of potential physical injury. In *Dulieu* v *White and Sons* (1901), the claimant suffered psychiatric injury when a horse-drawn van was driven into the public house where she was working. Kennedy LJ remarked that it was not necessary to suffer physical harm through impact. It was sufficient that the psychiatric injury was caused through a 'reasonable fear of immediate personal injury to oneself'.

The distinction between primary and secondary victims was considered in some depth by the House of Lords in *Page* v *Smith* (1995). The claimant was in a car accident caused by the negligent driving of the defendant. He was not physically injured but the incident sparked a recurrence of an illness, ME. The defendant was held liable.

Two important distinctions between primary and secondary victims were emphasised by the House of Lords:

❖ The primary victim does not need to show that psychiatric injury was foreseeable, whereas the secondary victim does. The primary victim merely needs to show that some kind of personal injury was foreseeable, and once this is established, it is irrelevant whether the primary victim suffers physical harm as well as psychiatric harm.

❖ On the issue of the recurrence of a condition to which the claimant was predisposed, the primary victim does not need to be a person of normal fortitude.

Lord Lloyd said, 'there is no difference in principle between an egg-shell skull and an egg-shell personality'. The 'eggshell personality' rule applies to claims for psychiatric injury; the defendant must take primary victims as he or she finds them.

The approach in *Page* was followed in *Simmons* v *British Steel plc* (2004), where the claimant had been physically injured in a workplace accident and consequently developed a severe skin condition. This condition led to him taking a lot of time off work, as a result of which he became depressed. The House of Lords held that his employer was liable for the skin condition and the depressive illness as well as the original injury, since it had exposed him to a foreseeable risk of physical injury, and it was therefore liable for all the injuries resulting from that risk.

Secondary victims

A secondary victim suffers psychiatric injury not as a result of being directly involved in the event or fearing for his or her own safety, but as a result of fearing for someone else's safety. More stringent criteria apply to secondary victims than to primary victims, not least because of the potentially endless liability that could attach to the defendant.

The control mechanisms applicable to secondary victims were explored thoroughly by the House of Lords in *Alcock* (1991), concerning the friends and relatives of victims of the Hillsborough disaster

The law of negligence has long recognised the duty owed to secondary victims. In *Hambrook* v *Stokes Bros* (1925), the successful claimant suffered nervous shock when she witnessed a driverless lorry careering down a narrow street in the direction of her children. Bankes LJ used as illustration a hypothetical situation in which a lorry was heading towards two mothers, each holding a baby. One suffered shock through fear for her own safety and one suffered shock through fear for the baby's safety. He questioned whether the law only allowed a claim in respect of the mother fearing for her own safety and concluded that both mothers would be able to claim. However, the Court of Appeal did stipulate that the secondary victim must perceive the event with his or her own sight or hearing. The law would not compensate for psychiatric injury brought about through communication by a third party.

The 'control mechanisms' applicable to secondary victims, which the Court of Appeal had begun to set out in *Hambrook*, were explored thoroughly by the House of Lords in *Alcock* v *Chief Constable of South Yorkshire* (1992). This was a test case involving a number of claimants who represented a range of relationships to those who had died or received serious injuries during the Hillsborough disaster, when police negligently allowed an excessive influx of fans into a football ground. This caused a huge crush at the front of the terrace. Ninety-five spectators were killed and over 400 were injured.

The claimants included parents, grandparents, siblings, spouses, fiancées and friends of the dead and injured. Some had been at the stadium at the time of the disaster, others had seen the events unfold live on television; some had gone to the stadium to look for someone they knew, others had to identify bodies in the mortuary.

In deciding that the claimants could not receive damages for the psychiatric harm they had suffered, the Law Lords all gave similar accounts of the control mechanisms applicable to secondary victims. They agreed that the general policy was not to compensate third parties, and that for third parties to be compensated, much stricter requirements had to be satisfied than those that applied to primary victims.

First of all, confirming the decision in *Page* v *Smith* (above), the secondary victim had to be able to prove that psychiatric injury was a reasonably foreseeable consequence of the defendant's negligence, and also that the claimant was a person of reasonable fortitude. After these tests had been met, the House of Lords laid down three further 'control tests' to determine whether claimants in such cases would succeed:

❖ There must be close ties of love and affection.
❖ The psychiatric injury must be caused through the victim's own sight and hearing of the event or the immediate aftermath.
❖ The injury must be caused by the sudden appreciation of a horrifying event.

Close ties of love and affection

Close ties of love and affection with the primary victim is to be presumed between spouses and between parents and children. However, the Law Lords emphasised that close ties could also exist in other kinds of family relationships and in close friendships. Close ties in these relationships (other than spouses or parent and child) must be proved by the claimant and are decided on a case-by-case basis.

Victim's own sight and hearing

The claimant must perceive the event with his or her own unaided senses. It is not sufficient to read about it or learn about it through a third party.

In *Alcock*, many of the claimants had watched the disaster unfold on television. The issue of whether simultaneous broadcasting of a disaster could be regarded as equivalent to seeing or hearing the event was left open. The Lords did not have to clarify the position on this because the television companies had conformed to the television authority's code of ethics and had not shown the suffering of any recognisable individual. Consequently, the Lords were in agreement that the pictures televised could not be equated to sight or hearing of the event or its immediate aftermath. However, the Lords did consider that there may be circumstances in which viewing live broadcasts could be equivalent to seeing or hearing the event.

Witnessing the accident itself or its immediate aftermath

The Lords agreed unanimously in *Alcock* that psychiatric injury could be caused through witnessing the immediate aftermath of the accident.

The extension of the law of negligence, to those who suffer psychiatric injury as a result of witnessing the immediate aftermath of an accident, was settled by Lord Wilberforce in *McLoughlin* v *O'Brian* (1982). The claimant was told that her family had been involved in an accident. She arrived at the hospital approximately 2 hours after the accident had occurred, where she saw her husband and two of her three children injured and covered in mud and oil. She learned from her husband that their other child had been killed. The other Law Lords agreed with Lord Wilberforce that the law should be extended to cover the immediate aftermath, as this was what justice demanded. As Lord Wilberforce had pointed out, there was little difference between this case and cases where claims had been allowed before. In *Benson* v *Lee* (1972), the successful claimant, a mother, was in her home 100 yards away from the accident when she was told by a third party that her children had been injured; she suffered shock upon running out and witnessing the accident scene.

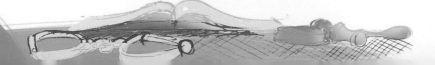

While it remains unclear precisely what amounts to the immediate aftermath in terms of time span, it appears that the victims must be in their post-accident state and not, for example, cleaned up. In *Jaensch* v *Coffey* (1984), the claimant saw her husband at the hospital before and between emergency operations. Deane J in the Australian High Court said:

> *The aftermath of the accident extended to the hospital to which the injured person was taken and persisted for so long as he remained in the state produced by the accident up to and including immediate post-accident treatment.*

In *Alcock*, the House of Lords overruled earlier cases, including *Hevican* v *Ruane* (1991), which had held that the immediate aftermath extended to witnessing a body in the mortuary.

Sudden appreciation of the event

The psychiatric injury must be induced by shock. Lord Ackner explained this in terms of 'the sudden appreciation by sight or sound of a horrifying event, which violently agitates the mind'. Psychiatric injury caused gradually over a period of time is not recoverable.

However, in *North Glamorgan NHS Trust* v *Walters* (2002), the Court of Appeal seemed to widen this rule. The claimant was the mother of a baby who died after receiving negligent treatment by the defendants. The baby was ill in hospital when his mother, who was staying at the hospital, woke up to find him choking and coughing up blood. Doctors told her that he was having a fit, but that it was not serious.

In fact, the baby had suffered a massive epileptic fit that had lasted an hour. Later that day, he was rushed to King's College Hospital in London, where the mother was told that her child had suffered such severe brain damage that he could not recover, and she was asked to consider switching off his life-support system. She and her husband agreed to do this the following day.

These events caused the mother to suffer a psychiatric illness, but the hospital argued there was no liability since it was not caused by a sudden shock but by a sequence of events that had taken place over 36 hours. The Court of Appeal disagreed and stated that the 'horrifying event' referred to in *Alcock* could be made up of a series of events — here, witnessing the fit, being told her son was severely brain-damaged after being told he was not, and then holding him in her arms while he died.

The injustice of the sudden shock requirement is illustrated by the case of *Sion* v *Hampstead Health Authority* (1994). A father suffered psychiatric injury as a result of watching his son die over a period of 14 days. His claim was unsuccessful as the illness was not induced by shock.

Psychiatric injury must be foreseeable

As explained above, while primary victims need only prove that personal injury — whether physical, psychiatric or both — was foreseeable, secondary victims must prove specifically that psychiatric injury was foreseeable. In *Page* v *Smith*, Lord Lloyd distinguished between primary and secondary victims. He said:

> *In claims by secondary victims...the defendant will not be liable unless psychiatric injury is foreseeable in a person of normal fortitude. These control mechanisms have no place where the claimant is the primary victim.*

Rescuers

The law recognises that danger invites rescue. People who are guilty of tort are thus expected to be liable to those who try to save their victims. As Stuart-Smith LJ commented in *McFarlane* v *EE Caledonia Ltd* (1994): 'A tortfeasor who has put A in peril by his negligence must reasonably foresee that B may come to rescue him, even if it involves risking his own safety.'

In *Chadwick* v *British Railways Board* (1967), the claimant suffered anxiety neurosis as a result of helping at the scene of a railway crash in which 90 people were killed. He was asked, because of his small size, to crawl into the carriages to help the injured. The claim was successful. Danger and injury to passengers was foreseeable, as was danger and injury to someone who tried to rescue them. Similarly, in *Hale* v *London Underground* (1992), the claimant, who was a fireman involved in rescuing people from the fire in King's Cross underground station, was able to recover damages for the post-traumatic stress disorder caused by the event.

The question as to who qualifies as a rescuer was closely examined by the House of Lords in *White* v *Chief Constable of South Yorkshire Police* (1999). The claimants were police officers who suffered post-traumatic stress disorder as a result of helping to deal with the Hillsborough tragedy. The Court of Appeal held that three of the police officers qualified as rescuers because they gave assistance in the immediate aftermath of the disaster. The House of Lords reversed the Court of Appeal decision. Lord Steyn said that, in order to recover compensation for psychiatric injury, a rescuer must satisfy the requirement that he or she objectively placed himself or herself in danger, or reasonably perceived himself or herself as doing so. The claimants were not exposed to danger at any time, and neither did they believe that they were so exposed. They were, therefore, *not* rescuers.

This decision in *White* has since been criticised as limiting liability towards rescuers. However, Lord Steyn specifically referred to *Chadwick* as being an example of the claimant placing himself in danger: 'There was clearly a danger the carriage might collapse.' He also cited Waller J who, in deciding the 1967 case, had referred to the 'element of personal danger in what Mr Chadwick was doing'. Many key cases would appear to support the view of Lord Steyn.

Rescuers who are not able to prove the 'placed themselves in danger' criterion have the option to claim as secondary victims. The success of this depends on whether they are able to satisfy the control mechanisms.

Bystanders

The law of negligence does not allow bystanders to recover for psychiatric injury. As Lord Wilberforce explained in *McLoughlin* v *O'Brian*, the law denies claims of the ordinary bystander because 'such persons must be assumed to be possessed of fortitude sufficient to enable them to endure the calamities of modern life', and because 'defendants cannot be expected to compensate the world at large'.

The possibility of bystanders being able to claim successfully has not, however, been ruled out. In *Alcock*, Lord Keith said:

> *The case of a bystander unconnected with the victims of an accident is difficult. Psychiatric injury to him would not ordinarily, in my view, be within the range of reasonable foreseeability, but could not perhaps be entirely excluded from it if the circumstances of a catastrophe occurring very close to him were particularly horrific.*

While the judiciary has left this possibility open, the courts have nevertheless been reluctant to extend the law in this way. In *McFarlane* v *EE Caledonia Ltd* (1994), the claimant was on a support vessel some 100 yards from the oilrig on which he worked when the oilrig caught fire. He helped prepare the heli-hanger to receive casualties by moving blankets, and assisted two of the walking wounded as they arrived on the support vessel.

The claimant relied on the *dicta* of Lord Keith in *Alcock*, expressing the view that it was difficult to imagine a more horrific disaster than the holocaust on the Piper Alpha rig, especially as he knew his workmates were on board. The Court of Appeal held that he could not recover damages. Stuart Smith LJ said:

> *The court should not extend the duty to those who are mere bystanders or witnesses of horrific events unless there is a sufficient degree of proximity, which requires both nearness in time and place and a close relationship of love and affection between claimant and victim.*

Questions

1 Which case decided that pathological grief disorder could qualify as a medically recognisable psychiatric disorder?

2 What change to the psychiatric illness rule was made by *North Glamorgan NHS Trust* v *Walters* (2002)?

3 Define a primary victim.

4 What rules were laid down in *Page* v *Smith* (1995) regarding primary and secondary victims?

5 Define a secondary victim.

6 What 'control tests' were laid down in *Alcock* v *Chief Constable of South Yorkshire* (1991)?

7 What is the leading case on witnessing the aftermath of an accident?

8 How did *Jaensch* v *Coffey* (1984) extend this rule?

9 Why was the father's claim unsuccessful in *Sion* v *Hampstead Health Authority* (1994)?

10 What rule was laid down in *White* v *Chief Constable of South Yorkshire* (1999) regarding rescuers being able to qualify for damages for psychiatric injury?

11 Why was McFarlane's claim unsuccessful following the *Piper Alpha* oilrig disaster?

Sample exam question

Greenwater lake has recently been developed by its owners, Highlife Sports, to provide extensive leisure facilities. Some swimmers are in the habit of swimming beneath the surface in an area of Greenwater clearly marked out for powerboating only. While doing so, Jim surfaces into the path of a powerboat being driven by Kellie. In the resulting collision, Jim suffers severe facial injuries and Kellie is knocked out of the boat and has her arm severed by the propeller. Kellie's friend, Laura, who is in another boat, drags her out of the water to safety. The experience causes Laura deep emotional distress.

Adapted from AQA Unit 5 paper, June 2004

Consider what rights and remedies Laura may have against Highlife Sports.

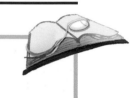

Further reading

Elliott, C. and Quinn, F. (2007) *Tort Law*, Pearson Longman.
Murphy, J. (2007) *Street on Torts*, Oxford University Press.
Pitchfork, E. D. (ed) (2000) *The Law of Tort*, Old Bailey Press.

Chapter 20

Economic loss

The law of tort does not generally allow recovery of compensation for pure economic loss — financial loss that is not the result of physical injury or property damage. As with the law relating to psychiatric injury, the rules concerning when a duty of care is owed have been adapted by the courts. In limited circumstances, a claim for economic loss suffered as a result of the defendant's negligence may be made when the loss:

* is the direct result of damage to property or personal injury (consequential economic loss)
* is caused by a negligent misstatement
* arises from circumstances the courts have held to fall within the extended Hedley Byrne principle

As with issues of psychiatric injury, remember that economic loss is a special duty situation within the law of negligence. A claimant therefore has to prove not only that the defendant owed a duty of care, but also that there was a breach of duty that caused the claimant's loss.

Consequential economic loss

The position, as clarified by Lord Denning in *Spartan Steel and Alloys Ltd* v *Martin and Co. Ltd* (1973), is that economic loss that is a consequence of physical damage or injury is recoverable in negligence, but there is no liability in respect of pure economic loss arising from negligent acts.

In *Spartan Steel*, the defendants negligently severed an electricity cable supplying power to the claimants' factory. As a result, the factory had to shut down. The claimants claimed compensation for:

* damage to goods in production at the time of the power cut (physical damage)
* loss of profit on the damaged goods (consequential economic loss)

❖ loss of profit on goods that could not be manufactured due to the power cut (pure economic loss)

The Court of Appeal held by a majority that compensation could be recovered for the damage to goods in production at the time of the power cut and the loss of profit that would have been made on those goods. That loss of profit was clearly a consequence of the physical damage to the goods. However, no damage had been caused in respect of the goods that would have been manufactured later that same day. The loss of profit in respect of those later goods was thus purely economic and not recoverable. In so deciding, the Court of Appeal followed the long established approach taken by the courts.

In *Weller and Co. v Foot and Mouth Disease Research Institute* (1966), an auctioneer's regular income from the sale of cattle was disrupted as the result of a ban on the movement of livestock following an escape of a virus from the defendants' laboratory. No liability could be imposed for the auctioneer's loss of profit, as it was purely economic.

In *Weller and Co. v Foot and Mouth Disease Research Institute* (1966), no liability could be imposed for the auctioneer's loss of profit, as it was purely economic

The justification for pure economic loss not being recoverable is one of policy. Clearly, all three types of loss suffered by the claimant in *Spartan Steel* were foreseeable, and according to the law of negligence alone should have been recoverable. However, the courts are cautious about allowing compensation claims in respect of pure economic loss because of the desire to limit the potential liability of defendants to a reasonable level. In *Spartan Steel*, Lord Denning MR stated:

> *At bottom I think the question of recovering economic loss is one of policy. Whenever the courts draw a line to mark out the bounds of duty, they do it as a matter of policy so as to limit the responsibility of the defendant.*

Compensation in respect of defective products is not recoverable in negligence. It is considered that liability in respect of defective products may only be imposed through the law of contract. There was some doubt about the relationship between negligence and contract following the decision of the House of Lords in *Junior Books Ltd* v *Veitchi Co. Ltd* (1983), in which a claim for compensation was allowed in respect of a defectively laid floor. However, subsequent judgements appear to have confined the decision to the facts of that particular case; by specifying that the flooring company should be used, the claimants had effectively created a sufficiently proximate relationship between themselves and the defendants.

In *D and F Estates Ltd* v *Church Commissioners for England* (1988), the claimants brought an action against the defendant builders in respect of negligent plasterwork, which had become loose and needed replacing. The claim was unsuccessful as the cost of repairing the defective plaster was pure economic loss. The loose plaster had caused neither damage to property nor personal injury.

Murphy v *Brentwood District Council* (1990) clarified the position regarding buildings and defective foundations. The claimant bought a property constructed on a concrete raft on an in-filled site. The raft foundation, which had been approved by the council, was defective and caused serious cracks to appear in the house. Unable to afford the cost of repairing the property to make it safe and inhabitable, estimated at £45,000, the claimant sold the house at a loss of £35,000. The defendant council was held not liable for the loss. The court held that foundations of a building could not be treated as separate from the building. The building was therefore defective and the cost of repairing the building was purely economic. The House of Lords overruled the decision in *Anns* v *Merton London Borough Council* (1978), where on similar facts a local authority was held liable in respect of negligently approving inadequate foundations.

Negligent misstatement

Traditionally, the claimant who suffers economic loss caused by statements would have had to bring an action in the tort of deceit. The law as it stands today developed from the dissenting judgement of Lord Denning in *Candler* v *Crane Christmas and Co.* (1951). In this case, the defendants negligently prepared a company's accounts. They were aware that the accounts were to be shown to the claimant in order to induce him to invest in the company. The claimant did invest, and lost his money. The court held that the defendants were not liable because they did not owe a duty of care to the third party — their responsibility was only to the client, with whom they had a contractual relationship.

Lord Denning's dissenting judgement was accepted by the House of Lords *in obiter* in *Hedley Byrne and Co. Ltd* v *Heller and Partners* (1964). A company called Easipower asked an advertising firm to run a campaign. The advertising firm approached Easipower's bank for a credit reference. The bank gave a satisfactory reference without checking the company's current financial standing. It included the disclaimer 'without responsibility on the part of this bank or its officials'. Easipower went into liquidation and the advertising firm lost over £17,000. The House of Lords held that liability for economic loss arising from a negligent misstatement could arise in such circumstances, but that in this particular case the defendants were not liable because of the disclaimer.

Special relationship

The House of Lords held that in addition to the requirements of foreseeability, proximity and it being fair, just and reasonable to impose a duty of care, there must be a special relationship between the parties for a duty of care to give careful advice to arise. However, the Law Lords all gave differing accounts of what amounts to a special relationship. Lord Reid said a special relationship arises:

> ...where it is plain that the party seeking information or advice was trusting the other to exercise such a degree of care as the circumstances required, where it was reasonable for him to do that, and where the other gave the information or advice when he knew or ought to have known that the inquirer was relying on him. I say 'ought to have known' because in questions of negligence we now apply the objective standard of what the reasonable man would have done.

Lord Morris emphasised the importance of the defendant possessing a special skill that he or she exercises to assist another, and then stated:

> If, in a sphere in which a person is so placed that others could reasonably rely on his judgement or his skill or on his ability to make careful inquiry, a person takes it on himself to give information or advice to, or allows his information or advice to be passed on to, another person who, as he knows or should know, will place reliance on it, then a duty of care will arise.

Lord Devlin said that he was happy to adopt any of the other Law Lords' statements. He also expressed his respect for the statement by Denning LJ in *Candler* v *Crane* about the circumstances in which a duty exists to take care in making a statement.

The need for the claimant in a negligent misstatement action to prove the existence of a special relationship, in addition to the usual requirements, is based on policy. Words have a greater propensity than physical articles to spread and, in the classic words of Cardozo CJ in *Ultramares Corp.* v *Touche* (1931), could subject the maker of the statement to 'liability in an indeterminate amount for an indeterminate time to an indeterminate class'. The judiciary has therefore limited the circumstances in which the maker of a negligent misstatement will be liable to compensate those people whom they cause to suffer economic loss. In *Hedley Byrne*, Lord Reid stated:

> Another obvious difference is that a negligently made article will only cause one accident, and so it is not very difficult to find the necessary degree of proximity or

neighbourhood between the negligent manufacturer and the person injured. But words can be broadcast with or without the consent or the foresight of the speaker or writer. It would be one thing to say that the speaker owed a duty to a limited class, but it would be going very far to say that he owed a duty to every ultimate 'consumer' who acts on those words to his detriment.

To prove that a special relationship exists between the claimant and defendant, the following requirements must be met:

❖ The defendant must possess a special skill.
❖ The claimant must rely on the statement to his or her detriment.
❖ The reliance must be reasonable.

The defendant must possess a special skill

The defendant must possess special skill in giving the advice sought. In *Mutual Life and Citizens Assurance Co.* v *Evatt* (1971), the Privy Council held that an insurance company did not owe a duty of care in advising that it was safe for the claimant to invest in another company, Palmer. A duty only arose when the defendant was in the business of giving that type of advice, or had professed to have special skill or knowledge in the field in which the advice was given.

This decision has been criticised, and there were two dissenting judgements in this case, from Lords Reid and Morris, both of whom had sat in *Hedley Byrne*. The fact was that, in advising Evatt as it did, Mutual Life took on the job of advising him as to whether it was safe to invest in Palmer and did implicitly indicate that he could safely rely on that advice. The narrow ground on which Lord Diplock gave the leading judgement was that Evatt had failed to prove that Mutual Life held itself out as possessing any special expertise to judge whether or not it was safe to invest in Palmer. This meant that it was not possible to say that a duty of care was owed to Evatt not to mislead him as to the soundness of Palmer.

The defendant will thus not be liable for statements made informally or during a social situation. Lord Reid (in *Hedley Byrne*) stated:

Quite careful people often express definite opinions on social or informal occasions, even when they see that others are likely to be influenced by them, and they often do that without taking that care which they would take if asked for their opinion professionally, or in a business connection.

A case that seemingly provides an exception to this is *Chaudhry* v *Prabhakar* (1989), in which the claimant had asked a friend to find a suitable car for her. The friend recommended a car that was later discovered to have been in an accident. A key fact in this case was that Prabhakar had discouraged the claimant from getting a qualified mechanic to examine the car before buying it. By doing so, the defendant had indicated to her that his advice that the car was in good condition could be safely relied upon.

The claimant must rely on the statement to his or her detriment

There must be actual reliance and consequent detriment suffered. In *JEB Fastener Ltd v Marks Bloom and Co.* (1983), a negligent statement was made about the value of a company's stock. The claimant did not succeed in his claim, as he had not relied on this advice. He had bought the company in order to secure the services of the company's two directors, and it was also held that before he took over the company, the claimant knew that its accounts were unreliable.

The reliance element of a special relationship has been important in determining the liability of surveyors in giving house valuations. In *Yianni* v *Evans* (1981), the claimants were purchasers of a property bought with the aid of a mortgage from a building society. The defendants were instructed by the building society to value the property in order to establish that it was worth the value of the mortgage. The defendants' valuation stated that the property was suitable as security for a loan of £12,000. The claimants did not have their own survey carried out but relied on the favourable report of the defendants. They purchased the property and then discovered that the property needed £18,000 worth of repairs. The High Court held the defendants were liable. Park J said the defendants knew that the part of the report confirming that the property was sufficiently valuable to be security for the loan would be passed to the claimants:

> I am sure that the defendants knew that their valuation would be passed on to the claimants and that the defendants knew that the claimants would rely on it when they decided to accept the building society's offer.

He referred to evidence that 90% of applicants for building society mortgages over the previous 6 years had relied on building society surveys. Also important was the fact that the house was at the lower-value end of the property market. Accordingly, the purchasers would have been of modest means and therefore not be expected to obtain an independent valuation.

This decision was approved by the House of Lords in *Smith* v *Eric S Bush* (1990), which also concerned the liability of surveyors in respect of building society valuations. The claimant purchaser was able to rely on the valuation, despite the inclusion of a disclaimer in the report. The disclaimer was not reasonable under the **Unfair Contract Terms Act 1977**. These cases are authority for property of a modest value.

The reliance must be reasonable

The courts seem to regard reliance as reasonable where it is foreseeable. In *Caparo* v *Dickman* (1990), guidelines were given by the House of Lords as to when reliance

may be foreseeable/reasonable. The defendant auditors were held not to be liable to the claimants for the negligent preparation of accounts. The claimants relied on the accounts to purchase further shares and eventually take over the company. The accounts were inaccurate and misleading, and the claimants consequently incurred financial loss.

Lord Bridge, having considered the relevant case law, said:

> *The salient feature of all these cases is that the defendant giving advice or information was fully aware of the nature of the transaction which the claimant had in contemplation, knew that the advice or information would be communicated to him directly or indirectly and knew that it was very likely that the claimant would rely on that advice or information in deciding whether or not to engage in the transaction in contemplation.*

Reliance was held not to be foreseeable by the defendants in this case. However, it was held that there was insufficient proximity between the auditors and the company's shareholders.

Soon after this decision, the case of *James McNaughton Papers Group Ltd* v *Hicks Anderson and Co.* (1991) was heard by the Court of Appeal. Bearing similar facts to *Caparo*, the defendants were accountants who prepared accounts at short notice for the chairman of a company. The accounts were then shown to the claimants, who relied on them to their detriment in bidding for and taking over the company. Neill LJ identified a number of factors that are important in ascertaining whether a duty of care exists, as follows:

❖ the purpose for which the statement is made
❖ the purpose for which the statement is communicated
❖ the relationship between the adviser, the advisee and any relevant third party
❖ the size of any class to which the advisee belongs
❖ the state of knowledge of the adviser
❖ reliance by the advisee

In that case, it was decided there was no duty owed to the claimants because the draft accounts were not prepared for their benefit, and even more importantly, the defendants would reasonably expect a party to a takeover to take independent advice and not rely solely on draft accounts.

This case was distinguished in *Morgan Crucible Co.* v *Hill Samuel* (1991), because in that case the defendants had made representations to the claimants, who were thinking of taking over the company, as to the financial health of the company, with the object of persuading the claimants to increase their bid. The claimants subsequently discovered that they had bid too much. It was held that if these facts were proved, the claimants had an arguable claim against the defendants.

Extended Hedley Byrne principle

In addition to the courts permitting the recovery in negligence of economic loss arising from personal injury, damage to property or a negligent misstatement, there are some circumstances in which liability has been imposed that do not fall squarely within these exceptions to the general rule against recovery. There does not appear to be a consistent principle applied in these circumstances, although recently there has been an attempt to fit them into the so-called 'extended Hedley Byrne principle'.

The difficulty has usually arisen in cases where the courts have clearly been in favour of imposing liability but there is an absence of reliance on the part of the claimant. This was the problem facing the courts in the so-called 'wills cases'.

In *Ross* v *Caunters* (1979), a solicitor prepared a will but failed to ensure that it was appropriately witnessed. The will was witnessed by the claimant spouse of the beneficiary, and this resulted in the legacy being void. The claimant successfully sued the solicitor for the economic loss sustained, despite not having acted in reliance on the solicitor. Sir Robert Megarry VC described the basis of the solicitor's liability to others as 'either an extension of the Hedley Byrne principle or, more probably, a direct application of the principle in *Donoghue* v *Stevenson*'. He further explained that where a solicitor is instructed to carry out a transaction that benefits a third party, that third party is clearly within contemplation as being likely to be affected, and the fact that the loss is purely financial should be no bar to a claim.

Sixteen years later, the House of Lords approved this decision in *White* v *Jones* (1995). A testator had cut his daughters out of his estate following a quarrel. The testator and his daughters were then reconciled, and he instructed the solicitor to prepare a new will including a £9,000 legacy to each of the daughters. The solicitor failed to act on the instructions before the testator died. The daughters' claim that the solicitor owed them a duty of care in these circumstances succeeded. Lord Goff gave the leading judgement. The problem in not allowing the claim would be that the testator and his or her estate would have a valid claim but have suffered no loss, while the disappointed beneficiary would have suffered loss but have no claim. This would result in no potential claim against a negligent solicitor. The issue was described as being 'a point of cardinal importance in the present case'. Lord Goff said that under the Hedley Byrne principle, the assumption of responsibility by the solicitor to the client should in law be held to extend to the intended beneficiary, to prevent the beneficiary being deprived of his or her legacy in circumstances where neither the testator nor the testator's estate has a remedy against the solicitor.

White v *Jones* must be regarded as a landmark case insofar as it rewrites the Hedley Byrne rules. As Margaret Brazier and John Murphy write in *Street on Torts* (10th edition):

White v Jones *does, at a minimum, establish three crucial principles governing liability for pure economic loss.*

1 *A duty to avoid causing such loss is confined to special relationships within which the D has assumed responsibility for protecting the claimant's economic welfare.*

2 *Such a relationship will arise only where the claimant is readily identifiable as an individual or a member of a class of persons for whom the D undertakes responsibility in the performance of a particular task.*

3 *Hedley Byrne relationships are not confined to negligent misstatements and careless advice. Provision of services, including service at the behest of a third party (as was the case in White) may create a special relationship in appropriate conditions. Reliance is not an essential ingredient of a special relationship.*

Questions

1 Briefly explain why there need to be special rules to deal with pure economic loss.

2 What losses suffered by the claimants were compensated in *Spartan Steel and Alloys Ltd* v *Martin and Co. Ltd* (1973)? Which loss was not compensated?

3 Why was Brentwood Council not liable for its negligence in not ensuring that the building foundation was sound?

4 In which case did Lord Denning (in a dissenting judgement) argue that defendants should owe a duty of care to prevent certain people suffering pure economic loss?

5 Briefly explain the requirements listed in *Hedley Byrne* (1964) that must be fulfilled for a special relationship to exist.

6 Why has the decision in *Mutual Life* v *Evatt* (1971) been criticised?

7 What particular fact in *Chaudhry* v *Prabhakar* (1988) clearly persuaded the court to impose liability on the defendant?

8 What rule is illustrated by *JEB Fastener* v *Marks Bloom and Co.* (1983)?

9 Which two cases involving property valuations resulted in the surveyors being held liable to pay compensation to the house owners?

10 Why were the defendants in *James McNaughton Papers Group Ltd* v *Hicks Anderson and Co.* (1991) not held to be liable?

11 Why, on the other hand, did the Court of Appeal rule in *Morgan Crucible Co.* v *Hill Samuel* (1991) that the defendant could be liable?

12 What rule is the basis of 'extended Hedley Byrne' liability?

13 Why, in *White* v *Jones* (1995), did Lord Goff decide that the solicitors had to be held liable to the beneficiaries of the will?

Sample exam question

Bonnie owns and publishes *Invest,* a journal that is well respected in the business and financial sector for its accurate assessment of the likely economic success of new inventions. Callum invests heavily in an invention by Doug after seeing it highly praised in an article written by Earl, one of *Invest*'s journalists. Fritz also sees the article and speaks directly to Earl about Doug's invention, after which he too invests heavily in it. Both Callum and Fritz lose all the money they have invested, when it later appears that there is a fundamental weakness in Doug's invention that Earl has failed to spot.

Adapted from AQA Paper 5, January 2007

Discuss the rights and remedies, if any, available to Callum and Fritz against Earl and against Bonnie in connection with the loss of the investment money.

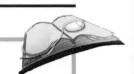

Further reading

Elliott, C. and Quinn, F. (2007) *Tort Law*, Pearson Longman.
Murphy, J. (2007) *Street on Torts*, Oxford University Press.
Pitchfork, E. D. (ed) (2000) *The Law of Tort*, Old Bailey Press.

Chapter 21

Occupiers' liability

Before the Occupiers' Liability Act 1957 was passed, occupiers' liability was dealt with by common law. The law relating to occupiers was complicated because different levels of care were owed to the various categories of claimant. However, the law has now been greatly simplified by codification in the Occupiers' Liability Acts of 1957 and 1984.

Occupiers' Liability Act 1957

This statute outlines the duty owed to lawful visitors.

Who is the occupier?

Section 1(2) of the 1957 Act states that a person who is to be treated as the occupier is the same as the person who would at common law have been treated as the occupier. The common-law position is illustrated by *Wheat* v *Lacon* (1966). The owners of a pub put it in the hands of a manager, who was authorised to take lodgers. One lodger was injured while using an unlit staircase. The House of Lords held that the owners could still be sued as occupiers because they retained some control over the state of the premises. Thus two or more people can be occupiers. This question of 'control' is crucial and in each case is a question of fact to be decided by the judge.

In *Harris* v *Birkenhead Corporation* (1976), the council served a compulsory purchase order on a house. After the residents had moved out, the council failed to board up the house and the claimant, a 4-year-old child, was able to enter the house through an unsecured door; he then fell out of a second-floor window. It was held that the council was liable, since it had the legal right to control the premises and was in the best position to prevent accidents.

The control test was also used in *Bailey* v *Armes* (1999). The defendant couple lived in a flat above a supermarket. From one of their windows, it was possible to gain access to a flat roof, on which their son was allowed to play. They had instructed him not to take any other children onto the roof. Although the supermarket owners owned the roof, they had no knowledge of the child playing there. One day, the son persuaded an 8-year-old boy to climb up onto the roof from the garden. The boy fell and was injured. Both the couple and the supermarket owner were sued, but the Court of Appeal ruled that neither defendant could be considered an occupier because they did not have a sufficient degree of control over the roof area.

To whom is the duty owed?

The **Occupiers' Liability Act 1957** abolished the common-law distinction between various categories of entrant and created instead a single category of 'lawful visitors'. A lawful visitor is anyone who is present on the premises by the occupier's invitation, with the occupier's express or implied permission, or in the exercise of a legal right. As well as people who have received an invitation, this includes those who have paid for the right of entry, for example to a theatre or theme park. Those who visit as a result of implied permission include meter readers, delivery men or the fire brigade dealing with a fire.

Lawful authority also covers police and others exercising rights granted by warrant. Casual visitors, such as political canvassers or door-to-door salesmen, are also included, following the general rule that any person has the right to come as far as the front door unless steps are taken to prevent this, such as a locked gate or warning notice.

Interestingly, people who use a right of way are not considered to be visitors and accordingly are not owed a duty of care. This was confirmed in *McGeown* v *Northern Ireland Housing Executive* (1995), where the appellant was walking along a public footpath that ran over the defendant's land. She tripped in a hole and was injured. Her case was rejected on the ground that people who used rights of way are neither trespassers nor lawful visitors and are accordingly owed no duty. Lord Keith justified this decision on the grounds that:

> ...*rights of way pass over many different types of terrain, and it would place an impossible burden on landowners if they not only had to submit to the passage over them of anyone who might choose to exercise them but also were under a duty to maintain them in a safe condition.*

Under the **Countryside and Rights of Way Act 2000**, there is a general right to walk over open land that falls within the description of 'mountain, moor, heath or down'; this is commonly referred to as the 'right to roam'. The Act provides that

People exercising the 'right to roam' are not visitors under the Occupiers' Liability Act 1957, but are instead covered by the 1984 Act

people exercising this right are not 'visitors' within the meaning of the 1957 Act; they are, however, covered by the 1984 Act.

The invitation or permission may be issued by someone other than the occupier. The occupier's wife or husband or children may invite a friend into the family home, and permission to enter commercial premises does not normally require the express authority of the board of directors. A more difficult situation arises where an employee, or junior member of the family, violates an express instruction not to allow visitors. In *Stone v Taffe* (1974), a pub manager had been instructed not to let friends remain on the premises after closing time except for a bona fide private party notified in advance to the brewery and the police. He ignored this instruction, and a guest fell on unlit stairs. The brewery was held liable. The guest was a lawful visitor since he did not know of the prohibition and believed he was on the premises by invitation.

Where is the duty owed?

The 1957 Act imposes a duty on occupiers of premises. 'Premises' is given a broad meaning by s.1(3), and may be 'any fixed or movable structure, including any vessel, vehicle or aircraft'.

Besides covering houses, building and the land itself, premises have also been held to include:

* ships in dry dock — *London Graving Dock v Horton* (1951)
* vehicles — *Hartwell v Grayson* (1947)
* lifts — *Haseldine v Daw and Son Ltd* (1941)
* ladders — *Wheeler v Copas* (1981)

What is the duty owed?

Section 2(1) provides that the duty owed is the common-law duty of care. Under s.2(2), the common-law duty of care is stated as:

> *...a duty to take such care as in all the circumstances of the case is reasonable to see that the visitor will be reasonably safe in using the premises for the purposes for which he is invited or permitted by the occupier to be there.*

The duty is not absolute but requires the occupier to take reasonable care. The occupier will be judged by the negligence standard of the reasonable person. Liability of the occupier is dependent on whether he or she has done or not done what the reasonable person would have done or not done.

In *Martin* v *Middlesbrough Corporation* (1965), a schoolgirl slipped in the playground and cut herself on a broken milk bottle. The council was held liable because it had not made adequate arrangements for disposing of the bottle. Similarly, in *Cunningham* v *Reading FC* (1992), a football club was liable to police officers injured by lumps of concrete thrown by visiting Bristol City fans. The club knew from past experience that the visiting crowd was likely to contain a violent element, who had thrown concrete on a previous visit some 4 months earlier, but had made no effort to remove or repair the loose concrete in spite of the relatively low cost of doing so.

However, in *Perry* v *Harris* (2008), no liability was imposed. The defendant had organised a children's party and had hired a bouncy castle and a bungee run. Her attention was diverted briefly by a child on the bungee run at the same time as the claimant performed a somersault on the bouncy castle. Before the claimant had time to get to his feet, another much taller and older boy also performed a somersault and his heel accidentally struck the claimant's forehead, causing severe and permanent brain damage. The High Court judge ruled the defendant was liable, holding that she should have given the bouncy castle her uninterrupted supervision and that she had therefore breached her duty of care. However, on appeal it was held that this standard of care was unreasonably high, and that the defendant had acted reasonably in concluding she could supervise both the castle and the bungee run at the same time.

The duty is, however, limited, in that it is only owed in respect of the purpose for which the visitor is permitted to be on the premises. No duty is owed under the Act to entrants who use the premises for other purposes. As Lord Scrutton LJ memorably said in *The Calgarth* (1927): 'When you invite a person into your house to use the stairs, you do not invite him to slide down the banisters.' Entrants who exceed the scope of the occupiers' permission become non-visitors under the 1984 Act in the event that they suffer injury.

Duty owed to children

Section 2(3)(a) provides that an occupier must be prepared for children to be less careful than adults. The premises must be reasonably safe for a child of that age.

The reasoning for this is that what may pose no threat to an adult may nevertheless be dangerous to a child. In *Moloney* v *Lambeth LBC* (1966), a 4-year-old fell through a gap in railing guarding a stairwell and was injured. An adult could not have fallen through the gap, so such an injury would have been impossible. The occupier was held liable.

In *Perry* v *Butlins Holiday World* (1998), the 3-year-old claimant badly cut his ear when he fell onto a brick wall. The wall was low and built of sharp bricks, and was near an open area where children's shows were performed. The Court of Appeal held this case was borderline, but the design of the wall, together with its position where children were likely to be, meant that the defendants had breached their duty of care.

Similarly, a child is unlikely to appreciate risks as an adult would, and may be attracted to the danger. Consequently, an occupier should guard against any kind of allurement that places a child visitor at risk of harm. In *Glasgow Corporation* v *Taylor* (1922), a 7-year-old ate poisonous berries in a botanical garden and died. The shrub on which the berries grew was not fenced off in any way. The corporation was held liable as it knew that the berries were poisonous and should have expected that a young child might be attracted them. The same approach was taken in *Jolley* v *Sutton LBC* (2000). The House of Lords restored the decision of the trial judge in holding the defendant liable to a 14-year-old boy, who was seriously injured when an old boat fell on him. The boat was something that would be attractive to children, including those of the claimant's age, and some injury was foreseeable if children played on or around it.

The courts sometimes take the view that young children should be under their parents' supervision. In such circumstances, the occupier is not liable. In *Phipps* v *Rochester Corporation* (1955), a 5-year-old was injured, having fallen down a trench dug by the defendant on a piece of waste ground where the child frequently played. The defendant was not liable because the court held that the parents should have had the child under proper control. The corporation had granted only 'conditional licence' to children accompanied by an adult.

Duty owed to experts

Section 2(3)(b) provides that an occupier may expect that a person in the exercise of his or her calling will appreciate and guard against any special risks ordinarily incidental to it.

Where tradesmen fail to guard against risks that they should know about, the occupier will not be liable. A window cleaner injured because of the insecurity of some part of the outside of a building that he uses as a foothold or handhold in order to clean the windows is expected to guard against that risk, which is a common one for window cleaners. However, that would be no reason for the occupier not to be held liable if the window cleaner were injured because of a defect in the stairs he was climbing to clean upstairs windows.

In *Roles* v *Nathan* (1963), the occupier was not liable when chimney sweeps died after inhaling carbon monoxide fumes while cleaning flues. The sweeps did not accept the advice of the occupiers to complete the work with the boilers off, and in any case should have been aware of the risks. The occupier may not, however, expect experts to guard against risks not incidental to their trade. Lord Denning in this case pointed out that the outcome would have been different if the sweeps had been killed by a basement staircase giving way, as such a risk is not incidental to cleaning chimneys.

Furthermore, the occupier may not expect experts to exercise more than the usual safeguards particular to their trade to guard against risks that are created by the occupier's negligence. In *Ogwo* v *Taylor* (1987), a householder who started a fire by his careless use of a blowlamp was liable for injuries suffered by a fireman in fighting the fire. The risk was one that the fireman could not effectively guard against. Similarly, in *Salmon* v *Seafarer* (1983), the owners of a chip shop were liable. They had failed to turn of a chip fryer, which then started a fire and injured the defendant fireman who was fighting the blaze.

For what damage may the occupier be held liable?

Section 1(3)(b) states that the Act applies not only to personal injury and death but also damage to property, including property that does not belong to the visitor.

Warnings

Section 2(4)(a) provides that the occupier's liability is discharged if the occupier gives effective warning of the danger. The warning must be sufficient to enable the visitor to be reasonably safe. In *Roles* v *Nathan* (1963), Lord Denning explained the provisions of this section:

> *Supposing for instance, that there was only one way of getting into and out of premises and it was by a footbridge over a stream which was rotten and dangerous. An occupier puts up a notice 'This bridge is dangerous'. In such a case, s.2(4)(a) makes it clear that the occupier would nowadays be liable. But if there were two footbridges one of which was rotten, and the other safe a hundred yards away, the occupier could still escape liability, even today by putting up a notice 'Do not use*

this footbridge. It is dangerous. There is a safe one further upstream'. Such a warning is sufficient because it does enable the visitor to be reasonably safe.

In some circumstances, a mere warning may be insufficient to safeguard the visitor, and the occupier may be obliged to set up barriers. In *Rae* v *Mars* (1990), a warning was ineffective in respect of a deep pit inside the entrance of a dark shed. The occupier was liable.

There is, however, no specific obligation to display a warning notice when the danger is one that should be obvious to any visitor. In *Cotton* v *Derbyshire Dales* (1994), a walker was injured after falling from a high path along dangerous cliffs in a much-visited area. There was no notice warning of the danger. The Court of Appeal said the absence of a notice was not a breach of the common duty of care. The danger was obvious to visitors exercising reasonable care for their own safety. A similar decision was reached in *Darby* v *National Trust* (2001), where a man drowned while swimming in a pond at a National Trust property. The Court of Appeal decided that since drowning was such an obvious risk, there was no requirement to warn against it.

Negligence of independent contractors

Under s.2(4)(b), an occupier will not be liable for loss or injuries suffered by his or her visitors when the cause of damage is the negligence of an independent contractor hired by the occupier. The reasoning behind this is that the contractor will be covered by his or her own insurance. This section effectively confirms the common-law position, whereby there is not normally any vicarious liability for torts committed by independent contractors.

Two requirements must be met for this section to apply:
❖ It must be reasonable for the occupier to have entrusted the work to the independent contractor. In *Haseldine* v *Daw* (1941), the occupier was not liable for the negligent repair of a lift, as this was a job requiring specialist skills. Delegation of work to an independent contractor would be deemed to be reasonable where it was the normal commercial practice to do so, for example employing contractors for office cleaning.
❖ The occupier must take reasonable steps to satisfy himself or herself that the contractor was competent and that the work had been properly done. Only reasonable steps must be taken. If the work is of a highly complex and technical nature, it is less reasonable to impose this obligation. However, if the risk is obvious, the occupier will be expected to discover it. In *Woodward* v *The Mayor of Hastings* (1945), the occupiers were liable when a child was injured on school steps that were negligently left icy after the contractors had cleaned off snow. The risk should have been obvious to the occupiers.

In *Bottomley* v *Todmorden Cricket Club* (2003), the claimant was injured while helping with a fireworks display on the cricket club's land, organised by an independent contractor. The club argued that since the display was organised by independent contractors, albeit for the club's benefit, it had no liability under the 1957 Act. Dismissing the cricket club's appeal, Brooke LJ said an occupier in such circumstances can usually escape liability by showing that he or she has taken reasonable care to select competent and safe contractors. In this case, however, there was no written safety plan and the cricket club had not insisted that the independent contractor take out adequate public liability insurance.

Excluding liability

Under s.2(1), the occupier can extend, restrict, modify and exclude liability to his or her visitors. However, exclusion clauses are subject to restrictions:
* They do not apply in the case of strangers, for example a tenant's visitors, because they have had no opportunity to agree to the exclusion.
* They fail against children who may be unable to read or to fully understand their implications.
* They are not allowed in respect of death or personal injury caused by the occupier's breach of duty under the 1957 Act by virtue of the **Unfair Contract Terms Act 1977**. This restriction applies where the premises are occupied for the business purposes of the occupier.

Defences

The occupier may raise the general defences of contributory negligence and *volenti non fit injuria*.

Contributory negligence

Under the **Law Reform (Contributory Negligence) Act 1945**, damages are reduced according to the claimant's responsibility for the damage suffered.

Volenti non fit injuria

The defence of *volenti non fit injuria* (voluntary assumption of risk) was explained in Chapter 18 (pages 235–37). The risk must be fully understood by the visitor.

In *Simms* v *Leigh RFC* (1969), a visiting rugby player was tackled near the edge of the pitch, collided with a concrete wall and broke a leg. The wall was 7 feet 3 inches from the touchline; league regulations stated that it should be at least 7 feet away. The judge found as fact that it was not proven that the injury had resulted from the collision with the wall, as it could have been from the tackle alone. However, *in obiter* the judge said that even if causation had been proved, the claimant had been *volenti* to the risk of injury on a ground laid out in accordance with league rules. There would thus be no liability when the injury was sustained within the normal rules of the game.

Mere knowledge of the risk is insufficient. The risk must be accepted. In *White* v *Blackmore* (1972), general knowledge that jalopy racing was dangerous did not mean that the claimant had accepted inadequate safety arrangements.

The claimant must freely choose to consent. In *Burnett* v *British Waterways Board* (1972), a claimant on a barge entering the defendant's dry dock had no choice but to be there. The defence of consent was therefore unavailable.

Occupiers' Liability Act 1984

The Occupiers' Liability Act 1984 was passed to clarify the law relating to categories of claimant not covered by the 1957 Act and outlines the duty owed to trespassers. The harshness of the judicial approach in *Addie* v *Dumbreck* (1929) — whereby the occupier's duty was to refrain from causing deliberate or reckless injury — was to some extent mitigated by the decision of the House of Lords in *British Railways Board* v *Herrington* (1972). A young child was injured when he gained access to an electrified railway line through vandalised fencing. Lord Diplock said the duty owed to a trespasser was limited to taking reasonable steps, as would be taken by a person of ordinary humane feeling, to enable the trespasser to avoid the danger. This duty became known as the 'duty of common humanity'.

Following the *Herrington* decision, the question of liability to trespassers was referred to the Law Commission; its report in 1976 formed the basis of the Occupiers Liability Act 1984.

Who is the occupier?

Section 1(2) of the 1984 Act states that the word 'occupier' bears the same meaning as under the Occupiers' Liability Act 1957. An occupier under the 1984 Act will thus, as stated by Lord Denning in *Wheat* v *Lacon* (1966), be a person who has a sufficient degree of control over the premises.

To whom is the duty owed?

Section 1(1) of the 1984 Act states that the duty is owed to persons other than visitors. Under s.1(2), it is provided that the word 'visitor' bears the same meaning as under the 1957 Act. The 1984 Act is clearly intended to provide for those categories of entrant not provided for under the 1957 Act.

Usually, entrants covered by the 1984 Act will be trespassers. However, the Act also applies to people who, without the permission of the occupier, are involuntarily on the premises, to persons exercising a private right of way, and to members of the public entering under an access order or agreement made under the **National Parks and Access to the Countryside Act 1949**.

It is expressly provided by s.1(7) that the 1984 Act does not apply to persons using the highway. Users of highways maintained at public expense are regulated by the **Highways Act 1980** (which is beyond the scope of the AQA specification).

Where is the duty owed?

The duty is owed by the occupier of premises. Under s.1(2) of the 1984 Act, premises are stated as including any fixed or movable structure. Section 1(9) defines 'movable structure' as including any vessel, vehicle or aircraft. The meaning of premises is thus the same as under the 1957 Act.

State of the premises

The duty owed to trespassers requires the occupier to take reasonable steps to ensure the trespasser is not injured or killed by reason of the danger arising 'due to the state of the premises or to things done or omitted to be done on them'. The 1984 Act therefore *only* deals with cases where someone trespasses on an occupier's property and is injured or killed because the property has a dangerous feature.

This was the case in *Tomlinson* v *Congleton BC* (2003). Here, the claimant was severely injured when he visited a public park and, ignoring warning notices about swimming in the lake, waded into the lake and then dived in, hitting his head on the shallow sandy bottom and fracturing his spinal cord. The House of Lords allowed the appeal from the Court of Appeal and dismissed the claimant's action. Lord Hoffman stated:

> There was nothing special about the lake; there were no hidden dangers. It was shallow in some places and deep in others, but that is the nature of lakes. Nor was the council doing or permitting anything to be done which created a danger to persons who came to the lake.

A similar decision was reached in *Keown* v *Coventry Health Care Trust* (2006), where a young boy climbed up a fire escape and fell 30 feet, breaking his arm and suffering severe brain damage. On appeal, it was held that any danger was due to the claimant's activity on the premises and was not due to the state of the premises. The fire escape was a normal fire escape and the premises were required by law to have means of egress in case of fire.

In what circumstances is the duty owed?

In *British Rail* v *Herrington* (1972), the Law Lords gave differing accounts of the circumstances in which the duty of common humanity is owed. These circumstances are now clarified in the 1984 Act.

Section 1(3) states that an occupier of premises owes a duty to a non-visitor if:

(a) he or she is aware of the danger or has reasonable grounds to believe that it exists

(b) he or she knows or has reasonable grounds to believe that the other is in the vicinity of the danger concerned or that he or she may come into the vicinity of the danger

(c) the risk is one against which, in all the circumstances of the case, he or she may reasonably be expected to offer the other some protection

Both (a) and (b) are subjective — that is, they relate to the knowledge of the defendant. If the defendant is unaware of the danger or unaware that the person may come on to the premises, then he or she will not be liable, even if such facts would be obvious to the reasonable person. In *Swain* v *Natui Ram Pun* (1996), a child trespassing on the roof of the defendant's factory fell off and was seriously injured. Dismissing his claim, the court said the factory was surrounded by substantial fences and there was no evidence of previous trespass. Therefore, the defendant had no reasonable grounds to believe there was anyone in the vicinity of the danger. *Obiter*, Pill LJ said that s.1(3)(b) imposes a subjective test based on the occupier's actual knowledge of facts giving such grounds, not on what he ought to have known.

The effect of this subsection is also illustrated by *White* v *St Albans DC* (1990). The claimant fell into a trench while taking a short cut across the defendant's land. He argued that the fact the defendant council had fenced the land showed it was aware of the risk of trespass, so satisfying the requirement of s.1(3)(b). In dismissing this argument, the Court of Appeal (per Nicholls LJ) upheld the decision of the trial judge:

> *The purpose of the fencing was to deter people from going on to the levelled surface from the highway. Whether one adopts a subjective or objective approach, I do not think the defendants had reasonable or any grounds to believe that anyone would use the levelled surface as a short-cut to the car park, and so come into the vicinity of the danger.*

However, the third requirement (c) is both subjective and objective. The focus is on 'all the circumstances of the case', which may include the purpose of the entry, the age and capabilities of the non-visitor and the financial resources of the occupier. The majority of the House of Lords in *Herrington* held the view that the financial resources of the occupier should be considered. They also thought that the circumstances in which the duty was owed should be based on the knowledge of the occupier.

What is the duty owed?

Section 1(4) states that the duty owed by an occupier to a non-visitor is:

...to take such care as is reasonable in all the circumstances of the case to see that he does not suffer injury on the premises by reason of the danger concerned.

This is a significantly lower duty than that imposed under s.2(2) of the 1957 Act. Indeed, the Law Commission, in its report that led to the creation of the 1984 Act, stated:

It will be evident that the duty towards the trespasser under our recommendations is of a quite different character from the 'common duty of care' under the Occupiers' Liability Act 1957. Under the latter that duty is, in short, owed to all visitors and the occupier has to take reasonable care to see that they are reasonably safe. Under the former, while the duty is one which is owed potentially to all trespassers, the question of the extent of the duty does not arise at all unless, in the first place, the court decides as a question of fact that the danger is one against which, in all the circumstances, it is reasonable for the occupier to offer some protection.

In respect of what damage is the duty owed?

Section 1(1) states that the duty owed under the 1984 Act applies in respect of injury. In s.1(9), 'injury' is defined as meaning death or personal injury, including disease and any impairment of physical or mental condition. By virtue of s.1(8), the 1984 Act does not apply in respect of damage to property.

Warnings

Section 1(5) states that the occupier may discharge his or her duty by:

...taking such steps as are reasonable in all the circumstances of the case to give warning of the danger concerned or to discourage persons from incurring the risk.

The level of warning required to discharge the occupier's duty under the 1984 Act is thus lower than that required under the 1957 Act. The 1984 Act does not require the warning to be sufficient to enable the entrant to be safe in remaining on the premises. Rather, the emphasis is on making the potential entrant aware of why he or she should not come onto the premises.

Excluding liability

The Law Commission, in its 1976 report, expressly provided that occupiers should be able to exclude liability to non-visitors, subject to the exclusion satisfying the requirement of reasonableness. However, as no mention of exclusion is made in the 1984 Act, it may be concluded that the duty imposed on occupiers in respect of trespassers is intended to be non-excludable.

Defences

The occupier may raise the general defences of contributory negligence and *volenti non fit injuria*.

Contributory negligence

Under the **Law Reform (Contributory Negligence) Act 1945**, damages are reduced according to the claimant's responsibility for the damage suffered.

Volenti non fit injuria

The defence of *volenti* is expressly provided for by s.1(6), which states that 'no duty is owed to a person in respect of risks which he willingly accepts as his'.

In *Ratcliff* v *McConnell* (1997), a 19-year-old student climbed over a locked gate at night and dived into a swimming pool, which was closed for the winter and partially drained. He dived into the shallow end and hit his head on the bottom, sustaining serious injuries. He sued the defendant under the 1984 Act and the trial judge found in his favour, subject to a deduction for contributory negligence. Allowing the defendant's appeal, Stuart-Smith LJ said there were several warning notices around the pool, and the dangers of diving into water of unknown depth were too well known to need any further express warning. The claimant had accepted the risks, and under s.1(6) of the 1984 Act his claim must fail.

Participation in dangerous sporting activities

Before the defence of *volenti* can be established in sporting cases, the defendant must show that the claimant consented not only to some risk of harm, but also to the particular risk that occurred.

In *Gillmore* v *LCC* (1938), the claimant was a member of the physical training class run by the defendant. During an exercise in which the members of the class were lunging at each other, he was injured through losing his balance on a floor that was slippery due to the defendant's negligence. It was held that while the claimant had consented to the risk incidental to doing physical training, he had not consented to the additional risk of doing these activities on a slippery floor.

In *Trustees of Portsmouth Youth Activities Committee* v *Poppleton* (2008), the Court of Appeal ruled that:

> ...adults who choose to engage in physical activities which obviously give rise to a degree of unavoidable risk may find that they have no means of recompense if the risk materialises so that they are injured.

In that case, the claimant was taking part in 'bouldering' — a form of free climbing without the aid of ropes — when he fell head first onto shock-absorbing matting while leaping from the climbing wall to a cross beam (copying a more experienced friend). The claimant had both signed a 'disclaimer form' and registered at reception, and was therefore free to use the climbing wall without any further guidance or instruction from centre staff.

Questions

1. Give four examples of people who would be regarded as lawful visitors.

2. What test for occupiers did *Wheat* v *Lacon* (1966) create?

3. Define the duty of care owed to lawful visitors in s.2(2) of the Occupiers' Liability Act 1957 and explain why in *Cunningham* v *Reading FC* (1992) the club was held liable.

4. Explain the contradictory decisions in *Glasgow Corporation* v *Taylor* (1922) and *Phipps* v *Rochester Corporation* (1955).

5. Explain what s.2(3)(b) states about expert visitors, and explain the decision in *Roles* v *Nathan* (1963).

6. Why were the defendants liable in both *Ogwo* v *Taylor* (1987) and *Salmon* v *Seafarer* (1983)?

7. What explanation did Lord Denning give about warnings in *Roles* v *Nathan* (1963)?

8. What rule about warnings was given in *Cotton* v *Derbyshire Dales* (1994)?

9. Why was the cricket club held liable in *Bottomley* v *Todmorden Cricket Club* (2003)? What action should the cricket club have taken to avoid liability?

10. Under the Occupiers' Liability Act 1984, what tests are laid down in s.1(3) to determine if the trespasser is owed a duty of care?

11. Why was the defendant not liable in *Swain* v *Natui Ram Pun* (1996) for the injuries sustained by the claimant?

12. What is the difference between the duty of care owed to lawful visitors and that owed to trespassers?

21

Sample exam question

Liam and Maurice visit Jarvis's house and gardens on the same day, on which there is torrential rain. Liam pays to enter, but Maurice manages to sneak in without paying. Jarvis's gardens are laid out in a number of levels, and the path between two levels consists of steep steps. Down one side of the steps is a low spiked fence, to which a handrail is attached. A notice at the top of the steps warns that extra care is necessary in wet weather. Liam slips and overbalances while running down the steps holding the handrail, and is jerked round onto the spikes of the fence, ripping his face open. Maurice stumbles on the crumbling edge of a step and falls down a number of steps, breaking his arm.

Adapted from AQA Unit 5 paper, January 2007

Discuss the rights and remedies, if any, available to Liam and to Maurice against Jarvis.

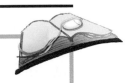

Further reading

Elliott, C. and Quinn, F. (2007) *Tort Law*, Pearson Longman.
Murphy, J. (2007) *Street on Torts*, Oxford University Press.
Pitchfork, E. D. (ed) (2000) *The Law of Tort*, Old Bailey Press.

Chapter 22

Nuisance

The tort of nuisance seeks to protect the claimant's ability to use and enjoy his or her land without due interference from the defendant. While it is usually straight-forward to identify nuisance, in most cases it will be private nuisance. The fact that there may be several people exposed to the nuisance does not 'convert' it into public nuisance.

Private nuisance

Professor Winfield in *Winfield and Jolowicz on Tort* defines private nuisance as 'unlawful interference with a person's use or enjoyment of land, or some right over, or in connection with it'. This tort action recognises the importance of the enjoyment of land, whether it belongs to the claimant or the defendant. This, in turn, means that not every interference with the claimant's land will amount to an actionable nuisance. Lord Wright commented in *Sedleigh-Denfield* v *O'Callaghan* (1940):

> *A balance has to be maintained between the right of the occupier to do what he likes with his own land, and the right of his neighbour not to be interfered with.*

The law expects a degree of reasonable tolerance between neighbours as to the uses to which each puts his or her land. Therefore, this tort insists that any interference is both **substantial** and **unreasonable**. Anything that causes actual physical damage meets this requirement, and it is also accepted that noise, smells and vibrations emanating onto the claimant's land can constitute nuisance.

Reasonableness in nuisance is different from the reasonableness in negligence. In negligence, the reasonableness of the defendant's conduct is the central issue. However, in nuisance the central issue is the reasonableness of the outcome of the defendant's conduct. The focus of a nuisance action is thus on the reasonableness of the interference caused to the claimant. The defendant cannot argue as a defence that he or she took reasonable care. In *Rapier* v *London Tramways Co.* (1893), Lindley

LJ noted: 'If I am sued for nuisance, and nuisance is proved, it is no defence to say and to prove that I have taken all reasonable care to prevent it.'

There may be occasions, however, where it may not be unreasonable even to cause an intolerable disturbance. In *Southwark LBC* v *Tanner* (2001), the claimants were tenants who lived in old houses with wholly inadequate soundproofing and who could hear everything their neighbours did. Although Lord Millett accepted that 'life in these conditions must be intolerable', the House of Lords found there was not an actionable nuisance. Despite the 'intolerable' effect of their everyday noises, it was not unreasonable for the claimants' neighbours to make such noises, as they were made as part of the ordinary and reasonable use of their property.

However, the conduct of the defendant is relevant in circumstances where he or she has acted maliciously.

What is unreasonable interference?

In deciding whether interference is unreasonable, the courts will take into account various factors:

❖ the nature of the locality
❖ whether the interference is ongoing
❖ the sensitivity of the claimant
❖ the motive or malice of the defendant

Nature of the locality

In an industrial area, fumes are less likely to be considered unlawful interference than in a rural area. Pollock J famously stated in *Bamford* v *Turnley* (1862): 'That may be a nuisance in Grosvenor Square which would be none in Smithfield market.' In a residential area, cocks crowing in the morning are more likely to be considered unlawful interference than in a rural area. In *Leeman* v *Montague* (1936), the claimant lived in a largely residential area and was regularly disturbed by the crowing of 750 cockerels on the defendant's land about 100 yards away. The court held that this constituted a nuisance.

In *Leeman* v *Montague* (1936), the crowing of 750 cockerels in a largely residential area constituted a nuisance

The nature of the locality may change over time from industrial to residential, and the courts have to address this possibility. In *Gillingham BC* v *Medway (Chatham) Dock Co. Ltd* (1993), Buckley J held that planning permission to develop a disused naval dockyard as a 24-hour commercial dock had changed the nature of the neighbourhood and, accordingly, local residents could not complain about the serious disruption caused by its operation. This case appears to suggest that the decisions of planning authorities may help to define the nature of a locality for the purposes of determining whether interference is unreasonable.

However, if there is physical damage to the claimant's property, the locality issue will not absolve the defendant from liability. In *St Helens Smelting Co.* v *Tipping* (1865), the claimant bought an estate near the defendant's smelting works and suffered damage to his trees and other crops, caused by the fumes. The defendants argued that there were many other smelting works in the area and so the nature of the locality prevented the interference from being unlawful. Lord Westbury LC said surrounding circumstances were relevant where enjoyment was concerned, but not where there was material damage. The claimant's action succeeded.

Whether the interference is ongoing

The law of nuisance is concerned with activities that are ongoing, i.e. a state of affairs. It is a matter of common sense that the claimant will have to tolerate some inconvenience in his or her enjoyment of land. What is unreasonable is when the interference occurs frequently and for long periods of time. In *De Keyser's Royal Hotel* v *Spicer Bros Ltd* (1914), the court was willing to issue an injunction for a temporary interference that consisted of pile-driving in the middle of the night, but confined the injunction to banning this work between 10 p.m. and 6.30 a.m.

However, the courts have at times held that seemingly one-off incidents are a nuisance. They have done this by finding that the preceding state of the defendant's land constituted the nuisance. In *Spicer* v *Smee* (1946), the claimant succeeded in claiming nuisance when his home was destroyed by fire caused by defective wiring in the defendant's home. The defective wiring was the state of affairs.

A further example is provided by *British Celanese Ltd* v *A H Hunt (Capacitors) Ltd* (1969). The defendants collected metal strips as part of their business. These metal strips were blown about by the wind and some landed on an electricity substation, causing a power failure to the claimant's factory. The defendants were held liable, the collection of metal strips on their land being the state of affairs.

Sensitivity of the claimant

A claimant cannot put his or her land to an unusually delicate use and then complain when that land is adversely affected to a greater extent than would usually be the case by his or her neighbour's activities. In *Amphitheatres Inc.* v *Portland Meadows* (1948), the claimant's action failed when his drive-in cinema was affected by the defendant's floodlit premises.

Similarly, in *Robinson* v *Kilvert* (1889), the unusually sensitive brown paper that the claimant manufactured was damaged when the defendant heated his cellar, thus

raising the temperature of the building. The defendant was not liable, as normal brown paper would not have been affected.

However, in *Network Rail Ltd* v *Morris* (2004), the Court of Appeal took a more considered approach. In this case, the claimant was complaining about electromagnetic interference from Railtrack's signalling system affecting the music of electric guitars in his recording studio. The Court recognised that, although this claim might have been dismissed in the past on the grounds of sensitivity, the use of electric and electronic equipment was now a common feature of modern life. As a footnote, Buxton LJ questioned the rule laid down in *Robinson* v *Kilvert*.

It should, however, be noted that if a claimant establishes that the defendant has infringed his or her right to ordinary enjoyment of his or her property, the defendant is liable for damage due to unusual sensitivity. In *McKinnon Industries* v *Walker* (1951), the claimant's orchids were damaged and his enjoyment of his land was adversely affected by fumes and sulphur dioxide gas from the defendant's factory. Although the defendant argued he should not be held liable for the damage to the orchids, since growing these was a delicate operation, the Privy Council rejected that argument, holding that as the right to ordinary enjoyment had been infringed, the claimant could also claim for this sensitive activity.

Motive or malice of the defendant

Where the defendant's activity is motivated by malice, the courts are more likely to hold such activity as unlawful. In *Christie* v *Davey* (1893), the claimant gave music lessons for approximately 17 hours per week. This annoyed her neighbour, who lived in the adjoining semi-detached house. He retaliated by banging trays on the wall, shouting and blowing whistles. The claimant was successful, as the defendant had acted deliberately and maliciously. North J held that 'what was done by the defendant was done only for the purpose of annoyance'.

When the activity is motivated by malice, the defendant cannot argue that the claimant is unusually sensitive. In *Hollywood Silver Fox Farm* v *Emmett* (1936), the defendant discharged his gun on his own property in order to frighten the plaintiff's silver fox breeding vixen, causing her to miscarry. Despite the delicate use of land by the claimant, the defendant's malicious intention rendered his actions a nuisance.

Who can sue?

Anyone with a proprietary interest in the land may bring an action in nuisance. This is usually the occupier, but may be a landlord who is out of possession. Members of the occupier's family cannot sue (but may sue in negligence if there is personal injury or damage to property).

An early example of this principle is provided by *Malone* v *Laskey* (1907). Mrs Malone and her husband occupied property provided by the husband's employers and sublet from Laskey, who operated an engine in adjoining premises. The vibrations created by the engine caused a bracket supporting a water tank in the Malones' house to collapse and injure Mrs Malone. Although the working of the engine was a nuisance, Mrs Malone's action failed as she had no proprietary interest in the property. (This case would be decided differently today, as wives now have statutory occupation rights.)

The principle established in *Malone* was upset in *Khorasandjian* v *Bush* (1993). The claimant, a young woman living with her parents, was receiving unwanted telephone calls and being otherwise harassed by a former boyfriend. In upholding the decision of the court of first instance, the Court of Appeal held that the claimant, as an occupier of property, had a right to bring an action in nuisance, notwithstanding that she had no legal or equitable interest in the land affected. However, the House of Lords in *Hunter* v *Canary Wharf* (1997) reaffirmed the principle of *Malone*. Lord Goff said the idea that the claimant need only a 'substantial link' with the property affected was too vague, and would transform nuisance from a tort against land into a tort against the person.

Who can be sued?

Anyone who causes a nuisance is liable for its creation and continuance. If the nuisance emanates from land, the occupier is primarily liable, and the owner not in occupation is liable only if he or she was the person who created or authorised the nuisance. This can be seen in *Tetley* v *Chitty* (1986), where the local council allowed a go-kart club to use its land and the noise disturbed local residents. Although the council argued it was not liable because it had neither created the noise nor permitted it, the court ruled that since such noise was an inevitable result of go-karting, and the council had allowed such use to be made of its land, it was liable for the nuisance.

In *Lippiatt* v *South Gloucestershire Council* (2000), the council had allowed a group of travellers to set up an unofficial camp on its land. The claimants were farmers on adjoining land who claimed that the travellers had used the land as a 'launching pad' for repeated entries to their farm, where they had caused damage. They sued the council on the ground that it had authorised the nuisance. Although the council tried to have this action struck out, the Court of Appeal held the claim was allowable.

An occupier is responsible for nuisances created by his employees, agent, family, guests and independent contractor. This is an exception to the general principle that employers are not liable for their independent contractors. In *Hole* v *Sittingbourne Railway* (1861), the independent contractor built a swing bridge so badly it would not open. The defendant employer was held liable. Similarly, in *Matania* v *NP Bank Ltd* (1994), the defendants were held liable for the nuisance created by the noisy building operations of their independent contractor.

Damage suffered must be foreseeable

The claimant may recover damages for any foreseeable loss that he or she has suffered as a result of the nuisance. The House of Lords in *Cambridge Water Co. Ltd v Eastern Counties Leather plc* (1994) held that the loss suffered must be of a type which is reasonably foreseeable. Lord Goff said:

> *It by no means follows that the defendant should be liable for damage of a type which he could not foresee; and the development of the law of negligence in the past 60 years points strongly towards a requirement that such foreseeability be a prerequisite of liability in damages for nuisance, as it is of liability in negligence.*

No liability in private nuisance for personal injury

Damages for personal injury are not recoverable *per se* in private nuisance. In *Hunter v Canary Wharf* (1995), the House of Lords reasserted the principle that nuisance is a tort against land and not a tort against the person.

Remedies

A person disturbed by a nuisance has four main remedies open:

* damages
* an injunction
* abatement
* a complaint to the local authority

Damages and injunctions

In a nuisance action, damages are often an inadequate remedy and are not usually awarded alone where the nuisance is likely to continue. In *Tetley* v *Chitty* (1986), McNeill J held the noise to be an inevitable consequence of the use for which permission had been given, so that the council was liable in private nuisance. Damages would have been wholly insufficient as a remedy, and an injunction was granted to restrain the council from permitting this activity.

Damages may be awarded where the damage done by the nuisance is quantifiable. Damages for past loss or inconvenience may also be awarded, together with an injunction to restrain any further nuisance. In *Hollywood Silver Fox Farm* v *Emmett*, the judge awarded damages and an injunction restraining the defendant from firing guns or making other noises near the fox farm during the breeding season.

An injunction is usually the preferred remedy for the claimant, since it requires the defendant to bring the nuisance to an end. It also has the advantage of flexibility, in that it can be tailored to meet the exact circumstances of the case and produce a just solution (often a compromise).

In *Leeman* v *Montague* (1936) (details on page 279), the court granted an injunction restraining the defendant from carrying on his business in a manner that disturbed his neighbours. There was evidence suggesting that the defendant could easily rearrange his use of his land so that the cockerels were kept further away from the houses.

Similarly, in *Kennaway* v *Thompson* (1980), the owners of a number of lakeside homes complained of the noise caused by powerboat racing on the lake. Lawton LJ granted an injunction against the organisers of the racing, limiting both the number of days on which racing could take place and the number and power of boats allowed to take part.

The injunction is an equitable remedy and, as such, available at the discretion of the court. Where the claimant seeks an injunction, the court may decide to award damages instead if an injunction would not be in the public interest. In *Miller* v *Jackson* (1977), the claimant bought a house overlooking the village cricket ground. Cricket balls were frequently hit into her garden. The claimant sought an injunction. The Court of Appeal held the activity to constitute a nuisance but declined to grant an injunction on the basis that it would not be in the public interest to prevent the public playing cricket. Damages of £400 were awarded to cover both past and future inconvenience.

Similarly, public interest outweighed private interest in the more recent case of *Dennis* v *Ministry of Defence* (2003, unreported). The claimants lived directly below the flight path of RAF Harrier jets used in pilot training and sought an injunction in respect of the excessive noise. After hearing evidence that the noise level was very high, Buckley J awarded the claimants damages totalling almost £1 million, including £300,000 for the loss of value to their home. The public interest in maintaining the training programme at the RAF station was greater than the claimants' private interest. However, selected individuals should not bear the cost of the public benefit, and common fairness demanded that the claimants should be compensated.

In *Dennis* v *Ministry of Defence* (2003, unreported), the claimants were awarded damages in respect of excessive noise from RAF Harrier jets

It is important to consider the type of injunction that it is realistic for the judge to impose on the defendant. In most cases, a partial injunction is more appropriate than a total injunction. For example, a factory emitting noise and dust both day and night is not likely to be ordered to shut down. The judge in such a case could order the factory to restrict its operating hours and to fit noise and dust suppression equipment.

Abatement

Abatement is a form of self-help. The claimant is entitled to take steps to alleviate the nuisance, for example by cutting off the roots or branches of the defendant's tree that encroach onto his or her property. The claimant is even entitled, after giving due notice (except in an emergency) to enter onto the defendant's land to abate the nuisance, so long as he or she does no more damage than is strictly necessary for his or her purpose.

In *Lemmon* v *Webb* (1895), branches from the claimant's trees were overhanging the defendant's land. When the defendant cut them off, the claimant sought damages. The House of Lords held that, although a person must normally give notice before taking steps to abate a nuisance, this is not necessary in an emergency or if (as here) he or she can take the necessary steps without leaving his or her own land.

Complaints to the local authority

Under s.79 of the **Environmental Protection Act 1990**, a local authority has a duty to investigate any complaints of a statutory nuisance, including anything prejudicial to health or causing a nuisance arising from the state of premises, or any accumulation or deposit thereon, or smoke, fumes, gas, dust, steam, smells or noise emitted from them, or from any animal kept in an unsuitable place or manner. The local authority can issue an abatement order directing the occupier to eliminate the nuisance. Failure to comply is punishable by a fine, with an additional penalty for each day the nuisance continues.

This procedure does not allow the aggrieved neighbour to recover damages, but may in some cases be more effective in securing compliance than an individual civil action, especially in light of reduced availability of civil legal aid.

Public nuisance

Private and public nuisance are quite separate forms of unlawful conduct. There will be some situations where they overlap, but not every defendant who commits the tort of private nuisance will create a public nuisance and *vice versa*. As Professor Rogers writes: 'The essence of a public nuisance is that it is something which affects the comfort and convenience of the public as a whole rather than of an individual complainant.' This usually involves interfering with a public right or acting in a way that is generally contrary to the public interest. In many situations, such as where there is an actionable interference with the public right to free passage along a highway, there can be a public nuisance, even though nobody's interests in land have been affected.

Class of people

The nuisance must affect a class of people. Romer LJ in *Attorney General* v *PYA Quarries* (1957) stated that the nuisance would affect a class of people if it was 'so widespread in its range or indiscriminate in its effects that it would not be reasonable to expect one person to take steps to put a stop to it'. In this case, the quarrying operations of the defendants, causing vibrations and dust to affect houses in the vicinity, were held to be a public nuisance.

Public nuisance is a criminal offence

In *R* v *Johnson* (1997), the defendant was convicted of public nuisance in respect of several hundred obscene telephone calls made to more than a dozen women over a period of 6 years. Upholding his conviction, Tucker J said a single call would have been a private rather than a public nuisance, but cumulatively the calls materially affected the reasonable comfort and convenience of a class of Her Majesty's subjects. The jury, properly directed, had decided that the women were sufficient in number to constitute such a class.

Public nuisance usually arises on the highway

In *Attorney General* v *Gastonia Coaches* (1977), the defendant coach operators regularly parked eight coaches on the highway outside their offices, thereby inter-fering with the free passage of traffic. On the application of the Attorney General, the judge granted an injunction to restrain the defendants from causing a public nuisance by their parking.

Similarly, in *Wandsworth LBC* v *Railtrack* (2001), the droppings from pigeons roosting under a railway bridge fouled the pavements and sometimes landed on passers-by. This amounted to a public nuisance. Even though Railtrack had no general control over wild pigeons, it had the necessary knowledge, opportunity and resources to have taken steps to prevent this particular nuisance, and had not done so. The council could bring an action in public nuisance, even though it had statutory powers to deal with the pigeons itself.

These cases highlight a key distinction between public and private nuisance. In private nuisance, the claimant must have a proprietary interest in the land affected. This is not a requirement of public nuisance.

Civil proceedings

Civil proceedings to put an end to the nuisance may be brought in the public interest by the Attorney General, an individual with the consent of the Attorney General, or a local authority.

Individual actions in tort: special damage

A public nuisance only becomes actionable at the suit of the individual when particular damage has been caused to that individual over and above that suffered by the general public. Such a claimant has to show special damage.

In *Castle* v *St Augustine's Links* (1922), Castle was driving his taxi when a ball driven from the defendant's golf course struck his windscreen and caused him to lose an eye. There was evidence that balls driven from this particular tee frequently landed on the highway. This case also illustrates that damages for personal injury are recoverable in *public* nuisance.

Similarly, in *Benjamin* v *Storr* (1874), the claimant owned a coffee house in Covent Garden, adjacent to which was the defendant auctioneer's yard. Horses used for delivering goods to the defendant often obstructed access to the claimant's shop, and the smell of their urine was strong. The Court of Common Pleas held that the claimant had suffered direct and substantial damage over and above that suffered by the public at large, and was therefore entitled to sue in public nuisance. See also *Tate and Lyle* v *Greater London Council* (1983), where it was decided the claimants had suffered special damage as river siltation had blocked access to their own jetty and they had had to spend a lot of money having the riverbed dredged.

While it is clearly established that in private nuisance no action for damages in respect of personal injury can be made, in *Corby Group* v *Corby BC* (2008) the Court of Appeal in preliminary proceedings rejected the defendant council's claim that public nuisance could not cover personal injuries. In that case, a group of children born with physical deformities claimed these had been caused by the council's improper disposal of toxic waste.

Defences
Statutory authority

Many activities that interfere with the enjoyment of land are carried out by organisations operating under an Act of Parliament. Whether the defendant is able to rely on this defence depends on the discretion given to him or her by the Act of Parliament.

In *Metropolitan Asylum District* v *Hill* (1881), the defendants were given authority to build a smallpox hospital 'according to such plan, and in such manner, as they think fit'. The hospital was built in Hampstead and was held by the House of Lords to be a nuisance by virtue of its location. The defendants had the authority to build the hospital elsewhere. Similarly, in *Tate and Lyle* v *Greater London Council* (1983), the defendants were authorised by statute to design and build new ferry terminals. The defence of statutory authority only partially succeeded. It was decided that some degree of siltation of the River Thames was inevitable, but that if the defendants had taken reasonable care the damage caused to the claimant's business by the siltation would have been reduced.

These cases can be contrasted with *Hammersmith Railway* v *Brand* (1867). The defendants had statutory authority to run trains along tracks adjoining the claimant's property. The defendants were not liable. The damaging vibration was an inevitable consequence of running the trains and an injunction would defeat the intention of the legislature. More recently, in *Allen* v *Gulf Oil Refining Ltd* (1981), the defendant company was authorised by statute to construct and operate an oil refinery. A claim in respect of the noise, smell and vibrations made by the refinery was unsuccessful, as it was an inevitable consequence.

Planning permission

It has been argued that planning permission given by a local authority is also a defence against a nuisance action, but in *Gillingham Borough Council* v *Medway (Chatham) Dock Co.* (1993) this general argument was rejected. Here, the dock company had been given planning permission for the operation of a commercial port. Access to it was only possible via residential roads, which caused much traffic noise, and the council sued in public nuisance. The court held that the fact that planning permission had been granted for a particular activity did not mean that that activity could not give rise to liability in nuisance. However, the existence of planning permission could mean that the character of the neighbourhood had changed (from residential to commercial), which could in turn mean that what might formerly have amounted to a nuisance could now be considered reasonable. That was what was held to have happened in this case, and therefore the dock company was not liable.

Prescription

The nuisance may be legalised if the claimant has tolerated the activity for more than 20 years without complaint. However, time does not begin to run until the interference reaches a sufficient degree of severity to constitute a nuisance.

In *Sturges* v *Bridgman* (1879), the defendant had used a pestle and mortar on his premises for over 20 years. The claimant built a consulting room at the end of his garden, adjacent to the defendant's premises, and at this point the noise and vibration from the defendant's activity became unacceptable. The defendant was unable to use the defence of prescription as the nuisance had not existed until the consulting room was built, and he was held liable.

This defence is available in private nuisance but not in public nuisance.

Volenti non fit injuria

The defence of *volenti* applies when the claimant has expressly or impliedly consented to the nuisance.

Assumption of risk

The tenant of part of premises is deemed to accept the risk of nuisance arising from the condition of any part retained by the landlord.

In *Kiddle* v *City Business Properties Ltd* (1942), the claimant leased part of the defendant's premises. A gutter on the part of the premises retained by the defendant flooded and discharged water into the claimant's shop. There was no liability as the claimant had assumed the risk.

Contributory negligence

The **Law Reform (Contributory Negligence) Act 1945** provides that the claimant's damages will be reduced according to his or her responsibility for the damage he or she has suffered.

Concealed, hidden, unobservable defects in property

If the defendant can be shown to have been aware of the defect, this defence will fail.

In *Leakey* v *National Trust* (1980), the surface of a hill on the defendant's land was liable to crack, and debris had occasionally fallen onto the claimant's land. During the hot summer of 1976, the defendant was asked to attend to the danger but failed to do so. A large landslip subsequently damaged the claimant's property. The claimant's action in nuisance succeeded, as the defendant was aware of the danger.

Act of a third party

This defence will fail if the defendant can be proved to have been aware of the danger. In *Sedleigh-Denfield* v *O'Callaghan* (1940), a trespasser on the defendant's land put a pipe in a ditch. Three years later it became blocked, causing the claimant's garden to be flooded. The defendant was presumed to be aware of the danger, as his employees cleaned the ditch twice a year, and so was held liable.

Ineffectual defences

The activity is for the public benefit

The defendant cannot argue that his or her activity is beneficial to the public.

In *Bellew* v *Cement Co. Ltd* (1948), the dust and noise from a cement factory was held to be a nuisance. An injunction was granted, despite the fact that this meant closing the only cement factory in Ireland at a time when there was an urgent public need for building new homes.

Similarly, in *Adams* v *Ursell* (1913), the defendant's fish and chip shop was situated in a residential street. The residents complained that the smell from the shop interfered with their enjoyment of their homes. The nuisance action was successful. An injunction was granted to prevent the defendant continuing his business on the premises, in spite of the argument that the shop was of great benefit to the poorer residents who lived nearby and that closing the shop would cause great hardship to the defendant.

The claimant came to the nuisance

The defendant cannot argue as a defence that he or she was carrying on his or her activity before the claimant moved nearby.

In *Miller* v *Jackson* (1977), a housing estate was built next to a cricket ground. The claimants bought a house on the boundary of the cricket ground. They brought a successful nuisance action and were awarded damages in respect of the damage to property and interference caused by balls flying into their garden. The defendants' argument that cricket had been played on the ground for many years before the estate was built was no defence.

The defendant took all reasonable care to avoid the nuisance

Lindley LJ commented in *Rapier* v *London Tramways Co.* (1893): 'If I am sued for nuisance, and nuisance is proved, it is no defence to say and to prove that I have taken all reasonable care to prevent it.' More recently, in *Cambridge Water Co.* v *Eastern Counties Leather* (1994), Lord Goff stated: 'The fact that the defendant has taken all reasonable care will not of itself exonerate him.'

The rule in *Rylands* v *Fletcher*

The rule in *Rylands* v *Fletcher* (1868) was established when the case was heard in the Court of Exchequer in 1866. In this case, the defendants engaged a reputable firm of engineers to construct a reservoir on their land. Unknown to the defendants or their contractors, mineshafts under the defendants' land connected to the claimant's coal mine nearby. When the reservoir was filled, water poured down the shafts and flooded the claimant's mine. Although the defendants were neither themselves negligent nor vicariously liable for the negligence of their independent contractors, they were held liable.

Blackburn J formulated the rule in the following terms:

> *The person who, for his own purposes, brings on his land, and collects and keeps there anything likely to do mischief if it escapes, must keep it in at his peril, and if he does not do so, is* prima facie *answerable for all the damage which is the natural consequence of its escape.*

The rule requires the claimant to establish:
* a non-natural use of the land
* an escape of the thing brought onto the land
* damage caused by the escape
* the damage suffered being of a foreseeable type

Non-natural use

In his statement, Blackburn J makes clear that the rule applies where the defendant 'has brought something on his own property which was not naturally there'. This aspect of the rule was more fully explained by Lord Cairns when the case was appealed to the House of Lords. The phrase is flexible, and the courts have used this flexibility in their judgements.

In *Rickards* v *Lothian* (1913), Lord Moulton said that 'it must be some special use bringing with it increased danger to others, and must not merely be the ordinary use of the land'. However, in *Giles* v *Walker* (1890), when thistles grew where the defendant had cleared forest, it was held that thistles grew naturally and could not be considered as a non-natural use. Yet in *Crowhurst* v *Amersham Burial Board* (1878), the planting of a yew tree whose branches protruded onto adjoining land and then poisoned cattle was held to be a non-natural use of land.

Therefore, a non-natural use of land may be 'that which in its natural condition was not in or upon it', or, alternatively, the use may be non-natural due to quantity or volume. In *Rylands* v *Fletcher,* bringing water on to the land in quantities sufficient to fill a reservoir was held to be a non-natural use.

Subsequent case law indicates that there is no set principle on which it can be determined whether the use is non-natural, despite judicial attempts to formulate such a principle. The following have been held to be examples of non-natural use:

❖ the storing of water, gas and electricity in bulk in mains
❖ the use of a blowlamp to thaw pipes in a loft
❖ the storage of ignitable material in a barn
❖ the storage of chemicals

In *Rickards* v *Lothian*, the Privy Council commented that a water supply to a lavatory was a necessary feature of town life and therefore a natural use. Lord Moulton commented that a water supply is 'in the interests of the community'. These words have since been subjected to judicial scrutiny. In *British Celanese Ltd* v *A H Hunt (Capacitors) Ltd* (1969), the defendants stored metal strips on their land. In deciding that this constituted a natural use, Lawton J, approving the 'in the interests of the community' test, commented that the metal foil was there for use in the manufacture of goods that were needed for the general benefit of the community.

The expansion of what courts considered to be 'in the interests of the community' was, however, halted by the House of Lords in *Cambridge Water Co.* v *Eastern Counties Leather* (1994), where the defendants operated a tannery and used a chlorinated solvent to degrease the pelts. The solvent seeped through the floor, and then through soil and layers of rock, and ultimately drained into the plaintiff's borehole situated just over a mile away. Consequently the water, which was destined for domestic use, became unfit for human consumption. The case was decided on the issue of foreseeability of damage. However, Lord Goff commented that, despite the fact that the chemicals were commonly used in the tanning industry and that the small industrial community was worthy of support, 'the storage of substantial quantities of chemicals should be regarded as an almost classic case of non-natural use'.

Escape

There must be an escape from the defendant's land of the thing brought onto that land.

The leading case on escape is *Read* v *Lyons and Co. Ltd* (1947), where the House of Lords held the claimant's action must fail as there had been no escape of the exploding shell from the defendant's land. Viscount Simon explained that there must be an escape from a place that the defendant has

In *Ponting* v *Noakes* (1894) there was no escape

occupation of, or control over, to a place that is outside his or her occupation or control. Similarly, in *Ponting* v *Noakes* (1894), there was no escape. A horse was poisoned when it reached its head over onto the land of the defendant and ate leaves from a yew tree. The dangerous leaves had not escaped from the defendant's land. However, in *Hale* v *Jennings Bros* (1938), a tenant of a stall at a funfair suffered personal injuries as the result of an escape of the defendant's chair-o-plane. It was held that this escape from one place of entertainment at a fairground to another was sufficient.

Damage caused by the escape

When he formulated the rule in *Rylands* v *Fletcher*, Blackburn J said that the defendant would be liable 'for all the damage which is the natural consequence of its escape'. Blackburn J envisaged the rule applying to all types of damage. The case of *Rylands* v *Fletcher* itself illustrates that the rule applies to damage to land.

The rule has also been held to apply to damage to chattels. In *Jones* v *Festiniog Rly Co.* (1868), Blackburn J allowed the plaintiff's action to succeed when sparks from a railway engine set fire to his haystack.

Economic loss would also appear to fall within the rule, so long as it is direct. In *Weller and Co.* v *Foot and Mouth Disease Research Institute* (1966), the claimant, a cattle auctioneer, did not succeed when the escape of a virus caused a loss of profit to his business after making a third party's cattle unsaleable. The auctioneer's loss of profit was contingent upon the cattle owner's loss and hence was indirect. However, in *Ryeford Homes* v *Sevenoaks District Council* (1989), Judge Newey QC was of the opinion that economic loss was recoverable under the rule in *Rylands* v *Fletcher* when it was 'a sufficiently direct result of an escape of water from sewers'. The claimant in this case failed as the defence of statutory authority was successful.

Since the second half of the twentieth century, the courts have decided that the rule does *not* apply to personal injury. In *Transco* v *Stockport MBC* (2003), Lord Hoffman referred to *Cambridge Water Co.* v *Eastern Counties Leather,* in which the House of Lords stated that the rule in *Rylands* v *Fletcher* was a special form of nuisance and concluded that personal injury was therefore not recoverable, as the rule is a tort against land.

Damage must be of a foreseeable type

In formulating the rule in *Rylands* v *Fletcher*, Blackburn J stated that the defendant should 'answer for the natural and anticipated consequences'. These words indicate that liability is dependant upon the damage being foreseeable. This issue was clarified in *Cambridge Water Co*. The House of Lords held the defendants were not liable, on the basis that the harm caused to the claimant's water supply was unforeseeable. Lord Goff stated: 'Foreseeability of damage of the relevant type should be regarded as a prerequisite of liability.'

Who can sue?

Throughout most of the twentieth century, the courts held that a claimant did not need to have a proprietary interest in the land. In *British Celanese Ltd*, Lawton J commented: 'Once there has been an escape in this sense, those damnified may claim. They need not be the occupiers of adjoining land or indeed of any land.' However, the position on this issue appears to have changed. In *Hunter* v *Canary Wharf*, the House of Lords held that a claimant in the tort of nuisance must have a proprietary interest in the land affected. In *Cambridge Water Co.,* Lord Goff expressed the view that the rule in *Rylands* v *Fletcher* was an extension of the law of nuisance. The combination of these decisions leads to the conclusion that a proprietary interest in the land affected is now required by the claimant. This conclusion was supported by Neuberger J in *McKenna* v *British Aluminium* (2002).

Who can be sued?

In Blackburn J's original formulation of the rule, the person who will be sued is the person who accumulates the particular thing that escapes. Subsequent case law seems to indicate that occupancy, as well as ownership of the land, falls within the rule. Lord Macmillan in *Read* v *Lyons* specifically stated that the rule in *Rylands* v *Fletcher* was 'a principle applicable between occupiers in respect of their land'.

Defences

Act of third parties

This defence is not available where the defendant ought reasonably to foresee the action of the third party and take steps to prevent it. In this respect, it is useful to compare *Hale* v *Jennings Bros*, where the escape of the chair-o-plane was caused by a passenger tampering with it, with *Rickards* v *Lothian,* where the escape of water was due to a water tap on the defendant's premises being turned on by an unknown third party. In the former case, the defence did not apply, whereas in the latter it did.

There was also immunity from liability in *Box* v *Jubb* (1879), where the defendant's reservoir overflowed because a third party, conducting operations upstream, discharged an unusually large quantity of water without giving any warning.

Act of God

This defence applies where the escape is caused by natural causes that no human foresight could have guarded against. It was successful in *Nichols* v *Marsland* (1876), when four bridges on the claimant's land were destroyed by flooding when the banks of his artificial lakes burst during a violent thunderstorm.

However, it is only in rare circumstances that the defence is successful. In *Greenock Corporation* v *Caledonian Railway Co.* (1917), unprecedented rainfall was held not to be an act of God. Lord Finlay LC said: 'Floods of extraordinary violence must be anticipated as likely to take place from time to time.'

Statutory authority

The success of this defence depends on whether the authority is obligatory or discretionary. In *Green* v *Chelsea Waterworks Co.* (1894), the claimant's premises were flooded when the defendants' water main burst. The defendants were not liable. They were obliged by statute to keep the water main charged at high pressure and it was inevitable that occasional bursts would cause such damage.

Default of the claimant

In *Ponting* v *Noakes* (1894), the claimant was unsuccessful when her horse stretched over to the defendant's land and ate poisonous leaves. Not only was there no escape, but the damage was caused by the actions of the claimant's horse.

Contributory negligence

Under the **Law Reform (Contributory Negligence) Act 1945**, damages are reduced according to the claimant's responsibility for the damage suffered.

Consent of the claimant

This defence applies where the claimant expressly or impliedly consents to the accumulation of the particular thing on the defendant's land. In *Peters* v *Prince of Wales Theatre (Birmingham) Ltd* (1943), the claimant leased his shop from the defendant. The shop was flooded when the sprinkler system burst in the adjoining theatre, also belonging to the defendant. The claimant was held to have impliedly consented to the existence of the sprinkler system, which was present at the commencement of his lease.

Questions

1 What is Professor Winfield's definition of nuisance?

2 Which rule of private nuisance is illustrated by *Rapier* v *London Tramways Co.* (1893)?

3 Why did the judge in *Gillingham BC* v *Medway (Chatham) Dock Co. Ltd* (1993) decide that there was no liability in nuisance, despite the degree of disruption caused by the dock company?

4 What rule is illustrated by *McKinnon Industries* v *Walker* (1951)?

5 What effect will 'malice' have in a nuisance claim?

6 Which two cases could be used as examples of malice?

7 What is the rule about who can sue in a nuisance action? What is the leading case?

8 What rule is illustrated by *Tetley* v *Chitty* (1986)?

9 In *Kennaway* v *Thompson* (1980), what remedy did the judge order?

10 Explain what is meant by 'abatement' of a nuisance? Give a case example.

11 Under which Act can a person make a complaint to a local authority concerning a nuisance?

12 Explain why the defence of prescription was not allowed in *Sturges* v *Bridgman* (1879).

13 Provide three examples of non-natural use in *Rylands* v *Fletcher* (1868).

14 In *Cambridge Water Co. Ltd* v *Eastern Counties Leather plc* (1994), what did Lord Goff describe as 'an almost classic case of non-natural use'?

15 What important rule was confirmed by the *Cambridge Water* case?

Sample exam question

Previously a quiet lake overlooked by a few cottages, Greenwater has recently been developed by its owner, Highlife Sports, to provide extensive leisure facilities, including swimming and powerboating. In consequence, the owners of the cottages, including Irene, have experienced a large increase in noise, especially at weekends and during frequent competition weeks, when traffic and parking problems have also made it difficult for them to leave or return to their properties. Additionally, damage to a diesel oil storage tank, owned by Highlife Sports, resulted in a leak that caused extensive contamination of Irene's vegetable garden.

Adapted from AQA Unit 5 paper, June 2004

Consider what rights and remedies the owners of the cottages, including Irene, may have in connection with the noise and other problems caused by the leisure activities and the oil spillage.

Further reading

Elliott, C. and Quinn, F. (2007) *Tort Law*, Pearson Longman.
Murphy, J. (2007) *Street on Torts*, Oxford University Press.
Pitchfork, E. D. (ed) (2000) *The Law of Tort*, Old Bailey Press.

Chapter 23

Vicarious liability

Vicarious liability is not an individual tort but a principle under which liability is imposed on a party in respect of torts (or crimes) committed by others. Vicarious liability arises most often in employment relationships. If an employee commits a tort in the course of his or her employment, the employer is liable regardless of whether he or she personally has committed a tort.

The principle of vicarious liability is clearly a policy decision of judges. It is based on two facts:

❖ an employer is better able to stand the loss, especially since the introduction of compulsory employer insurance
❖ the principle encourages employers to maintain higher standards of conduct — employee training and supervision — in the running of their businesses

It is also argued that if the employer should take the profits created by his or her employees, he or she should also be liable for their negligence.

There are two key requirements for the imposition of vicarious liability on the employer: the tort (or crime) must (a) be committed by an employee and (b) be committed in the course of his or her employment.

However, before considering these requirements, it is essential to consider the tortious action of the employee. Unless the employee has committed a tort, the employer cannot be held vicariously liable.

Who is an employee?

There is no single set test for the courts to apply in deciding whether the wrongdoer is an employee. This is due to the broad range of employment relationships that exist, and the shortcomings of the tests developed so far by the courts.

Control test

The control test was the first attempt by the courts to establish a mechanism by which to decide whether the wrongdoer is an employee.

In *Collins* v *Hertfordshire County Council* (1947), Hilbery J explained that as the worker was an employee, the employer 'can not only order or require what is to be done but how it shall be done'. In this case, the defendant was not held liable for the negligence of a surgeon that resulted in the death of a patient, because Hilbery J concluded that the council could not control how the surgeon performed his duties.

The inadequacy of the control test as the sole determining factor was recognised by Lord Thankerton in *Short* v *J W Henderson Ltd* (1946). He suggested that further key features of an employment relationship included the power to select, suspend and dismiss, the power to control the method of working and the payment of wages.

The decision of Hilbery J was much criticised in *Cassidy* v *Ministry of Health* (1951). A patient suffered permanent injury to his hand, allegedly through the negligence of the surgeon performing the operation. The surgeon was held to be the employee of the hospital authority. Lord Denning explained that the determining factor of whether the worker was an employee was not that the employer controlled the method of work, but rather that the employer had the power to select and dismiss.

The control test nevertheless remains useful as a determining factor in some circumstances, for example when employees are hired out to work for others. In *Mersey Docks* v *Coggins and Griffith* (1947), a harbour board hired out a crane and driver to the claimant under a contract, making the driver the servant of the claimant. When an accident occurred through the driver's negligence, the court held he was still effectively the servant of the harbour board. The harbour board was responsible for paying the driver and retained the power of dismissal, and it also controlled the way the driver operated the crane.

However, in *Viasystems* v *Thermal Transfer* (2005), which involved the negligence of an employee working for one company but under the supervision of another company, it was held by May LJ there was no reason in principle why both employers should not be vicariously liable if both had some control over his actions — in such a case, liability would be equally shared. Yet in *Hawley* v *Luminar Leisure* (2006), the Court of Appeal decided that a nightclub was vicariously liable for a doorman, even though he was employed by another company. Applying the control test, it was found that the security firm provided the personnel, but the club had greater control over the work done. Distinguishing this case from *Viasystems*, the court ruled that the original employer had no control over what the doorman did or how he did it.

Economic reality or multiple test

The present approach used by the courts is the economic reality or multiple test, which recognises that a single test of employment is unsatisfactory. It was developed by McKenna J in *Ready Mixed Concrete* v *MPNI* (1968). A contract between the defendant firm and its driver provided for the driver to own his own lorry (bought with money loaned by an associate finance company). It was the responsibility of the driver to maintain the lorry and do whatever was needed to make the lorry and a driver available throughout the contract period. McKenna J said factors to be considered when determining the existence of a contract of employment include:

❖ whether there is payment of a wage
❖ whether tools for the job are provided by the employer or the worker
❖ whether the worker has to obey orders
❖ the exercise of control over the way the work is done
❖ the acceptance of the business risk

No one factor is conclusive by itself. McKenna J stipulated three conditions must be met before an employment relationship is identified:

❖ The employee agrees in return for a wage or other remuneration that he or she will provide his or her work and skill for the employer.
❖ The employee agrees expressly or impliedly to be subject to the employer's control.
❖ The other terms of the contract are consistent with there being a contract of employment.

In this case, the claimant driver had taken a certain business risk and so was held to be an independent contractor and not an employee.

The economic reality test has since been modified so that all factors in the relationship should be considered and weighed according to their significance. Relevant factors, in addition to those mentioned above, include the method of payment, tax and National Insurance contributions and self-description.

In some workplace situations, the parties may have decided the status of the employment relationship for themselves. The most usual reasons for having a contract for services whereby the worker is self-employed, as opposed to a contract of service giving the worker employee status, are to avoid tax deductions under the PAYE system and to take advantage of a more favourable level of NI contributions. From the view of the employer, the advantage of hiring a worker on a self-employed basis is that the worker does not have the extensive provision of statutory employment rights afforded to employees, for example the right to redundancy pay. However, a case illustrating the inconclusiveness of the parties' description of their working relationship is *Ferguson* v *John Dawson Ltd* (1976). The claimant was employed as a self-employed labourer on a building site. This meant that the claimant paid less income tax. When the claimant was injured as a result of falling off the roof, the defendants argued that their duty to provide a guardrail was only owed to employees. The court held that, despite the self-description of the working relationship, the claimant was, in reality, an employee. The defendants controlled what work was done, and how and when the claimant did it.

Course of employment

The employer will only be held vicariously liable for the torts (crimes) of the employee if the employee was acting in the course of employment at the time of the wrongdoing.

Until the case of *Lister* v *Hesley Hall Ltd* (2001), the **Salmond test** was used to determine whether an employee's tort was committed in the course of his or her employment. Under this test, an employee's tort will have been committed in the course of employment if it was either:

❖ a wrongful act authorised by the employer, or
❖ a wrongful and unauthorised mode of doing some act authorised by the employer

Authorised acts carried out in an unauthorised manner

Broadly speaking, this category of acts is concerned with circumstances in which the employee is doing what he or she is employed to do but in a manner that has not been authorised by the employer. There are many different means by which an act may be unauthorised.

Acting over-zealously

In some situations, the act may be carried out in an unauthorised way because the employee has acted over-zealously to protect the property of the employer.

In *Vasey* v *Surrey Free Inns* (1996), the claimant was refused entry to a club by two doormen who were employees of the defendant. In a temper, the claimant kicked and damaged a glass window before walking away. The doormen chased the claimant across the car park and assaulted him with a cosh. The Court of Appeal held the club was vicariously liable for the assault. The doormen were doing their job, i.e. using force to protect their employer's property, albeit it in an excessive way.

However, where the employee, while at work, uses violence to settle a personal dispute, the courts will hold his or her actions to be beyond the scope of his or her employment.

In *Warren* v *Henlys* (1948), a garage attendant used violent language in wrongly accusing a driver of trying to leave the garage without paying. After paying, the driver told the garage attendant he would report him to his employers. The attendant punched the driver in the face. The driver claimed damages. The garage owners were not held to be vicariously liable. The actions of the garage attendant were of personal vengeance, not an unauthorised way of performing his job, and so were outside the course of employment.

Acting in an impliedly unauthorised way

An act may be conducted in an impliedly unauthorised way because the employer would have prohibited it had he or she thought about it.

In *Century Insurance* v *Northern Ireland Road Transport* (1942), an employee petrol tanker driver was delivering petrol to a garage. While the petrol was being transferred into the tankers, he lit a cigarette and negligently threw away the lighted match, causing an explosion and extensive damage. The House of Lords held the driver was acting in the course of his employment. Part of his job was to wait while the petrol was transferred. Although lighting the cigarette was for his benefit, this was not enough to relieve the employers of their liability.

Acting in an expressly prohibited way

Sometimes the employee will perform an authorised act in a manner expressly prohibited by the employer. Provided the employee is doing acts he or she is employed to do, the employer will be held vicariously liable.

In *Limpus* v *London Omnibus* (1862), the drivers of horse-drawn buses were expressly forbidden to race their vehicles. One driver did so and caused an accident. The company was held to be vicariously liable. The driver was doing what he was authorised to do (driving the bus) but was doing so in an expressly unauthorised manner. This case can be compared to *Iqbal* v *London Transport Executive* (1973). A bus conductor, trying to be helpful, drove a bus, despite having been specifically forbidden to do so. His negligent driving caused damage. The employers were held not to be vicariously liable. The act of driving the bus was not an act the conductor was employed to do.

Rose v *Plenty* (1976) is another decision illustrating the courts' approach to expressly prohibited modes of performing employment duties. A milkman, against express orders to the contrary, took a 13-year-old boy to help him on his round. The boy was injured as a result of the milkman's negligent driving. The Court of Appeal held the dairy to be vicariously liable. The milkman was doing what he was employed to do, i.e. deliver milk, but was doing so in an expressly unauthorised way.

'Frolics of their own'

An employer will not be vicariously liable for activities performed by an employee that have no relevance to the job he or she is employed to do. In these circumstances, the employee is said to be 'on a frolic of his own'.

In *General Engineering Services* v *Kingston and Saint Andrew Corporation* (1989), firemen working a 'go-slow' in support of a pay claim took 17 minutes to complete a 3.5-minute journey. By the time the firemen arrived at the fire, the claimant's factory had been completely destroyed. The Privy Council held that the employers were not vicariously liable for the damage. The firemen's action was not an unauthorised way of doing their job, but was tantamount to a refusal to do their job at all.

A similar approach was taken by the Court of Appeal in *Heasmans* v *Clarity Cleaning* (1987). The defendants were contracted to clean the claimant's offices. A cleaner employed by the defendants used the claimant's telephones to make a number of long-distance calls totalling approximately £1,400. The defendants were not vicariously liable. While the cleaner's employment had put him in the position to make the calls, it was a wholly unauthorised act and therefore not in the course of his employment.

When employees who travel from place to place as part of their job take a detour for their own benefit, they are acting outside the course of employment. In *Storey* v *Ashton* (1869), a wine merchant's driver and clerk went out to deliver some wine and collect empty bottles. On the way back, they took a detour in order to fetch a cask belonging to the clerk, and ran over the claimant. The claimant sued for damages. The court held the employer was not vicariously liable. The driver was not on his employer's business at the time of the accident, but on 'a frolic of his own'. This case is easily distinguishable from *Smith* v *Stages* (1989) (page 303), in which the employees had clearly been on the employer's business.

Activities outside normal hours of work

The course of employment includes not only activities carried out during normal hours of work but also activities that are closely connected.

In *Ruddiman and Co.* v *Smith* (1889), an employee went to wash his hands a few minutes after his working day ended. He left the tap running and the resulting overflow damaged the claimant's adjoining premises. The court held that the negligent act was incidental to the employment and accordingly the employers were vicariously liable.

Collecting one's wages at the end of the working day has also been held to be within the course of employment. In *Staton* v *National Coal Board* (1957), the claimant's husband, having completed his work for the day, was killed by the

defendant's negligent employee who was on his way to collect his wages. The defendant was held vicariously liable.

Activities of the employee while off the employer's premises may also be sufficiently related to their employment to fall within the principle. In *Weir* v *Chief Constable of Merseyside* (2003), an off-duty police officer was held to be acting in the course of employment when he assaulted the claimant and manhandled him down some stairs and into a police van following an argument about personal matters. The officer had identified himself to the claimant as a police officer and had acted as one, albeit badly, and that was sufficient.

Liability for employee's torts committed while travelling to and from work

The general position is that most journeys to and from work are outside the course of employment. However, journeys where employees are being paid for the time during which they are travelling and for which they are receiving travel expenses may be within the course of employment.

In *Smith* v *Stages* (1989), an employee was injured while travelling home due to another employee's negligent driving. The employees had worked 24 hours without a break and decided to drive straight back, having had no sleep. The House of Lords held the employer to be vicariously liable. The employees were paid wages to cover the journey time and had been given expenses to cover a return rail fare.

Discrimination

A more generous approach to what constitutes the 'course of employment' is adopted by the courts in circumstances where anti-discrimination legislation applies. In *Jones* v *Tower Boot Company* (1997), a young black worker was subjected to racist taunts and physical abuse by workmates. The Employment Appeal Tribunal held the actions of the employees to be outside the scope of their employment. The Court of Appeal, reversing the decision of the Employment Appeal Tribunal, held that the **Race Discrimination Act 1976** made the employer liable for all discriminatory acts committed by employees in the course of their employment. The employer was therefore vicariously liable.

Lister test

In *Lister* v *Hesley Hall Ltd* (2001), the defendants ran a boarding house for children who attended a nearby school. The defendants employed a married couple to run the boarding house. Unfortunately, the husband sexually abused a number of the children, who sued the defendants, claiming that they were vicariously liable for the torts committed by their employee.

Had the Salmond test been used to determine whether or not the employee was acting in the course of his employment, the claimants' case would have been dismissed — there was no way in which it could be argued that the employee was doing something he was employed to do by sexually abusing the claimants. The House of Lords in this case instead adopted a different test, which had been developed in two Canadian cases. Under this test, an employee is held to have acted in the course of his employment when he or she commits a tort 'so closely connected with his employment that it would be fair and just to hold the employee's employer vicariously liable for the tort'.

A good illustration of the use of this Lister test is provided by *Gravil* v *Carroll* (2008). A semi-professional rugby player, C, punched an opponent, G, in an off-the-ball incident during a match, causing serious injury to G's eye. G sued C and C's club (Redruth) for damages. Reversing the trial judge's decision, the Court of Appeal said Redruth was vicariously liable for C's behaviour on the grounds that the club was closely connected with his employment with it.

Sample exam question

Miko works 3 days each week as a financial consultant in the National Bank. Her contract with the bank forbids her from giving advice on any financial products other than those offered by the bank. She is paid a commission on all sales that she succeeds in negotiating with clients. While advising Neil, who has sought advice in the bank, Miko recommends a financial product not offered by the bank. Neil acts on the advice but loses a lot of money when the financial product proves totally unsuitable for his needs.

Adapted from AQA Unit 5 paper, June 2004

Consider what rights and remedies Neil may have against the National Bank (assume that Miko has committed the tort of negligence against Neil).

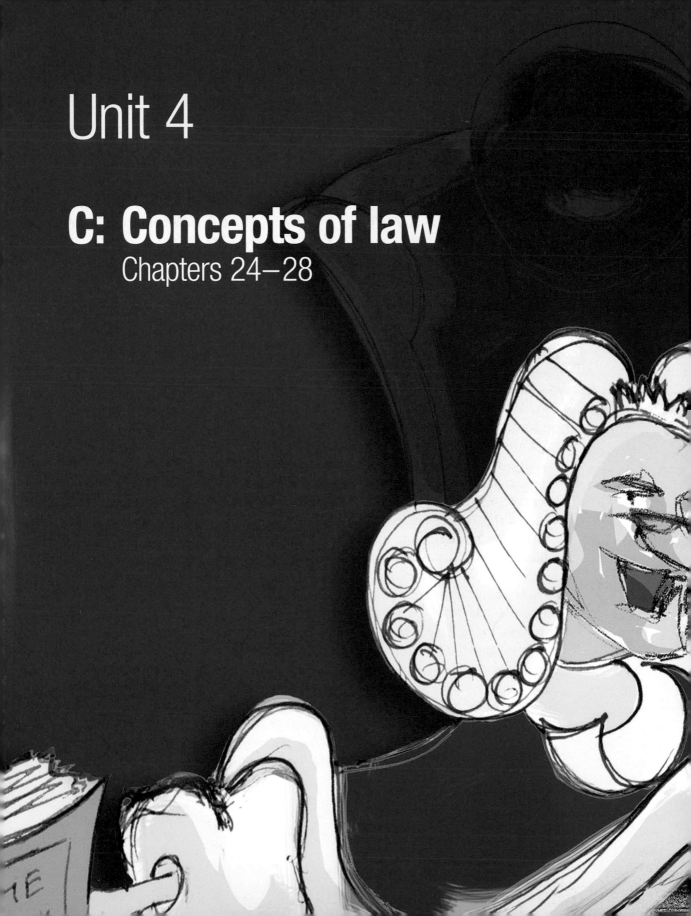

Unit 4

C: Concepts of law
Chapters 24–28

Chapter 24

Law and morality

Legal and moral rules

Characteristics of legal rules

Sir John Salmond, writing in the early twentieth century, described law as 'the body of principles recognised and applied by the state in the administration of justice'. John Austin, in *The Province of Jurisprudence*, defined it as a command issued from a sovereign power to an inferior and enforced by coercion. In Britain, this sovereign power is Parliament, although legal rules are also made by judges.

In *The Concept of Law*, H. L. A. Hart sets out his classification of law. In order to survive, every social group must have a set of primary rules that impose certain duties concerning standards of behaviour. These rules may relate to crimes or impose civil duties. More developed societies have a set of secondary policies that include rules of change, allowing specified bodies or persons to develop new laws. These are supported by rules of adjudication, which provide for authoritative decisions to be made when disputes arise. Professor Hart criticised Austin's command theory for being too limited: while it covers criminal laws, it does not cover laws that do not command people to do things. For example, the law of contract does not command people to make contracts but sets out conditions that must be met for an agreement to be legally binding.

American writer Karl Llewellyn also focused on law being necessary for the survival of a social group, in his 'law-jobs theory'. For Llewellyn, the law has certain functions to perform in a society, including the prevention and resolution of disputes within a group.

While theories differ, they essentially agree on the following as being characteristic of legal rules:

* Compliance with legal rules is compulsory, and not a matter of choice. Such rules are imposed on and govern all members of society and must be obeyed. In Britain, everyone is bound by the Offences Against the Person Act 1861, which stipulates (among other things) that people cannot intentionally or recklessly cause serious harm to another. The same principle of compulsory compliance applies to judicial decisions, for example *R* v *R* (1991), which established that a man could be found guilty of raping his wife.
* Breach of legal rules results in state sanctions and procedures. For example, breach of the criminal law may result in being arrested, charged and prosecuted through the criminal courts. If a person is found guilty, a criminal sanction such as a fine or a period of detention may be imposed.
* Legal rules are made and take effect at a precise time. A precedent is created in the judgement of a case and applies to future cases in lower courts. A piece of legislation will take effect on a specified commencement date. For example, the Smoke-free (Premises and Enforcement) Regulations, which implemented the ban on smoking in public places, were made on 13 December 2006 but came into effect on 1 July 2007.

Characteristics of moral rules

In *An Introduction to Law*, Phil Harris defines a society's 'code of morality' as a set of beliefs, values, principles and standards of behaviour.

Compliance with moral rules is voluntary, in that people have a choice as to whether or not they obey them. People make personal decisions as to what they consider to be moral and immoral, and they may or may not be persuaded by the validity of a moral rule. It follows that the moral duties of different individuals vary. What one person considers immoral, another may not. For example, some people may believe that sex before marriage is immoral, while others consider it to be acceptable.

Moral rules develop gradually. They often stem from religious rules made thousands of years ago. Over time, conduct once considered immoral can become acceptable. For example, attitudes towards homosexuality continue to change.

Moral rules are enforced informally, usually through social or domestic pressure. A person who repeatedly tells lies or breaks promises, for example, may be shunned or ostracised by friends, family or work colleagues.

Distinctions between legal and moral rules

Many of the distinctions between legal and moral rules emerge through a discussion of their characteristics. It is useful, however, to consider the following:

❖ If there is disagreement regarding the content of a legal rule, reference can be made to a precedent or Act of Parliament to resolve it. Whether or not people agree with the legal rule, they will be able to accept it. This cannot be done with moral rules, which are open to dispute.

❖ Legal rules can be changed instantly, whereas moral rules evolve gradually. The legal rules regarding homosexual acts in private between consenting adults were changed instantly when the **Sexual Offences Act 1967** was passed. Society's moral acceptance of homosexuality, however, underwent and continues to undergo gradual change.

❖ Legal rules are enforced formally by state sanctions and procedures. Moral rules are enforced informally through social and domestic pressure; they are often supported not by the threat of punishment, but by a simple reminder of the rules' existence, and by an implied appeal to act in accordance with them.

❖ Legal rules can impose strict liability. This can be seen in both criminal and civil law. In criminal law, there are offences which, as stated by Lord Scarman in *Gammon (Hong Kong) Ltd* v *Attorney General of Hong Kong* (1985), are not truly criminal in nature but 'are concerned with an issue of social concern'. Many of these offences do not require *mens rea*. Examples of strict liability offences include selling lottery tickets to persons under the age of 16 (*Harrow London Borough Council* v *Shah*, 1999) and causing polluted matter to enter a river (*Alphacell* v *Woodward*, 1972). Despite the best efforts of the defendants in such cases not to commit the offences, they will be found guilty. In civil law, the tort of nuisance is concerned with preventing interference with the enjoyment of proprietary interests. In consumer law, the Trade Descriptions Act 1968 aims to protect consumers by outlining strict liability offences. Moral offences, however, can only be committed voluntarily with full *mens rea*.

When identifying the distinctions between legal and moral rules, it is important to consider the pluralistic nature of society. The moral codes of the various groups making up British society may vary, but all are obliged to comply with legal rules.

Relationship between legal and moral rules

Any legal system presupposes a certain amount of morality, because if law is not essentially moral there is no easy explanation of the obligation to obey. The relationship between law and morality, according to Sir John Salmond, is best described as two intersecting circles, with the area inside the intersection representing the common ground and the areas outside representing the areas distinctive to each.

You are required to explore both the coincidence and the divergence of legal and moral rules. However, to gain the best grades you must be able to show understanding of the complex relationship between law and morality. For example, you

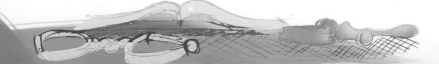

should consider not only how moral rules may influence a change in legal rules, but also the effects of legal rules on moral rules.

Coincidence of legal and moral rules

Long-established legal rules influenced by moral rules

Many long-established legal rules have a moral connection. These include the laws of murder and theft, which can be traced back to the Ten Commandments in the Bible.

Public morality may influence judicial change

Criminal law

The decision in *R* v *R* (1991) was influenced by the moral rule that a husband should not be able to force his wife to have sexual intercourse. The law prior to this case had been that on giving her consent to be married, a woman automatically gave consent to sexual intercourse for the rest of the marriage. Lord Keith said the decision was 'the removal of a common law fiction which has become anachronistic and offensive'.

The decision in *R* v *Brown and Others* (1993) was influenced by the moral rule that holds sadomasochistic activities as being unacceptable, even if consented to.

Contract law

In *Central London Property* v *High Trees House* (1947), Lord Denning created the equitable remedy of promissory estoppel. Prior to this, the common law had deemed that part-payment would not settle a debt, even if the creditor promised it would. This remedy reflects the moral rule that people ought not to break their promises.

Tort

The decision in *Chadwick* v *British Railways Board* (1967; see page 250) was influenced by the moral rule that people ought to help others who may be in trouble. A man who suffered nervous shock as a result of participation in a rescue operation was able to recover compensation and was not required to satisfy the criteria that applied to other secondary victims.

Public morality may influence legislative reform

Several major legislative reforms of the 1960s could be said to reflect the 'permissive' moral ideals of that decade. Abortion was legalised by the Abortion Act 1967, and the Sexual Offences Act 1967 legalised homosexual acts in private between consenting adults.

As public morality has shifted towards a greater acceptance of homosexuality, the law has followed by reducing the age of consent for such acts, from 21 to 18 in 1994, and from 18 to 16 in December 2000. Adoption legislation enacted in 2002 gives unmarried and gay couples the right to adopt a child, and the **Civil Partnership Act 2004** (which came into effect in December 2005) allows civil registrations that give gay and lesbian couples the same legal entitlements as marriage in areas such as employment, pensions and social security (although these are not officially regarded as marriages). However, the shift is arguably not complete, as the 2004 legislation does not allow religious ceremonies.

The Civil Partnership Act 2004 allows civil registrations that give gay and lesbian couples the same legal entitlements as marriage in certain areas

There has been no decriminalisation of assisted suicide in the UK, despite a considerable shift in public opinion, and it is still punishable by a maximum of 14 years' imprisonment. In 2005, the British Medical Association dropped its opposition to euthanasia and adopted a neutral stance on the issue. According to the British Social Attitudes Survey 2007, 80% of the public are in favour of giving terminally ill patients the right to die with the help of a doctor. In May 2006, the House of Lords rejected Lord Joffe's Assisted Dying Bill, which proposed that doctors should be allowed to prescribe a lethal dose of medication. The bill generated considerable debate between supporters of the right to die and supporters of better palliative care. However, Britain's major faith groups united to protest against the proposals, publishing an open letter that stated:

> *Assisted suicide and euthanasia will radically change the social air we all breathe by severely undermining respect for life...We, the undersigned, hold all human life to be sacred and worthy of the utmost respect.*

The courts have arguably moved towards addressing this issue. The doctrine of 'double effect', established in 2000 in the case of Dr David Moor, the first doctor in the UK to face murder charges for mercy killing, allows a doctor to administer potentially lethal drugs, provided the primary aim is to relieve pain and suffering, not to kill.

In 2008, euthanasia was put under the media spotlight as several British people sought assisted suicide in Switzerland. One of these was Daniel James, a young rugby player who had been paralysed by a rugby injury. In December 2008, the Director of Public Prosecutions (DPP) decided that it would not be in the public interest to prosecute his parents or a family friend who had helped with the travel arrangements. In fact, by then more than 100 UK citizens had gone to Switzerland to die, but there had been no prosecutions of their relatives. However, in a case brought by Debbie Purdy in October 2008, the High Court ruled that relatives could not be given a guarantee that they would not be prosecuted. In February 2009, this ruling was upheld by the Court of Appeal.

The ruling confirmed the decision of the House of Lords and the European Court of Human Rights (ECtHR) in the Dianne Pretty case (2001) that the DPP has no power to give an undertaking not to prosecute anyone who assists in a suicide. Currently, the law remains that assisted suicide or mercy killing is illegal, and the UK cannot allow the DPP to turn a blind eye to persons who want to assist their terminally ill or severely disabled loved ones to die.

Questions

1 Why do you think the majority of the population is in favour of giving terminally ill patients the right to die with the assistance of a doctor?

2 Why do you think the UK government has resisted attempts to change the law?

3 Why have other countries have been able to legalise assisted suicide?

Law reform may influence public morality

It can be argued that some legislation is introduced partly with the aim of educating the public to recognise morally unacceptable behaviour. Anti-discrimination legislation, for instance, aims to impart the message that treating others differently on the grounds of sex, race or disability is wrong. The **Disability Discrimination Act 1995**, as amended by the **Disability Discrimination Act 2005**, makes it unlawful to discriminate against disabled people in the areas of employment, education, access to goods, facilities and services (including larger private clubs and transport services), buying or renting of land and property, and the functions of public authorities (including the issuing of licences). The success of this Act in influencing public morality is, to an extent, limited by inconsistent legislation.

The **Abortion Act 1967** allows termination of a pregnancy at any time if there is a substantial risk that the child would be born with such physical or mental abnormalities as to be seriously handicapped. The time limit for termination in other circumstances is 24 weeks. The Disability Rights Commission has criticised this provision on the basis that it is incompatible with valuing disability and non-disability equally. It can be argued further that the 1967 Act allows eugenic abortion — termination of pregnancy in order to eliminate disabling genes from the human race.

Question

Can you think of any justification for having this apparent inconsistency in the law?

Law reform may result from a campaign to change public morality

In 1949, the Howard League for Penal Reform persuaded the government to appoint a Royal Commission on Capital Punishment. It then convinced most members of that commission to favour abolishing the death penalty. The government refused to implement the proposals because public opinion considered the death penalty to be morally correct. Subsequently, a pressure group called the National Campaign for the Abolition of Capital Punishment was set up. During the years 1955–57, public opinion was changed by the campaign, and the government introduced legislation to abolish the death penalty.

The pluralistic nature of society means coincidence is partial

The UK has a large multicultural, multiracial society, with citizens possessing different political ideals and following a variety of religions. Naturally, this leads to differing opinions on a number of moral issues.

For example, some people regard abortion as immoral, while others feel it is acceptable for medical reasons only. Even those in favour of abortion may disagree about the stage of pregnancy at which such a procedure should be allowed.

At the second reading of the **Human Fertilisation and Embryology Bill** on 20 May 2008, MPs voted against reducing the current 24-week abortion limit to 20 weeks by 332 votes to 190. MPs also rejected suggested limits of 12, 16 and 22 weeks.

While some people campaigned to lower the limit for abortion, others fought to maintain the 24-week limit

The health minister, Dawn Primarolo, was in favour of retaining the 24-week limit, arguing that there is no evidence requiring it to be lowered. She also pointed out that if the limit were lowered, the small number of women seeking late abortions would be forced to go elsewhere, thus defeating the purpose of the legislation in 1967 to prevent so-called 'backstreet' abortions. The chairman of the House of Commons health committee, Kevin Barron, also argued that there was no evidence in the survival rate of very premature babies.

The result of the vote was welcomed by the chief executive of the Family Planning Association, Julie Bentley, who said: 'FPA are delighted that Parliament has resisted cynical attempts by anti-abortion campaigners to reduce access to safe, legal abortion.'

Medical organisations, including the British Medical Association and the Royal College of Nursing, issued a joint statement, urging MPs to base their decisions on factual information. It said there is no evidence of a significant improvement in survival of pre-term infants below 24 weeks' gestation in the UK since 1990, when the time limit was reduced from 28 to 24 weeks.

However, the All-Party Pro-Life Group claimed that Parliament had voted against public opinion. Ian Lucas, coordinator of the group, said: 'We will continue to fight to reflect the wishes of the public and support the rights of the unborn child.' Conservative MP Nadine Dorries, who led the campaign to lower the limit, said a baby's rights should be considered at the point when it has a chance of life. Anti-abortion MPs are in favour of reducing the current limit because some babies are viable at 23 or 22 weeks; they claim that as many as 2,300 babies could be saved each year if the limit were reduced to 20 weeks. Jim Dobbin of the Pro-Life Group of MPs has said he would like to see a lower limit of 13 weeks. Lower limits are also the ultimate aim of some religious groups; for example, the Christian Medical Fellowship says it saw lowering the limit to 20 weeks as a 'first step'. Most of the shadow cabinet voted in favour of a 22-week limit, while Catholic cabinet ministers Ruth Kelly, Des Browne and Paul Murphy voted for a 12-week limit.

Research into the viability of babies born before 24 weeks has recently been conducted in a survey led by Professor David Field of the University of Leicester. The survey of 55,000 births in the Trent area during a 12-year period found that 18% of babies born at 23 weeks — 12 out of a total of 65 — and none of the 150 babies born at 22 weeks survived. Survival rates of babies born at 24 or 25 weeks improved from 36% during 1994–99 to 47% during 2000–05. Similar findings were made by a national study, Epicure 2, which reported its preliminary findings in April 2008.

Approximately 200,000 abortions are carried out in the UK each year. Of these, 87% are performed before 13 weeks, with less than 1% being carried out at more than 22 weeks. In 2007, almost 3,000 pregnancies were terminated between 20 and 24 weeks.

Questions

1 What reasons do some groups put forward for lowering the current abortion limit? What other reasons might people have?

2 What reasons are put forward for retaining the current abortion limit? What other reasons might people have?

3 Do you think another limit, i.e. a limit other than 24 or 20 weeks, might be more desirable? Give reasons for your answer.

It can be argued that it is impossible to achieve public consensus on any moral issue. Further examples to consider are as follows:

❖ *Gillick* v *West Norfolk and Wisbech Area Health Authority* (1986) concerned the prescription by doctors of contraceptives to girls under 16 without parental consent.

❖ *Re A (Children)* (2000) concerned a disagreement between doctors and the parents of Siamese twins on whether the doctors should operate to try to save the life of one of the twins. The case established the general defence of necessity, provided the following criteria apply:
– the act was needed to avoid inevitable and irreparable evil
– no more was done than was reasonably necessary for the purpose to be achieved
– the evil inflicted was not disproportionate to the evil avoided
The court decided that in the case of the twins the criteria were met and the defence could apply to what otherwise would be murder of the other twin.

❖ The Dianne Pretty (2001) and Debbie Purdy cases (2009) discussed on pages 310–11.

Selective abortion raises similar issues. As seen above, the Abortion Act allows termination of a pregnancy at any time if there is a risk of the foetus being seriously handicapped. This is a form of selective abortion — abortion because the foetus is perceived as possessing undesirable characteristics. Scientific advances make selective abortion more possible, as doctors are able to screen embryos for genetic abnormalities and unwanted qualities. In vitro fertilisation (IVF) raises a similar debate, whereby doctors are able to screen the fertilised embryos to ensure only healthy ones are implanted in the womb.

Pre-implantation genetic diagnosis (PGD) was developed to enable couples at risk of passing on serious genetic disease to have healthy children. Since it was introduced in 1990, it has been used to prevent the birth of children with conditions including Down's syndrome, cystic fibrosis, and sickle-cell anaemia. It has also been used to produce so-called 'saviour' children, created to improve or save an existing sibling's life. The Human Genetics Commission (HGC) has warned that such saviour siblings must be monitored to ensure their well-being and protected from becoming viewed as a spare-parts bank.

Josephine Quintavalle, of the group Comment on Reproductive Ethics, believes the potential impact of new technologies — such as those for saviour siblings — should have been thought of before:

> *These issues are absolutely what we have been worried about. And they should be thought about before children are used as guinea pigs in a social experiment...We can't imagine what it might be like for children born in these circumstances, and what might be expected of them in the future.*

Gender-selective abortion is not legal in the UK. Article 14 of the Council of Europe's 1997 Convention on Human Rights and Biomedicine states that techniques may not be used to choose a future child's sex, except in circumstances where serious hereditary gender-related disease is to be avoided. Using PGD for gender selection for non-medical purposes is prohibited by the Human Fertilisation and Embryology Authority, the UK's regulatory authority for IVF procedures. However, doctors can determine the sex of a foetus, and if this is communicated to parents it may result in sex-selective abortion.

All these issues have generated considerable debate, incorporating widely contrasting views. They illustrate the problem of trying to create legal rules in areas where there is no moral consensus.

Reasons for the overlap between legal and moral rules

There are several reasons for the broad overlap between legal and moral rules. Both aim to impose standards of conduct, without which human society would break down. In many of these standards, law and morality reinforce and complement each other as part of the fabric of social life.

It is therefore clear that legal rules do not exist in a vacuum, but, as Harris writes:

> ...are found side by side with moral codes of greater or less complexity. The relationship of law to moral rules and standards is therefore one of great and abiding importance in every human society, and certainly not least in our own.

Moral codes, then, can be said to supplement and underpin the force of legal rules that forbid immoral acts. The moral disapproval that such acts inspire is reinforced by the sanctions and remedies imposed by the law.

The close link between legal and moral rules is also demonstrated by the similarity of the normative language that they employ. Both are concerned to lay down rules or 'norms' of conduct for human beings, and in both moral and legal language this is expressed in terms of obligations, duties, or of what is right and wrong.

Divergence of legal and moral rules

Some legal rules appear to have no moral connection

There appears to be little moral justification for the fact that the smoking of tobacco and consumption of alcohol are legal while smoking cannabis is illegal. Likewise, what is the moral justification for closing pubs at 11 p.m.? And is it morally wrong to park on yellow lines or drive on a motorway at 72 miles per hour? There are some arguments, however, against the assertion that such laws have no connection with morals. It may be considered immoral, for example, to park in disabled parking spaces if you are not actually disabled, or to partially block roads, making access difficult for emergency service vehicles.

Some moral rules have little or no legal backing

As considered in connection with the law on tort, there is a moral duty to help those who may be in danger. The general position of the law, however, is that there is no liability for an omission to act. So, for example, the passer-by who fails to rescue someone who is drowning will not be held responsible. However, there are some exceptions in criminal law to this rule, such as where:

❖ a person creates a dangerous situation (as in the case of *R* v *Miller*, 1983)
❖ there is an assumption of responsibility
❖ there is a special relationship
❖ there is a contractual duty to act

The remedy of promissory estoppel (see page 97) is an exception to the general position of the law that there is no legal requirement to keep a promise. There is, however, a moral duty to do so.

Reasons for the divergence between legal and moral rules

As the examples above show, the law often shrinks from pursuing what may be seen as the path of morality. The reasons for this vary. It may be because the moral attitude may not be sufficiently widespread, and the law would not reflect popular morality. In certain fields of human activity, the law deliberately abstains from supporting the moral rule because the machinery of enforcement is felt to be too cumbersome to deal with the moral wrong — more social harm may be created than prevented by legal intervention. This was why the Wolfenden Committee recommended that homosexual acts in private between consenting adults should be decriminalised. It was also the reason that the legislature delayed making forced marriages illegal.

Forced marriages are conducted without the consent of one or both parties because pressure is put on them. Forced marriages are different to arranged marriages, which are conducted with the full consent of both parties and remain the preferred option of many people. All major faith groups condemn forced marriage, but it affects men and women worldwide and arises from cultural factors. In November 2008, the **Forced Marriage (Civil Protection) Act 2007** came into effect in England, Wales and Northern Ireland, making it an offence, punishable by a maximum of 2 years' imprisonment, to force someone into marriage.

The government was reluctant to introduce this protection legislation for fear of offending cultural sensitivities. However, as the then minister for racial equality, Mike O'Brien, stated in 1999, 'the government must respond sensitively to the issues of cultural diversity, but multicultural sensitivity is no excuse for moral blindness'.

Theories of law and morality
Natural law theorists

Natural law theorists argue that, in order to be valid, the law must coincide with natural law. Throughout history, many different views have been expressed as to what natural law is.

In the fourth century BC, the Greek philosopher Aristotle based his theory of natural law on the law of nature. He believed that the principles that governed the universe, and that explained how it was structured and how it functioned, could be discovered through observation and human reason.

By the Middle Ages, natural law theorists believed that the natural law was the divine law or the law of God. St Thomas Aquinas, writing in the thirteenth century, expressed the view that the universe was created by God, and that when God created humans he enabled them to know the truth. According to Aquinas, humankind is able to discover the truth of divine law through revelation, for example in the Holy Scriptures, through reflection and through practical reasoning. Aquinas believed that if human law was at variance with the divine law, it was not legal but rather a corruption of the law.

In more recent times, the influence of the Church has arguably declined. Professor Lon Fuller, in *The Morality of Law* (1964), refers to what he terms the 'inner morality of law'. For Fuller, a legal system is only valid if it conforms to eight procedural requirements. The laws must be:

* in existence, not made *ad hoc*
* published
* prospective, not retrospective
* understandable
* consistent
* possible to comply with
* not changed so frequently that people are unable to regulate their conduct by them
* administered by society in accordance with how they are announced

We have seen that public morality has influenced judicial development of the law. It would seem that many aspects of judicial law-making are incompatible with Fuller's procedural requirements. By its very nature, judge-made law is made *ad hoc*, and is retrospective, not always understandable and inconsistent. While the decision in *R v R* (1991) was welcomed on the basis that it reflected a shift in public morality, this decision is retrospective in effect. In *R v Crooks* (2004), the Court of Appeal upheld the conviction (in 2002) of the defendant, who had had sexual intercourse with his wife without her consent in 1970, 21 years before such behaviour was made a criminal offence.

While it can be seen that views as to what natural law is have varied and continue to vary, there is nevertheless a common thread. As Lord Lloyd of Hampstead points out in *Introduction to Jurisprudence*:

> *What has remained constant is an assertion that there are principles of natural law...the essence of natural law may be said to lie in the constant assertion that there are objective moral principles which depend upon the nature of the universe and which can be discovered by reason.*

Positivists

Jeremy Bentham rejected natural law as 'nonsense upon stilts'

Jeremy Bentham (1748–1832) rejected natural law theories as 'nonsense upon stilts'. His key criticisms were that natural law was based upon unprovable principles, and that natural law theorists confused legal issues with moral issues. For Bentham, the validity of a law did not depend on whether it was good or bad. What the law is and what the law ought to be should be treated as different issues. Bentham was primarily concerned with the promotion of the utility principle, i.e. the greatest happiness for the greatest number, and he believed that a law could be considered good or bad according to this principle. However, a law considered bad would not automatically be judged to be invalid.

John Austin (1790–1859) is credited with formulating the first coherent theory of positivism. He rejected the principle of natural law, whereby a law's validity depends on it not being in conflict with a 'higher law', whether natural or divine. For Austin, a law may be valid irrespective of its moral content. He defined law in terms of a command from a sovereign, whom the bulk of society is in the habit of obeying, enforced by a sanction. The origins of the command theory can be traced to Bentham and to Hobbes (1588–1679).

Professor Hart, in *The Concept of Law* (1963), also subscribes to the positivist view. However, he is critical of Austin's command theory in three respects:

❖ Not all laws resemble orders backed by threats. For example, while this definition is true of criminal law, it is not relevant in contract law or family law, which confer powers on people so that they may arrange their personal affairs.

❖ The requirement of the habit of obedience is impossible to apply when a new sovereign succeeds the old one.

❖ In most states, there are limitations on the legal powers of the sovereign.

Hart–Fuller debate

The Hart–Fuller debate took place during the years 1958–67. In essence, it was a response of both natural law theory and positivism to the views expressed by the German philosopher Gustav Radbruch on the validity of laws passed under the Nazi regime. Radbruch had been a positivist before the Nazi era, but the atrocities perpetrated during that period, apparently with legal approval, led him to believe that no law could be valid if it contravened basic moral principles.

Following the Second World War, many informers were tried as war criminals. In their defence, they typically argued that what they were doing was legal, as the law at that time made it illegal to make statements that were detrimental to the government. The approach of the German courts was to declare these Nazi laws invalid as they were 'contrary to the sound conscience and sense of justice of all decent human beings'. This approach was clearly in agreement with the natural law theorists and Fuller supported it.

Hart disagreed with Fuller. According to Hart, the law was valid despite being so fundamentally contrary to moral principles. Hart did not disagree that the law was immoral, only that it was invalid.

Hart–Devlin debate

The issue of how far law and morals should coincide was widely discussed in the late 1950s, when there was public concern about an apparent decline in sexual morality. This became known as the Hart–Devlin debate — not to be confused with the Hart–Fuller debate just discussed, which was concerned with the validity of legal rules that conflict with moral rules. The Hart–Devlin debate was concerned with the extent to which the law should enforce moral rules.

Statements reflecting the pluralistic nature of society can be found in the debates surrounding the legal reforms of the 1960s. The **Sexual Offences Act 1967**, legalising homosexual acts in private between consenting adults, was introduced following recommendations made by the Wolfenden Committee in its 1957 report. Two years after the publication of the Wolfenden Report, Lord Devlin, in *The Enforcement of Morals*, set out his criticisms of the Wolfenden recommendations. In 1962, Hart set out his arguments against Devlin's views in *Law, Liberty and Morality*.

Hart drew on the work of John Stuart Mill who, in his essay 'On liberty' (1859), stated:

> *The only part of the conduct of anyone, for which he is amenable to society, is that which concerns others. In the part which merely concerns himself, his independence, is of right, absolute. Over himself, over his own body and mind, the individual is sovereign.*

Mill and Hart put forward the view that the minority should not be made to conform to the will of the majority when in private, as this would amount to tyranny and be immoral. They thus recognised the pluralistic nature of society.

Hart argued that using law to enforce moral values was unnecessary, undesirable and morally unacceptable: unnecessary because society was capable of containing many moral standpoints without disintegrating; undesirable because it would freeze morality at a particular point; and morally unacceptable because it infringes the freedom of the individual. He also pointed out that objections to unusual behaviour are often prompted by ignorance, prejudice and misunderstanding.

Sir James Stephen, a leading criminal judge in the late nineteenth century, disagreed with Mill. In his work *Liberty, Equality, Fraternity* (1874), he stated:

> *I think that the attempt to distinguish between self-regarding acts and acts which regard others is like an attempt to distinguish between acts which happen in time and acts which happen in space. Every act happens at some time and in some space, and, in like manner, every act that we do either does or may affect both ourselves and others. I therefore think that the distinction is altogether fallacious and unfounded.*

He went on to say: 'There are acts of wickedness so gross and outrageous that they must be punished at any cost to the offender.' Stephen's view was that the prevention of immoral behaviour is an end in itself.

Devlin's views were more in line with those of Stephen. While Devlin believed that individual privacy should be respected, he stated: 'History shows that the loosening of moral bonds is often the first stage of disintegration...suppression of vice is as much the law's business as the suppression of subversive activities.' He believed that society shared a common morality and that the law should intervene to punish acts that offend that shared morality, whether done in public or private. Failure to intervene would result in the disintegration of society. He argued that individual liberty could only flourish in a stable society; disintegration of society through lack of a shared morality would, therefore, threaten individual freedom.

This debate must be discussed in relation to the coincidence of legal and moral rules. To perform well in your exam, you must be able to demonstrate detailed knowledge of the views of both Hart and Devlin, and explain how the debate has influenced the law in recent years.

Influence of Mill and Hart

In his report on prostitution and homosexuality, Sir John Wolfenden recognised the pluralistic nature of society and the importance of individual liberty, and in this way both his report and the resulting **Sexual Offences Act 1967** were influenced by the views of Mill and Hart. These views were also reflected in other reforming legislation of that period, such as the **Obscene Publications Act 1968** and the **Divorce Law Reform Act 1969**.

The majority of the House of Lords in *Gillick v Norfolk and Wisbech Area Health Authority* (1986) also adopted the Mill–Hart approach. They held that it was legal for doctors to offer contraceptive advice and treatment to girls under the age of 16, provided they were satisfied that the girls had sufficient understanding of the issues involved. The decision created what has become known as the 'Gillick-competent child'. In Lord Scarman's words, the principle is that 'parental rights are derived from parental duty' and that the 'dwindling right' of a parent as the child grows older:

> *...yields to the child's right to make his own decision when he reaches a sufficient understanding and intelligence to be capable of making up his own mind on the matter requiring decision.*

Influence of Stephen and Devlin

The dissenting judgements of Lords Brandon and Templeman in *Gillick* (1986) reflected concerns over the wider social implications. Brandon's dissent was based largely on the question of public policy and his concern for the criminal aspect of underage sex. Lord Templeman ignored case law and produced an opinion which read like a speech by Mrs Gillick, the most memorable line of which is: 'There are many things which a girl under 16 needs to practise but sex is not one of them.' These views were an echo of Devlin's concern about social disintegration.

The influence of Stephen and Devlin can be seen in a number of other judicial decisions. In *Shaw v DPP* (1962), the House of Lords ruled that a publication advertising the services of prostitutes was a conspiracy to corrupt public morals. Viscount Simmonds argued:

> *In the sphere of criminal law I entertain no doubt that there remains in the courts a residual power to enforce the supreme and fundamental purpose of the law, to conserve not only the safety and order, but also the moral welfare of the state.*

More recent decisions show that there is still judicial support for the Devlin viewpoint that some acts are intrinsically immoral, regardless of whether or not they harm others. In *Knuller v DPP* (1973), a case involving advertisements in a magazine placed by readers inviting others to contact them for homosexual purposes, the decision in *Shaw* was followed. In *R v Gibson* (1990), an artist exhibited earrings made from freeze-dried foetuses of 3–4 months' gestation. A conviction for the common law offence of outraging public decency was upheld.

Perhaps the most significant recent decisions are those of the House of Lords in *R v Brown and Others* (1993) and the European Court of Human Rights in *Laskey, Brown and Jaggard v United Kingdom* (1997). In the House of Lords case, the question was whether the defence of consent could be used in respect of sadomasochistic acts. The people involved were consenting adults and none of the activities was conducted in public or had resulted in the need for medical treatment. The activities concerned included whipping, caning, branding and nailing their genitals to pieces of wood. The House of Lords held that the defence of consent could not be applied to such practices and that such behaviour was not to be encouraged by relaxation of the law. When the defendants took their case to the ECtHR, they lost on the basis that there was no breach of Article 8 of the European Convention on Human Rights, as infringement of the right to respect for private life was justified by the need to protect health or morals.

Interpretation of Article 8 is also at the heart of the assisted suicide cases. The European Court of Human Rights continues to show preference for Devlin's view. In these cases, the claimants argue that the law preventing deciding when to end one's life breaches the right to respect for private and family life.

Questions

1 What was the Wolfenden Report?

2 Which nineteenth-century philosopher influenced Professor Hart?

3 Which nineteenth-century criminal judge influenced Lord Devlin?

4 Briefly explain the view of Hart and the reasons he put forward to justify it. Using examples, discuss how he influenced the development of the law.

5 Briefly explain the view of Devlin and the reasons he put forward to justify it. Using examples, discuss how he influenced the development of the law.

6 Which view, Hart's or Devlin's, did the Wolfenden Committee adopt?

7 What changes in the law were made following the recommendations of the Wolfenden Committee?

Conclusion

One of the difficulties for the law is not only that society is pluralistic, with a wide range of views on all moral issues, but also that these views are sometimes passionately held, allowing little scope for compromise. In general terms, it could be argued that a large section of society has come to adopt the view taken by Hart, and inevitably this has been reflected in both legislative changes and in judicial decisions such as *Gillick*. On the other hand, significant groups remain opposed to what they perceive as a dangerous weakening of the moral basis of law.

Moral issues often feature prominently in the media, and you are encouraged to use examples that are currently in the news. Abortion and other issues concerning the sanctity of life, such as euthanasia, stem-cell research and interventions in the field of human fertilisation, remain contentious.

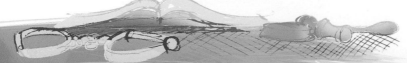

24

Another issue giving rise to strongly held views is that of fox hunting. In February 2005, the Hunting Act 2004 became law, making hunting with dogs illegal. However, the issue has remained on the political agenda, not least through court actions challenging the validity of the legislation. That hunting with dogs has continued cannot be in dispute, although since the Act was passed there has been an increase in drag hunting, which suggests that the legislation is having a morally educative effect.

You should be able to discuss some of these issues in the context of the Hart–Devlin debate, and make judgements about how far in practice law and morality are linked, and whether it is appropriate for the law to be used to resolve moral issues.

Sample exam question

Explain the nature/characteristics of legal and moral rules and then consider the extent to which the law does and should reflect moral rules.

Further reading

Freeman, M. (2008) *Lloyd's Introduction to Jurisprudence*, Sweet & Maxwell.
Harris, P. (2006) *An Introduction to Law*, Weidenfeld and Nicolson.
Mitchell, A. (2005) 'Exploring law and morality', *A-Level Law Review*, Vol. 1, No. 1, pp. 28–29.

Chapter **25**

Law and justice

The meaning of 'justice'

'Justice' has many meanings. The definition given in the *Oxford English Dictionary* is 'just conduct; fairness', and this is the common understanding of the word. The definition of 'just' is 'acting or done in accordance with what is morally right or proper'. The definition of 'fair' is 'free from discrimination, dishonesty...in conformity with rules or standards'. Lord Lloyd emphasises the difficulty in defining justice precisely:

> *Justice, whatever its precise meaning may be, is itself a moral value, that is one of the aims or purposes which man sets himself in order to attain the good life.*

It would appear that conceptions of justice vary from age to age, person to person and according to existing economic relations.

While justice is simplified in the dictionary by the idea of 'fairness', Chaim Perelman recognised that justice has several meanings. In his essay, 'De La Justice' (1945), he set out six possible meanings of the word:

1. 'to each according to his works' (rewards are based on contribution)
2. 'to each according to his needs' (people receive what they need)
3. 'to each according to his merits' (people get what they deserve)
4. 'to each according to his rank' (people may enjoy privileges according to status)
5. 'to each according to his legal entitlement' (people receive what the law says they should)
6. 'to each equally' (all people receive the same)

While recognising these different meanings, all of which he explained in terms of distributive justice, Perelman believed that once the type of justice subscribed to by a society was identified, all individuals had to be treated the same. He subscribed to the theory of formal justice.

Justice, according to the law, can be formal, substantive, distributive or corrective, or any combination of these types:

❖ Formal justice, often referred to as procedural justice, requires equality of treatment in accordance with the classification laid down by rules.
❖ Substantive justice is concerned with whether or not rules are just.
❖ Distributive justice is concerned with the fair allocation of benefits and burdens within society.
❖ Corrective justice requires the righting of wrongs through fair remedy or punishment.

Theories of justice

There are numerous theories of justice. It is important to be able to explain and evaluate these theories and their relationships with each other, and to understand their application to modern society. You will notice that many of the theorists mentioned are referred to in Chapter 24 on law and morality. It is important to remember that there is an obvious connection between morality and justice, and theorists were often developing ideas that related to both. Natural law theorists would argue, for example, that if laws were not founded on certain fundamental principles they could be neither moral nor just and would not be valid, while positivists rejected the notion that there was a 'higher' source of law and argued that laws could still be valid even if they were not based on acceptable ideas of morality or justice.

Aristotle

The Greek philosopher Aristotle introduced the principles of distributive justice and corrective justice.

❖ The principle of **distributive justice** requires that the allocation of assets in society should be proportional to a person's claim on them. Aristotle argued that this did not necessarily mean equal shares. Distributive justice considers the merits of the parties, so that it is unjust if unequal parties have equal shares.
❖ The principle of **corrective justice** requires that where distributive justice is disturbed by wrongdoing, there should be a means of restoring the original position. This might be done by imposing penalties or awarding compensation.

St Thomas Aquinas

Aquinas's **natural law theory** makes the assumption that if higher law is followed, the result will be justice. An unjust law might be contrary to human good or against the higher law derived from God. A law which goes against this God-derived law will always be 'unjust' and should not be obeyed. Some Roman Catholics today would argue that this applies to laws legalising abortion. Members of many faith groups would find it difficult to obey laws that compelled them to break what they regard as fundamental principles. Interesting examples are the law in France forbidding the wearing of religious symbols in state institutions such as schools, and the exemption given to Sikhs in the UK from the requirement to wear a crash helmet when riding a motorcycle.

In more recent times, the influence of the Church has declined, and natural law theorists have based their ideas on different kinds of fundamentals. As we saw in Chapter 24, Professor Lon Fuller in *Morality of Law* refers to the 'inner morality of law', and considers a legal system as valid only if it conforms to eight procedural requirements. While it can be seen that views of what natural law is have varied and continue to vary, there is nevertheless a common thread. In the words of Lord Lloyd of Hampstead, there are 'objective moral principles which depend upon the nature of the universe and which can be discovered by reason'.

Jeremy Bentham

The **theory of utilitarianism** was developed by Bentham. The aim of utilitarianism is to maximise human happiness by increasing pleasure and diminishing pain. For the utilitarian, justice is concerned with promoting 'the greatest happiness of the greatest number'. The sum of human happiness is assessed by numerical means, and each person's happiness is equal in value.

Utilitarianism has been influential in legal reform and appears to be based on democratic principles. In democratic societies, citizens must comply with laws made by a government elected by the majority. It is a secular theory, not based on religious principles defensible only by faith; and maximising happiness is a policy often applied on both a national political level and among friends and family. However, utilitarianism can be criticised for being difficult to apply in practice: it is questionable whether happiness can be directly or precisely measured.

Another criticism is that utilitarianism is concerned with the consequences of an act and not the means by which it is achieved. Thus, torture may justify the end result of obtaining information. Individuals are not regarded as important, and the complete misery of a few is justified if it increases the happiness of the many. Strict utilitarianism is not concerned with individual rights but rather with the needs of society. This is in conflict with other theories of justice, such as that of Rawls and Marx, who regard the rights of the individual as all-important.

Bentham also rejected natural law theory as being based on unprovable principles. For Bentham, the validity of a law did not depend on whether it was good or bad.

The approach of John Stuart Mill was to modify strict utilitarianism through a recognition of some individual rights. As seen in Chapter 24, Mill influenced Hart in the development of the 'harm to others' theory. Thus the law should only restrict individual rights in order to avoid harm to others.

Positivism

John Austin is credited with formulating the first coherent theory of positivism, and he developed the ideas of Bentham. Like Bentham, Austin also rejected the principle of natural law. For Austin, a law may be valid irrespective of its moral content or whether it delivers justice. Professor Hart in *The Concept of Law* also subscribes to the positivist view. He points out that it is possible to administer unjust laws in a just manner and vice versa.

John Rawls

In *A Theory of Justice* (1971), John Rawls sets out justice as fairness:

> *The main task clearly is to determine which principles of justice would be chosen in the original position… The idea of the original position is to set up a fair procedure so that any principles agreed to will be just… It seems reasonable to suppose that the parties in the original position are equal, that is, all have the same rights in the procedure for choosing principles; each can make proposals, submit reasons for their acceptance and so on.*

In order to avoid the situation whereby people exploit social and natural circumstances to their own advantage, Rawls places these people in the original position behind a 'veil of ignorance', whereby:

> *…the parties do not know certain kinds of particular facts. First of all, no one knows his place in society, his class position or social status; nor does he know his fortune in the distribution of natural assets and abilities, his intelligence and strength and the like.*

Furthermore, people behind the veil of ignorance do not know what they will value as good or bad, or what economic or political situation, level of civilisation and culture are prevalent in their society. According to Rawls, two principles would be chosen as a result of these circumstances:

> *First: each person is to have an equal right to the most extensive basic liberty compatible with a similar liberty for others. Second: social and economic inequalities are to be arranged so that they are both (a) reasonably expected to be to everyone's advantage, and (b) attached to positions and offices open to all.*

Rawls subscribes to the theory of distributive justice but rejects the notion of utility. He believes that justice is achieved through rules that create inequality only if that inequality is of benefit to all, not merely to the greatest number. Furthermore, the equal right to liberty cannot be denied in favour of greater social or economic advantages.

Rawls's theory of justice is reflected in both English law and in the European Convention on Human Rights. Rawls subscribes to **liberalism**, which is primarily concerned with freedom and the autonomy of individuals. The European Convention reflects this in that it ensures that individuals are given the positive rights Rawls regards as important, including freedom of speech and assembly and freedom from arbitrary arrest and seizure. However, the derogation clauses depart from Rawls's theory, allowing for a denial of rights in certain circumstances, for example:

> *...in the interests of national security, public safety or the economic well-being of the country, for the prevention of disorder or crime, for the protection of health or morals, or for the protection of the rights and freedoms of others. (Article 8)*

Only the last point arguably reflects Rawls's theory, in that individual liberty can be limited if it will result in greater liberty overall.

Marxism

Karl Marx, like Rawls, subscribed to an ideal of justice rather than to an actual existing system. For Marx, the ideal society meant: 'From each according to his ability, to each according to his needs.' He argued that justice cannot be achieved until the ideal society is in place, as any other society is defective and justice therein impossible. However, Marx also propounded the view that: 'Once the new productive arrangements appear, there will be no need for principles of justice for production or distribution.' This implies that no one would find it necessary to rely upon institutional apparatus to recognise his or her rights. Justice for Marx would be the existence of his ideal society, and there would apparently be no need for a law to conform to.

Karl Marx

Such sentiments were also expressed by the eighteenth-century theorist David Hume:

If every man had a tender regard for another, or if nature supplied abundantly all our wants and desires...the jealousy of interest, which justice supposes, could no longer have place. Increase to a sufficient degree the benevolence of men, or the bounty of nature, and you render justice useless.

It is clear that Britain does not correspond to the ideal society as envisaged by either Hume or Marx.

Robert Nozick and the minimal state

Nozick rejected the distributive theories of justice of Rawls and Marx on the basis that they involved unwarranted interference with the inherent rights of individuals. Instead, he developed the **entitlement theory** of justice, according to which goods are already encumbered with ownership. He maintained that individuals have natural rights to the enjoyment of life, health, liberty and possessions, free from interference by others. Rather than being concerned with equality, the entitlement theory stipulates that the state should only intervene to protect natural rights: inequalities are a fact of life. It holds that the state should play a minimal role and is not justified in diminishing or increasing the natural rights which an individual possesses.

According to Nozick, there are three ways in which property can be justly acquired:

❖ if it was previously not owned by anyone and is acquired through effort or skill
❖ if it is validly transferred by its previous owner
❖ if it is transferred by court order to rectify a previous unjust acquisition

Redistribution of individuals' rights is not justified for any social purpose. Legal systems such as that operating in the UK, which go further than merely enforcing natural rights, do not comply with Nozick's theory of justice.

Natural justice and the rule of law

It would be reasonable to claim that if a legal system is to be based on justice, it must incorporate the principles of natural justice and the rule of law.

Phil Harris, in *An Introduction to Law*, argues that the idea of natural justice 'has no mysterious or magical meaning: it simply refers to a duty to act fairly'. This is based on two requirements: that each party should have the opportunity to be heard and that no one should be judge in his or her own cause.

The theory of the rule of law, as outlined by British jurist and constitutional theorist A. V. Dicey in the nineteenth century, is that 'no person is punishable except for a distinct breach of the law established in the courts' and also that no man is 'above the law, but that every man, whatever his rank, is subject to the ordinary law of the realm' (*An Introduction to the Study of the Law of the Constitution*, 1885).

The relationship between law and justice

Some exam questions may ask you to explain what law is and how it differs from the idea of justice. As explained on page 306, Sir John Salmond described law as 'the body of principles recognised and applied by the state in the administration of justice'. John Austin defined it as a command issued from a sovereign power to an inferior and enforced by coercion. Compliance with legal rules is compulsory; they govern all members of society and must be obeyed. Breach of legal rules will result in state sanctions and procedures.

As we have seen, natural law theorists argue that unjust laws do not deserve to be treated as laws. Natural law theory holds that certain ideal principles or values exist and that the law should correspond to these if it is to be regarded as genuine. The source of these ideal principles or values may be morality, reason or God. Positivists, on the other hand, would hold that for a law to be valid, all that is required is that it should issue from a competent legislator after following the prescribed process.

The differences between these two views became clear during the Hart–Fuller debate (see page 319). In essence, this was a response of both natural law theory and positivism to the views expressed by Gustav Radbruch on the validity of laws passed under the Nazi regime that seemed to grant legal approval to the perpetration of atrocities. Radbruch, a positivist before the Nazi era, came to believe that no law could be valid if it contravened basic moral principles and fundamental principles of justice.

Once the Second World War ended, the approach of the German courts was to declare these Nazi laws invalid. Fuller, a natural law theorist, approved of this approach. He maintained that law and morality cannot be separated and that the postwar courts were entitled to hold Nazi rules not to be law. To call the Nazi system 'legal' and to call its rules 'laws' was a false description of what they were. They were instruments of an arbitrary and tyrannical regime.

An example referred to by Fuller concerned a German woman who was prosecuted after the war for denouncing her husband to the authorities in accordance with the anti-sedition laws of 1934 and 1938. He had made derogatory remarks about Hitler and was prosecuted and convicted of slandering the *Führer*, which carried the death penalty. Although sentenced to death, the husband was not executed but was sent as a soldier to the Eastern front. He survived the war and on his return instituted proceedings against his wife.

She argued that she had not committed a crime because a court had sentenced her husband in accordance with the law of the time. She was convicted of 'illegally depriving another of his freedom', a crime under the German Penal Code 1871, which had remained in force throughout the Nazi period. The Nazi laws were, the

court said, 'contrary to the sound conscience and sense of justice of all decent human beings'.

Hart argued that the decision of the court was wrong, as the Nazi law of 1934 was valid; Fuller contended that the Nazi regime was so 'lawless' that nothing that it implemented could qualify as law. Hart insisted that the question of what law is must be separated from the question of whether it is moral or just.

Questions

1 Explain the characteristics of laws.
2 Do you share the view that because the Nazi laws were contrary to the sense of justice of all decent human beings they could not qualify as laws at all?
3 Do you think that justice was done in the case referred to by Fuller?
4 What are the implications of this view for those who live under such regimes?

The extent to which there is justice under English law

Exam questions may require you to explain in theory what justice is, and then to discuss to what extent it is achieved in practice. However, a common weakness is to define justice well and to give examples of justice in operation, but not to link these two parts. In this respect it is important that you explore the extent to which substantive legal rules, legal institutions and legal processes achieve justice in the UK.

In questioning whether English law complies with the requirements of formal, substantive, distributive and/or corrective justice, examples of rules, institutions and processes from many parts of the specification can be used. These examples can then be related to the meanings and theories of justice and examined in order to assess how successful they are in achieving justice. In 'Exploring law and justice' (*A-Level Law Review*, Vol. 1, No. 2), Andrew Mitchell recommends that candidates make a table of examples to illustrate aspects of the English legal system that appear to reflect formal, substantive, distributive and corrective justice. His suggestions for investigation — some of which are explored in this chapter — together with further examples, are summarised in Table 25.1. He also recommends research into some miscarriages of justice.

The extent to which the English legal system is just depends on which theory/definition of justice is used, but the majority of people, with the possible exception of Marxists, would agree that most of the system is just and leads to just results most of the time. However, there are many occasions when people claim that they have not received justice.

Table 25.1 Examples of different kinds of justice

Formal justice	Substantive justice	Distributive justice	Corrective justice
• Right to a fair trial — Article 6 ECHR • Rules against judicial bias — *ex parte Pinochet* • Rules of natural justice • Rule of law • Judicial review • Jury — conscience/perverse verdicts • Civil and criminal appeal processes • Provisions to achieve access to justice • Consistency through the operation of judicial precedent — like cases treated alike • Problem of deterrence in sentencing and of inconsistent sentencing in Magistrates' Courts	• The policy underpinning contract — to protect the weaker party; consideration of consumer laws is useful • Policy in tort — to shift loss from the victim to the wrongdoer • Role of equity to supplement policy in contract (specific performance, promissory estoppel) and tort (injunctions in nuisance cases) • Strict liability in both civil and criminal law • Incorporation of the ECHR into English law • Broad scope of discrimination law	• Parliament's responsibilities in making law, particularly when imposing burdens, such as taxes, on citizens • Role of the law in balancing conflicting interests in family, employment, immigration and welfare disputes	• Sentencing in criminal law • Civil law remedies • Mandatory sentence for murder — reform — the Tony Martin case

Judicial review

One of the ways in which the rule of law is guaranteed is by having an independent judiciary able to review the decisions of politicians and public officials. Judicial review is instrumental in upholding the rule of law; it is a means of formal justice.

Judicial review does not examine the merits of a decision, but simply whether the body or individual in question was within their rights in making the decision. If a decision is *ultra vires* (goes beyond their powers), it can be quashed.

Procedural *ultra vires* arises where proper procedures have not been followed, e.g. there has been a breach of natural justice, as in the Pinochet case (see page 334).

Substantive *ultra vires* arises where the content of the decision was outside the power of the body that made it. One of the problems with substantive *ultra vires* is that it is difficult for judges to control the actions of public bodies if the discretionary powers granted to such bodies are wide. For example, in *R* v *Secretary of State for the Environment ex parte Norwich City Council* (1982), the wording of the Housing Act 1980 allowed the secretary of state to 'do all such things as appear to him necessary or expedient' to enable council house tenants to buy their council houses. The courts accepted that, in cases where sales were proceeding slowly, this gave him the right to remove the power from the local authority and exercise it himself.

It could be argued that the real test of whether a system is based on the principles of justice is how it copes with direct or perceived threats to the security of the state. It has been suggested that the reliance by governments on the requirements of national security has inhibited judicial review of their decisions.

In *R* v *Secretary of State for Home Affairs ex parte Hosenball* (1977), the Court of Appeal held that an American journalist could be deported, even though the rules of natural justice had not been followed, because the decision was made on the grounds of national security. Similarly, in *Council of Civil Service Unions* v *Minister for the Civil Service* (1985), the government decision to ban employees at the Government Communications Headquarters (GCHQ) from membership of trade unions was upheld on the basis that it was claimed to be necessary for reasons of national security.

However, the passing of the Human Rights Act 1998 has enabled judges to review even primary legislation to determine whether it complies with the European Convention on Human Rights. In *A and others* v *Secretary of State for the Home Department* (2004), the House of Lords took the view that the detention of foreign nationals without trial under s.21 of the Anti-Terrorism, Crime and Security Act 2001 was not justified, even though the government argued that they were a threat to national security.

The government has responded to this judicial decision by releasing the detainees, but under control orders greatly restricting their freedom. It has also secured new legislation (Prevention of Terrorism Act 2005) allowing for the use of such control orders in the future for both British and foreign terror suspects. These too have been successfully challenged, though on more limited grounds.

It would appear that judges are now more ready to uphold the rights of unpopular individuals and to require that the rules of natural justice are followed despite the national security argument.

Judicial independence

Judicial independence, as required under the doctrine of the separation of powers, is fundamental to the rule of natural justice that no one should be a judge in his or her own cause — *nemo judex in causa sua*.

This principle can be seen operating in *R* v *Bow Street Metropolitan Stipendiary Magistrate, ex parte Pinochet* (1999), in which the House of Lords decided that General Pinochet, the former dictator of Chile, should be extradited to Spain to face serious charges of human rights abuse. When it was revealed that Lord Hoffman, one of the Law Lords who heard the case, had links with Amnesty International (a human rights organisation involved in the proceedings), the House of Lords annulled the decision and reheard the case without Hoffman.

In this case, Lord Browne-Wilkinson emphasised that while financial interest had been the basis for disqualification from presiding over previous cases, this need not be the only reason for disqualification. The House of Lords stated that the absolute impartiality of the judiciary required a rule that automatically disqualified a judge who was involved, whether personally or as a director of a company, in promoting the same causes in the same organisation as the parties to the case.

Judicial impartiality also requires that a judge has no relationship or acquaintance with any party or witness involved in a criminal or civil case. In *Morrison* v *AWG Group Ltd and another* (2006), the Court of Appeal held that a High Court judge should have recused himself (stood down from hearing the case). He had acknowledged that he had known a witness appearing for the claimants for some 30 years, and consequently that witness was replaced by another. The judge then resolved to hear the case. Lord Justice Mummery stated that in such a situation a judge should stand down to avoid any perception of bias, however unjustified such a perception might be.

Formal or procedural justice and equality of treatment

Formal justice, often referred to as procedural justice, requires equality of treatment in accordance with the classification laid down by rules. In *The Concept of Law*, Hart linked the idea of formal justice with that of morality. He agreed that like cases should be treated in the same way, a principle that seems to be common to most theories of justice; but he argued that this raised important questions as to what makes cases alike or different. It may be that, on occasions, treating people differently is justified. This issue can be illustrated by reference to any discrimination legislation and the interpretation of it by the national and European courts.

An interesting example is *R (Carson)* v *Secretary of State* (2005), in which a British pensioner living in South Africa claimed she should receive the same cost-of-living increases as pensioners still living in the UK. The House of Lords rejected her claim. Lord Hoffmann, while accepting the principle that everyone is entitled to equal treatment by the state, argued that the claimant was being treated differently from a pensioner who lived in the UK because the situations were different.

Another recent example is *Burden and Others* v *UK* (2008). In this case, the European Court of Human Rights held that two elderly sisters, who had lived together for 30 years in property they had inherited, could not be compared to a married or same-sex couple under the Civil Partnership Act 2004. The court said that they had not been discriminated against and therefore there had been no breach of Article 14 of the European Convention on Human Rights.

This case can be contrasted with *Ghaidan* v *Mendoza* (2004), in which the tenant of a privately rented flat died, and his gay partner (who had lived with him) sought to take over as a statutory tenant, claiming he had been living 'as the wife or husband' of the deceased tenant. Lord Nicholls in the House of Lords judgement said that Article 14 of the European Convention required like cases to be treated alike, and unlike cases not to be treated alike. He added that the circumstances that justify two cases being regarded as unlike are infinite, but that there were certain grounds of factual difference which were not in themselves acceptable as a basis for different legal treatment. Differences of race, sex or religion are obvious examples, and sexual orientation is another. The majority of the House agreed, and granted the statutory tenancy.

Questions

1 From the three cases above relating to equality of treatment, suggest some criteria for deciding when it is fair to treat people differently to others in similar circumstances.

2 Do you think that each of the cases was decided fairly?

Access to justice

The rules relating to equal access to justice in England seem to have become more substantially unjust in recent years. Government funding for legal cases was introduced by the Legal Aid Act 1949, with the aim of providing the means for everyone to have access to justice, rather than just those who could afford it. The system was means-tested and demand-led, so that all those who applied would receive funding, provided they fell within the eligibility criteria. When the system was first introduced, approximately 80% of the population was eligible for some government funding; however, the expense to the taxpayer of this system persuaded successive governments to alter the means test so that fewer people qualified, and by the early 1990s only 40% of the population was eligible for legal aid. The majority of the population fell into what was referred to as the 'middle income trap': too rich to qualify for legal aid yet too poor to fund legal action themselves.

The position has been improved to some extent by the **Access to Justice Act 1999**, but problems remain. The Act introduced a limit on the amount of funding available, so that when the money runs out, no funding is available. The limits for eligibility remain high. Also, certain types of action are excluded from the system, such as personal injury cases, although these can be pursued through conditional fee arrangements. However, not all of those who may have qualified for legal aid under the old system can find a lawyer willing to accept their case on a conditional fee. Lawyers are only willing to accept those cases they feel sure of winning. All of these issues mean that some people have access to the legal system, while others do not.

The rules regarding government funding suggest that formal justice is denied. The law in general cannot be applied impartially if certain sections of society are denied access to it. It can also be argued that such rules are substantially unjust because they have the effect of denying equal access.

Civil justice system

The civil justice system as it operated before 1999 was widely criticised as unfair. Elliott and Quinn, in *The English Legal System*, comment that:

> *While conflicting interests may mean it is impossible to achieve a civil justice system that satisfies everyone, there were serious concerns that the civil justice system before April 1999 was giving satisfaction to only a small minority of users.*

In his final report, published in 1996, Lord Woolf identified a number of goals that a civil justice system should have. The first two of these were that it should be just in the results it delivers and fair in the way it treats litigants. The changes proposed by Woolf were implemented in the **Civil Procedure Rules 1999**. He described these as 'a new landscape for civil justice for the twenty-first century' and they certainly represent a significant reform. The overriding objective in the rules, with their emphasis on pre-action protocols and pro-active case management by judges, is that the courts should deal with cases justly; and this objective is to prevail over all others.

The new system has generally been welcomed as an improvement, although the reforms were described by Michael Zander, a leading academic, as being 'fundamentally flawed'. For example, he points out that procedural timetables for the fast track may not work fairly because lawyers, for a variety of reasons, may not be able to keep to the prescribed timetables. This could result in sanctions being imposed on parties deemed to have caused the delays, thus punishing them for what in effect are the failings of their lawyers.

Criminal justice system

There have always been miscarriages of justice. For example, Timothy Evans was hanged in 1950 after being convicted of murder. The real murderer was identified shortly afterwards, and Evans was pardoned (posthumously) in 1966. Mahmood Hussein Mattan and Derek Bentley were hanged for separate murders in 1952; their convictions were eventually quashed by the Court of Appeal in 1998. But it was the miscarriage of justice cases in the 1980s and 1990s, such as the Guildford Four, the Maguires and the Birmingham Six, that raised the most disturbing questions about the way the criminal justice system was operating. These cases suggested that in their eagerness to get convictions in what were dreadful murders, the police had been prepared to compromise some of the principles of formal justice. In particular, there were concerns about confessions and the treatment of the defendants while they were in custody, and also about the reliability of forensic evidence.

When Judith Ward was cleared in 1992 after serving 18 years for the bombing of a coach on the M62 motorway, which killed 12 people, the Court of Appeal said that a grave miscarriage of justice had occurred:

> In failing to disclose evidence…the West Yorkshire police, the scientists who gave evidence at the trial, and some of those members of the staff of the DPP and counsel who advised them…failed to carry out their basic duty to seek to ensure a trial which is fair to both the prosecution…and the accused.

Arguably, however, the system did eventually deliver justice, because the appeal system led to the convictions being quashed and compensation being paid in all these IRA cases, and in others such as the Tottenham Three and the Bridgewater Four. The **Criminal Appeals Act 1995** tried to rectify some of the shortcomings of the system: under s.2(1) of this Act, the Court of Appeal should allow an appeal if it thinks the conviction is 'unsafe', regardless of technicalities.

A further aspect of the criminal justice system that arguably promotes justice is trial by jury. Juries are free to do justice as they see fit, and do not have to give reasons for their decisions. While this may lead to inconsistencies in decision making — a breach of formal justice — the jury has on some occasions refused to apply legal rules in order to reach a verdict that is fair in the circumstances. In *R* v *Ponting* (1985), the jury refused to convict a civil servant charged with an offence under the Official Secrets Act. Ponting had given documents that revealed that the government had lied to an opposition MP in its account of the sinking of an Argentinian ship during the Falklands War. In delivering the 'not guilty' verdict, the jury resisted pressure to convict from both the government and the judge.

Justice for victims?

The Stephen Lawrence case led to calls to relax the 'double jeopardy' rule

The Stephen Lawrence case demonstrates that there can also be concerns about whether the institutions of the state operate fairly in the interests of all those affected by crime. Stephen Lawrence was murdered in an apparently racially motivated attack in 1993. The Macpherson Inquiry was set up by the government, as a result of concerns expressed about the way the police handled the case, and it concluded that the investigation was 'marred by a combination of professional incompetence, institutional racism and a failure of leadership by senior officers'.

In this case, it is clear that Stephen's family feels an enormous sense of injustice, compounded by the fact that a private prosecution brought against the three men suspected of killing Stephen failed. Victims, unlike defendants, do not get a second chance and the recognition that those acquitted of Stephen's murder could not be tried again, regardless of any new evidence that might emerge, led to calls for the 'double jeopardy' rule to be relaxed. As a result, the Criminal Justice Act 2003 allows for people acquitted of certain serious offences, including murder, to be retried, provided that both the DPP and the Court of Appeal are satisfied that there is 'new and compelling evidence' and that it is in the interests of justice to have a retrial. The relevant clauses became law in April 2005, and Joshua Rozenberg writing in the *Daily Telegraph* suggested that there might be as many as 35 murder cases that could be retried as a result of the change in the law. The first such case concerned William Dunlop, who had been acquitted of the murder of his girlfriend in 1989, but while in prison for another offence, he confessed the murder to a prison officer. As soon as the Criminal Justice Act reforms came into effect, prosecutors applied for a retrial and he pleaded guilty to murder in 2006.

The case of Damilola Taylor also focuses on the frustration felt by the families of victims when there are unsuccessful prosecutions. The response of some of the press to the 2002 acquittal of the defendants in this case was, in the words of the *Daily Mirror*, that this was 'another murdered black boy betrayed by British justice'. However, David Pannick, in an article in *The Times* (7 May 2002), argued that although 'justice was battered and bruised by the Taylor case', it survived the ordeal. He pointed out that 'show trials' do not take place in Britain and that justice can be served when defendants are acquitted because the jury is not satisfied of guilt beyond reasonable doubt. He also claimed that although mistakes were made, 'none

of the errors of which the police have been accused in the Taylor case could, if avoided, have resulted in a conviction'.

The police persevered with the investigation and in August 2006, two brothers, Danny and Ricky Preddie, then aged 18 and 19, were convicted of manslaughter. They had originally been arrested a few days after Damilola was stabbed in the leg with a broken bottle near his home in Peckham, but vital leads were missed by a forensic laboratory and investigators. Forensic evidence was later picked up by a private science laboratory, and this convicted the defendants.

The case of *A* v *Hoare and Others* (2008) also drew attention to the difficulties victims face in getting justice. The case, heard by the House of Lords, involved five claimants in four joined appeals who sought damages for personal injuries caused by sexual assault.

In 1989, the defendant, Hoare, had been convicted of attempted rape and given a life sentence. In 2004, having been released on licence, he won £7 million on the National Lottery, and later that year the claimant began an action seeking civil damages. Her claim was struck out: the judge stated that the cause of action had arisen at the time of the offence, and since the claim had not been brought until some 15 years later, it was barred by s.2 of the Limitation Act 1980.

In each of the four cases, the lower courts had felt bound by the House of Lords' decision in *Stubbings* v *Webb* (1993), which was that the shorter 3-year time limit in s.11, which the judge has the power to disapply under s.33, did not apply to claims for sexual assault. The fact that the defendant had not hitherto been worth suing was irrelevant. After considering the legislative history and the evident injustice arising from the earlier decision, the House of Lords exercised its power under the Practice Statement 1966 to depart from its own previous decision. It sent the claim by Hoare's victim back to the High Court so that the judge could decide whether or not to exercise discretion to allow the claim to proceed. These cases are a reminder that all criminal assaults are also actionable torts, and it is open to victims to sue for damages as well as having their attacker prosecuted. In most cases, as with Hoare in 1989, there is little point in doing this because the defendant is unlikely to have substantial assets.

It is also possible to bring a civil action in situations where the defendant has been acquitted. The logic of such an action is that the burden of proof is different in civil cases and it may be possible to prove something on the balance of probabilities when it has not been possible to prove it beyond reasonable doubt.

In December 2005, property baron Nicholas van Hoogstraten was held responsible by the High Court for the murder of a business rival — despite having been cleared in the criminal courts. Mr Raja was in the process of suing van Hoogstraten over a business deal at the time of his death. He was stabbed and shot after answering the door at his home on 2 July 1999. Justice Lightman in 2005 ruled that van Hoogstraten 'recruited two highly dangerous thugs' to murder Raja in order to halt a civil action that he was bringing against him. The finding was central to a £6 million civil action brought against the property tycoon by the dead man's family. Robert Knapp and David Croke — who were, according to the judgement, van Hoogstraten's henchmen — were sentenced to life for the murder at the Old Bailey in 2002. Van Hoogstraten was sentenced to 10 years for manslaughter, but his conviction was quashed by the Court of Appeal. After the 2005 hearing, the Raja family said in a statement: 'Naturally, we are very pleased with the court's findings, but it has been a devastating and uphill struggle to get here.'

In recent years, the civil courts have increasingly been used to litigate against people who have committed crimes where the state has been unwilling or unable to bring a prosecution. In some cases, the civil ruling has led to a fresh criminal prosecution. For example, in 1991 a High Court judge ruled that Michael Brookes had killed 16-year-old Lynn Siddons in 1978. Her family was awarded £10,641 in damages. The original police case was found to have been bungled, but a fresh criminal investigation then took place and Brookes was charged with the murder in 1992. In July 1996, he was found guilty after a 34-day trial, and sentenced to life in jail.

Another example is the current action being brought by the relatives of the Omagh bombing in 1998, which killed 29 people. There have not been any criminal prosecutions because authorities do not believe there is enough evidence to satisfy the criterion of proof 'beyond reasonable doubt'.

Questions

1 Explain how the outcomes of the Stephen Lawrence and Damilola Taylor cases could be seen as advancing justice.

2 Under what circumstances can victims benefit from the decision in *A* v *Hoare* (2008)?

DNA samples

The use of DNA samples raises the broader problem of the admissibility of evidence and the sense of injustice that victims feel when evidence clearly identifying someone as guilty is rejected by the court because of a procedural irregularity.

In *R* v *B* (2000) (*Attorney General's Reference No. 3 of 1999*), a man was charged with rape after the police found a match between DNA taken from the scene and a sample of his DNA taken on an earlier occasion that had not been destroyed subsequently as the law then required. The judge refused to allow any DNA evidence to be given and the trial collapsed; the Court of Appeal said the judge had been right, but the House of Lords said that the **Police and Criminal Evidence Act 1984** gave the judge discretion as to whether to allow the DNA evidence to be used. The fairness of a trial has to take account of fairness to the victim and to the public at large, as well as to the defendant. Lord Hobhouse argued that:

...respect for the privacy of defendants is not the only value at stake, that the purpose of the criminal law is to protect citizens from harm and that there must be fairness to all, to the victim and to the public as well as to the defendant...the interests of the victim and the public must be considered as well as the interests of the defendant.

A more recent judgement, and one that is likely to have far-reaching implications, is the unanimous ruling by 17 judges in the European Court of Human Rights in December 2008, in a case brought by Michael Marper and a 19-year-old named in court only as S. Both had had fingerprints and DNA taken, but neither was convicted. Since 2005, legislation in England and Wales has allowed the data of those arrested but not convicted to be retained on the DNA database; consequently, more than 800,000 of the 5.1 million samples on the database belong to people with no criminal conviction. In a landmark judgement, the European Court of Human Rights held that retaining the fingerprints and DNA samples of people acquitted of crime, or when proceedings are dropped, breaches a person's right to respect for private life under Article 8. The judges were highly critical of the fact that the DNA samples could be retained without a time limit and regardless of the seriousness of the offence or the age of the suspect. The profiles of the two men are now expected to be taken off the database, but the Home Office stated that the current policy of taking and retaining the DNA of innocent people will remain until it delivers its formal response to the European Court.

The UK has been a pioneer in developing its DNA database, which is larger than that in any other European country. In a response to the ruling, Home Secretary Jacqui Smith claimed that 'DNA and fingerprinting are vital to the fight against crime, providing the police with more than 3,500 matches a month'. These matches lead to many successful prosecutions, which to many victims of crime would clearly be welcome. However, one barrister supporting the European Court decision said that 'the accumulation of vast swathes of personal information including a person's DNA when that person is not suspected of a criminal offence is simply unacceptable in a democratic society'.

Some people claim that accumulating such personal information as DNA is unacceptable in a democratic society

Question

What arguments could be presented for and against the view that justice will be better served by the destruction of DNA samples taken from innocent people?

Substantive criminal law

Provocation and diminished responsibility

Provocation and diminished responsibility are partial defences to murder and if pleaded successfully result in a conviction for voluntary manslaughter. The aim of the partial defences is to provide substantive justice, whereby those who kill but are not fully responsible for their actions are not found guilty of murder.

The provocation defence has been topical in recent years due to the perceived unfairness it affords to women. The problem is the requirement set out in *R* v *Duffy* (1949) for a 'sudden and temporary loss of self-control'. It has become apparent that the general impartial application of this defence results in injustice to women who, because they are generally physically weaker than men, are less likely to act spontaneously and therefore less likely to be able to rely on the strict interpretation of the defence. This situation has been mitigated to a certain extent by *R* v *Ahluwalia* (1992; see page 31), in which battered-woman syndrome was regarded as evidence of the 'abnormality of mind' required under the defence of diminished responsibility.

Clearly, there is still a need for some reform of this defence before it can be regarded as substantially just. The *Ahluwalia* decision in effect typecasts battered women as mentally impaired, having to rely on the defence of diminished responsibility, whereas males — apparently legally sane — may rely on the defence of provocation.

One proposal is to abolish the requirement of sudden loss of self-control. Another is to create a new defence of self-preservation, which would apply to both men and women, but which would take into account the way that women react. This would allow a defence to women like Ahluwalia, who kill out of fear but not in the heat of the moment. Critics of this proposal argue that it would create a licence to kill. It is questionable whether the proposed defence would result in more justice or would simply change the balance of injustice.

Intoxication

The defence of intoxication is useful in the context of justice because it illustrates the difficulty the law has in striking a balance that is fair to both victim and defendant. Currently, involuntary intoxication is a defence to crimes of specific but not basic intent.

It is clear that there is a problem here with applying the principles of justice. Formal justice requires consistency in the way rules operate and yet we treat basic and specific intent in different ways. The illogical nature of this approach is apparent. If intoxication can prevent a person forming a specific intent, it can surely also prevent someone recognising a risk and therefore being reckless. There is thus the potential injustice that someone can be found guilty even though he or she is clearly unable to form the *mens rea* for even a basic intent crime.

This problem was recognised by the House of Lords in *DPP* v *Majewski* (1977), but it firmly resisted the idea that intoxication should become a general defence, because this would be socially undesirable. Lord Salmon argued that while he accepted that there was 'a degree of illogicality in the rule that intoxication may excuse…one type of intention and not another…absolute logic in human affairs is an uncertain guide and a very dangerous master'. One important aspect of individual liberty, he argued, is protection against physical violence and, because the intoxication rule helps to achieve this, 'the rule works without imperilling justice'.

Strict liability

Another area of criminal law that can be explored in addressing the issue of whether the law achieves justice is that of strict liability offences — rules imposing liability in the absence of blameworthiness are arguably substantially unjust.

Tort law

It is useful to consider the strict liability torts of nuisance and *Rylands* v *Fletcher* (1868) — arguably unjust because they impose liability without blameworthiness. The circumstances in which a duty of care is owed in negligence can also be explored — one requirement is that it must be fair, just and reasonable to impose a duty.

Elements of distributive and substantive justice can be seen in the decision in *Donoghue* v *Stephenson* (1932), in which it was held that a duty of care is owed by the manufacturer to the consumer; and it can be argued that to impose a duty of care on someone who is doing his or her best, as in *Nettleship* v *Weston* (1971) and as required under the principle of *Bolam* (1957), is unjust.

Contract law

The policy underpinning contract law has increasingly moved away from *laissez-faire* towards protection of the weaker party. This can be seen through the development of consumer laws by the European Union, national legislation and case law. These laws aim to provide substantive justice through a system of just rules, and also to incorporate distributive justice in that rights are given to the weaker party.

There is a wealth of illustrative material that can be used when discussing this area, including the law relating to unfair contract terms and implied terms. Recent protective legislation includes the **Consumer Protection from Unfair Trading Regulations 2008**, which replace the main offences under the **Trade Descriptions Act 1968**, provisions in the **Consumer Protection Act 1987** relating to misleading price indications, the **Control of Misleading Advertising Regulation 1988** and further secondary legislation. The right of the consumer to cancel doorstep agreements is extended by the Cancellation of Contracts made in a Consumer's Home or Place of Work etc. Regulations 2008. The right to cancel is now applicable to both solicited and unsolicited visits.

The role of equity in contract is relevant to the extent to which justice is achieved. The equitable remedies of specific performance and promissory estoppel were introduced to provide justice where the common law failed to do so.

Conclusion

It is clear that there are aspects of English law where the requirement for formal justice has not been met. This is also true of substantive justice, although arguably less so. However, a balanced view would point out that legislative reform such as the Human Rights Act 1998 and the Access to Justice Act 1999 have helped to ensure that procedures are more fair and individuals more likely to experience justice. Arguably, substantive justice does underpin the English legal system, and in the miscarriage of justice cases, for example, it was not the substantive law that was in question but the manner in which it was being administered.

It remains true, of course, that substantive law can be changed through enactment, so that laws regarded as unjust can be repealed. It is not so simple, however, to alter the behaviour of those administering the legal system.

Sample exam question

Consider what is meant by justice and discuss the extent to which the English law achieves justice.

Further reading

Freeman, M. (2008) *Lloyd's Introduction to Jurisprudence*, Sweet & Maxwell.
Mitchell, A. (2006) 'Exploring law and justice', *A-Level Law Review*, Vol. 1, No. 2, pp. 26–27.

Chapter 26

Judicial creativity

Judicial creativity is concerned with whether or not judges make law, and the extent to which they do so. You should revisit the material on precedent and statutory interpretation covered in Unit 1 and develop it through illustrative material and consideration of how each of these elements aids or limits judicial creativity.

Creativity in judicial precedent

It is important to be able to address the *extent* to which judges can display creativity in the operation of the system of judicial precedent. Some mechanisms of precedent aid judicial creativity, and some impede it. In some areas of law, these mechanisms have been operational in either developing or restricting the development of the law.

Characteristics of precedent that limit judicial creativity

Requirement to follow previous decisions

The doctrine of precedent is based on the idea of **stare decisis**, which means 'to stand by what has been decided'. The courts are bound to follow the decisions made in earlier cases. The doctrine of precedent operates within a hierarchical court structure, with the lower courts being bound by precedents made in the higher courts.

The binding part of a judgement is called the **ratio decidendi**, meaning the legal reason for the decision. Once a *ratio decidendi* is created, it cannot be changed by judges until a case hinging on the same *ratio* is appealed to a higher court. Judgements made by the House of Lords therefore remain binding on all courts for many years. The rule in *Addie* v *Dumbreck* (1929) that an occupier owes no duty of care to a child trespasser was not changed until *British Railways Board* v *Herrington* (1972).

Lord Denning campaigned for many years to free the Court of Appeal from being bound by its own decisions and by the House of Lords, in order to allow greater flexibility. The essence of his argument was that because most binding precedents are set by the Court of Appeal and the House of Lords, it is necessary for a case to reach the House of Lords before it can be changed. In the majority of cases, the final appeal is to the Court of Appeal. Because comparatively few cases are appealed to the House of Lords, the Court of Appeal is, in the majority of cases, the final court to make a decision.

In the cases of *B* v *B* (1978) and *Cantliff* v *Jenkins* (1978), the Court of Appeal held that under the **Domestic Violence and Matrimonial Proceedings Act 1976**, injunctions preventing or restricting access to property could be made to protect wives but not mistresses, unless the mistress was the sole owner or sole tenant of the property. In *Davis* v *Johnson* (1979), Lord Denning persuaded two of the other four judges to join him in departing from these decisions in the Court of Appeal. He said:

> On principle, it seems to me that, while this court should regard itself as normally bound by a previous decision of the court, nevertheless it should be at liberty to depart from it if it is convinced that the previous decision was wrong. What is the argument to the contrary? It is said that if an error has been made, this court has no option but to continue the error and leave it to be corrected by the House of Lords. The answer is this, the House of Lords may never have an opportunity to correct the error, and thus it may be perpetuated indefinitely, perhaps forever.

Lord Denning also refused to follow some House of Lords decisions when sitting in the Court of Appeal. In *Schorsch Meier GmbH* v *Hennin* (1975), the Court of Appeal did not follow *Re United Railways of the Havana and Regla Warehouses Ltd* (1961), in which the House of Lords had decided that damages could only be awarded in sterling. The *Schorsch Meier* case did not progress further. It was a year later before another case based on the same legal principle, *Miliangos* v *George Frank Textiles* (1976), reached the House of Lords. Using the Practice Statement 1966, the House of Lords overruled the decision in *United Railways* and held that damages could be awarded in foreign currency. However, Lord Denning was rebuked by Lord Cross, who said:

> It is not for any inferior court — be it a County Court or a division of the Court of Appeal presided over by Lord Denning — to review the decisions of this House. Such a review can only be undertaken by this House itself under the declaration of 1966.

While unsuccessful in terms of achieving any reform of the doctrine of precedent, Lord Denning's campaign was successful in highlighting the characteristics of precedent that impose restrictions on the Court of Appeal. In order to develop the law in areas acknowledged as needing reform, he had to disregard the rules.

Dependency on cases being brought before the courts

The judiciary is dependent on cases being brought before the higher courts for the opportunity to create law. For example, judges had felt since the 1960s that the old rule of a builder not owing a duty in tort to the person to whom a property was sold was unfair. In *Dutton* v *Bognor Regis UDC* (1972), Lord Denning said *in obiter* that the builder should owe a duty of care to the purchaser of property, but the opportunity to follow this persuasive precedent did not arise until 1978 in *Batty* v *Metropolitan Property Realisations Ltd*.

Characteristics of precedent that aid judicial creativity

Practice Statement 1966

Under the 1966 Practice Statement, the House of Lords has the power to depart from its previous decisions when it appears 'right to do so'. The Law Lords have used this power sparingly because of an overall desire to achieve certainty in the law.

However, despite the limitations set out in the Practice Statement, and the self-imposed restraint that has characterised the Law Lords in a majority of cases heard since 1966, the statement has been used to bring about significant changes in the law. Notable examples are:

❖ no participant can use duress as a defence to a murder charge (*R* v *Howe*, 1987)
❖ *Hansard* can, in certain circumstances, be referred to when interpreting a statute (*Pepper* v *Hart*, 1993)
❖ the *mens rea* of recklessness should always be subjective (*R* v *G*, 2003, overruling *R* v *Caldwell*, 1982)

Find out what other areas of law have been corrected, updated and developed by the House of Lords' use of the Practice Statement. You may find it useful to look at the articles by Chris Turner and Sally Russell given in the Further reading section at the end of the chapter.

Overruling

Higher courts can always overrule earlier precedents set in lower courts. The House of Lords may also overrule its own decisions using the Practice Statement 1966, and the Court of Appeal (Civil Division) can overrule its own decisions using the exceptions in *Young* v *Bristol Aeroplane* (1944).

Overruling must not be confused with reversing, which involves a higher court changing the outcome of a case on appeal.

Distinguishing

Judges in all courts may avoid following a precedent by finding that the facts of the case before them are materially different from those of the case in which the binding precedent was set. In *Balfour* v *Balfour* (1919), Mrs Balfour was unable to enforce a maintenance agreement made with her husband. The *ratio decidendi* of the case was that there is no intention to create legal relations when agreements are made within marriage. In *Merritt* v *Merritt* (1970), the defendant husband sought to rely on the *Balfour* principle to avoid honouring an agreement he had made with his estranged wife. The court distinguished the case on the material difference that the agreement, albeit made within marriage, had been made after the couple had separated, and the husband had to transfer the house to the wife as agreed. The decision limited the scope of the *Balfour* principle and created a new rule in respect of separated couples.

Dissenting judgements

Judges in the higher courts may disagree with the legal principles being applied by the majority judges in cases before them. In such cases, they may deliver a dissenting judgement, in which they outline principles that they believe should apply.

Dissenting judgements are persuasive precedents and may be followed in future cases. Some key areas of law have developed from dissenting judgements. The law on negligent misstatement was developed from the dissenting judgement of Lord Denning in *Candler* v *Crane Christmas* (1951). The majority judges held that account-ants, who prepared a company's accounts knowing that they would be relied upon by third parties, owed no duty of care. Lord Denning, however, stipulated the circum-stances in which such a duty should be owed. His judgement formed the basis of the decision in *Hedley Byrne* v *Heller* (1964), in which it was held that, had there not been a disclaimer, the claimants could have recovered compensation caused by the negligent misstatement. The circumstances later outlined in *Caparo* v *Dickman* (1990) for when such a duty should be owed are similar to those originally outlined by Lord Denning.

Obiter dicta statements

When delivering judgements, judges sometimes speculate on what their decision *would have been* had the facts been slightly different. These *obiter* statements are persuasive and may become the *ratio decidendi* of future cases.

The neighbour principle, set out in the House of Lords by Lord Atkin in *Donoghue* v *Stevenson* (1932), is regarded as the foundation of the modern law of negligence with regard to determining when a duty of care is owed. The criminal defence of consent has also been developed through *obiter* statements. In *R* v *Brown and Others* (1993), the defendants, who had engaged in sadomasochistic activities, were unable to rely on consent when prosecuted under the **Offences Against the Person Act 1861**. However, the Lords stated *in obiter* that consent could be a defence to painful practices such as tattooing and piercing. In *R* v *Wilson* (1996), the defendant husband was able to rely on this defence when he used a hot knife to brand his initials onto his wife's buttocks at her request. The Court of Appeal held that the defendant was engaged in body decoration, which was similar to body piercing or tattooing.

Further examples of persuasive precedent

Persuasive precedents are not binding, but judges may choose to follow them.

Examples of creativity aided by persuasive precedent include *R* v *R* (1991), where the House of Lords was influenced by Court of Appeal arguments on the issue of rape within marriage, and *The Wagon Mound* (1961), where a decision of the Judicial Committee of the Privy Council on remoteness of damage was followed in the English courts.

The Privy Council has also been influential in developing the defence of provocation, in spite of conflicting House of Lords authority. In *Attorney General for Jersey* v *Holley* (2005), a nine-member Privy Council decided by 6 to 3 to follow its decision in *Luc Thiet Thuan* (1997) rather than the more recent decision of the House of Lords in *R* v *Morgan Smith* (2000). The Court of Appeal in *R* v *James and Karimi* (2006) has since followed *Holley* rather than *Smith (Morgan)*.

The Court of Appeal

In practice, the Court of Appeal makes a great deal of new law. A good example is *R* v *Nedrick* (1986), which clarified the law on oblique intent and has become the leading judgement, despite several earlier House of Lords decisions. It was also the Court of Appeal in *R* v *Prentice* (1994) that effectively reintroduced gross negligence manslaughter into modern law. However, as we have seen, the Court of Appeal does not have the power to overrule its own earlier decisions.

Areas of judge-made law

Evidence of the ability of judges to be creative and develop the law, despite the constraints of precedent, is provided by the fact that in a number of significant areas of law, almost all the rules are judge-made. Questions on this topic present an opportunity to refer to areas of substantive law in detail. For example, in criminal law you can consider the rules on the *mens rea* of murder, on involuntary manslaughter and on defences such as intoxication and self-defence. In contract law, the rules on formation and discharge of contract are obvious examples. In tort, you can refer to areas such as the development of the rules relating to nervous shock or economic loss, private nuisance and the rule in *Rylands* v *Fletcher*.

Another area of tort that judges have begun to develop is invasion of privacy. At present, this new tort can arguably be more accurately described as the 'misuse by publication of personal information'. There have been many cases in recent years in which people in the public eye have attempted to prevent intrusion into their private lives. The English judges have, to an extent, followed the decision of the European Court of Human Rights in *Von Hannover* (2004), in which it was held that paparazzi photographs of the Princess of Monaco engaged in activities concerning her personal life, for example dining in restaurants or going out jogging, were an infringement of her right to privacy under Article 8 of the ECHR — the right for respect for private and family life. Article 10 did not override this right because there was no public interest in publication of the photographs.

In *Murray* v *Express Newspapers and Another* (2008), the author J. K. Rowling and her husband (Neil Murray) brought an action for invasion of privacy. A photographer had covertly taken a picture of the couple and their son walking down a street, which was subsequently published in the *Sunday Express Magazine*. The Murrays had been unaware of the picture being taken, and had clearly not consented to its publication.

The decision in *Murray* v *Express Newspapers and Another* (2008) was overturned by the Court of Appeal

At first instance, the Murrays' claim that publication of the photographs was a breach of their son's right to respect for his private and family life was unsuccessful. The first instance judge, Mr Justice Patten, acknowledged that this was a test case and pointed out that, prior to the Human Rights Act, the law did not recognise any right to privacy and that there was still no general cause of action for 'invasion of privacy'. The decision was overturned by the Court of Appeal. Sir Anthony Clarke, Master of the Rolls, held that the clandestine taking of photographs of people while engaging in their personal lives, in the knowledge that if asked the subject of the photograph would not consent, followed by the sale of the photographs for publication, could amount to a breach of Article 8. Although this case concerned a child, the decision was not specifically confined to children. In the Hugh Grant case (2008), photographs of Liz Hurley, her husband and Hugh Grant while on holiday were taken by a picture agency and sold to newspapers. The newspapers that published the pictures settled out of court, but the agency was found to have invaded Grant's and Hurley's privacy, primarily on the basis that the taking of the photographs had not been consented to.

These decisions were followed in the recent case of *Mosley* v *News Group Newspapers Ltd* (2008), in which the Formula One boss successfully sued the *News of the World* in respect of an article headed 'F1 boss has sick Nazi orgy with 5 hookers'. The case did not develop the law in relation to the scope of a 'reasonable expectation of privacy', but it did deal with the issue of balancing Article 8 with Article 10. Further information about this decision is contained in Chapter 28 on the balancing of conflicting interests.

Questions

1 What benefits of judicial law making are highlighted by these decisions?

2 What problems of judicial law making are highlighted by these decisions?

Creativity in statutory interpretation

Literal rule

In theory, judges should have little opportunity for creativity because their task is to apply statutes as they are written. Supporters of the literal rule argue that judges should do this in all circumstances. Judges who follow the literal rule are not creative and do not develop the law, even when common sense demands it. An example is *Fisher* v *Bell* (1961). A shopkeeper, who had displayed flick knives in his shop window, was charged under the Offensive Weapons Act 1959 with offering for sale an offensive weapon. The court held that no offence had been committed as, according to contract law, what he had done amounted to an invitation to treat and not to an offer.

Mischief rule

When interpreting a statute, judges may be creative in broadening or narrowing its application. This is particularly the case with the mischief and purposive approaches. The mischief rule requires judges to look back to the law before the Act in question was made, to determine the gap in the law the Act was intended to remedy.

In *Smith* v *Hughes* (1960), a prostitute was prosecuted under the Street Offences Act 1958, under which it was an offence to solicit in the street. In this case, the prostitute had attracted the attention of men in the street by tapping on her first-floor window. Using the mischief approach, the court held that the mischief the Act had been passed to prevent was men in the street being accosted by prostitutes. It therefore found her guilty. The application of the Act was thus made broader because it was not limited to situations where the prostitute was in the street.

A further example is *The Royal College of Nursing* v *Department of Health and Social Security* (1981), in which the House of Lords had to decide how the **Abortion Act 1967** should be interpreted. The Act stated that lawful abortion requires a pregnancy to be terminated by 'a registered medical practitioner'. In 1967, the method of producing an abortion was surgical and so needed to be performed by a doctor. However, due to technological advances, by the 1980s abortions were induced by drip-feeding a drug that discharged the foetus. This was performed by midwives and nurses. The House of Lords held that the mischief the Act had been passed to prevent was illegal backstreet abortion, and that therefore it was legal for midwives and nurses to administer the drugs.

Purposive approach

The purposive approach, being the modern version of the mischief approach, similarly provides opportunities for judicial creativity. It was the preferred approach of Lord Denning who, as long ago as 1950 in *Magor and St Mellons* v *Newport Corporation*, said:

> We do not sit here to pull the language of Parliament and of Ministers to pieces and make nonsense of it. That is an easy thing to do and it is a thing to which lawyers are too often prone. We sit here to find the intention of Parliament and of Ministers and carry it out, and we do this better by filling in the gaps and making sense of the enactment than by opening it up to destructive analysis.

The purposive approach allows for a broader interpretation of a word or phrase than the literal rule. In *R* v *Cockburn* (2008), the defendant had been convicted, under s.31 of the **Offences Against the Person Act 1861**, of setting a 'mantrap or other engine…with intent to cause grievous bodily harm'. The Court of Appeal upheld the conviction. Referring to the purpose of the Act, it held that a spiked metal object attached to the roof of a shed in such a way that it would fall on anyone opening the shed door was an engine. The defendant had claimed that the device was operated by gravity and was therefore not an engine.

The purposive approach has become increasingly popular among English judges, particularly since the UK joined the European Union. In many countries, the law is stated in general principles that can be applied to a broad range of circumstances. This necessitates a purposive approach to legislation. EU law is also drafted in such terms, and it is important that English judges take a purposive approach to interpreting acts of Parliament that have been passed to comply with European obligations.

Lord Denning, in *Bulmer* v *Bollinger* (1974), pointed out that when interpreting such legislation, English courts must depart from the traditional methods of interpreting domestic statutes and follow the European pattern: 'No longer must they examine words in meticulous detail. No longer must they argue about the precise grammatical sense. They must look to the purpose or intent.'

The European Convention on Human Rights is similarly set out in broad terms. The judges in the European Court of Human Rights, therefore, also use the purposive approach. The **Human Rights Act 1998** requires that all legislation be interpreted so that as far as possible it is compatible with the Convention. This will inevitably result in English judges increasingly using the purposive approach.

Following the House of Lords decision in *Pepper* v *Hart* (1993), judges may now make reference to *Hansard* in limited circumstances as an aid to interpretation. This decision was arguably brought about by the shift in favour from the literal to the purposive approach that has occurred in recent years, and it has certainly facilitated this approach.

Balance of the roles of Parliament and the judiciary

Constitutional position

Constitutionally, it is the role of Parliament to create law and, as Lord Radcliffe said, 'it is unacceptable constitutionally that there should be two sources of law-making at work at the same time'. The basis of the constitutional position is that Parliament is democratically elected (at least, the House of Commons is) and that the legislative programme will be influenced by the electorate. Judges, on the other hand, are not elected and are not necessarily representative of the population they serve.

The constitutional role of judges has changed in recent years through the UK's membership of the European Union. Section 2(4) of the **European Communities Act 1972** provides that European Community law should take precedence over English law. In giving effect to this section, English judges have been able to exercise powers that were not available to them in the past. For example, in *R* v *Secretary of State for Transport ex parte Factortame* (1990), the European Court of Justice held that domestic courts are entitled to ignore provisions of domestic legislation that are in conflict with provisions of directly enforceable European law. In this case, it was also held that domestic courts can suspend domestic legislation while awaiting a decision of the European Court of Justice.

The **Human Rights Act 1998** has also significantly altered the balance between the judges and Parliament. Section 3 requires legislation to be interpreted so that as far as possible it is compatible with the European Convention on Human Rights. This was most dramatically demonstrated in *A and Others* v *Secretary of State for the Home Department* (2004). The House of Lords held that s.23 of the **Anti-Terrorism, Crime and Security Act 2001**, in permitting the detention of suspected international terrorists indefinitely without charge or trial, was incompatible with Articles 5 and 14 of the European Convention on Human Rights.

Policy

Formulation of policy is the role of Parliament. Policy is a set of ideas about what should be done and sets out objectives and intended directions for change. Ronald Dworkin made a distinction between rules and principles on the one hand and policies on the other:

* A policy is a standard setting out of a goal to be achieved, usually in terms of the economic, social or political well-being of the community.
* A principle sets individual rights above communal well-being and imposes a standard of justice or fairness or some other moral dimension.

Matters of policy should be left to the elected legislators; judges should concern themselves only with legal principles.

On the whole, judges tend to agree with this view, at least in what they say. However, they are sometimes placed in positions where they have to make policy decisions. First, judges have a role in judicial review and as guardians of individual rights. By giving priority to individual rights over policy, and thereby ruling against the government, they will be making decisions that could be seen as political and that have an impact on policy goals. For example, the House of Lords decision in *A and Others* v *Secretary of State for the Home Department* (2004) — that detention of suspected international terrorists without trial or charge is unlawful — will inevitably have an impact on how the government deals with terrorism in the future.

The second problem for judges is that they sometimes have to make controversial decisions, which will inevitably have policy implications. In *Gillick* v *West Norfolk and Wisbech AHA* (1985), the issue for the judges to decide was whether girls under the age of 16 should be prescribed contraceptives without parental consent. There was no consensus on the issue and Parliament had given no guidance. The House of Lords held that a girl under 16 could be prescribed contraceptives without parental consent if she fully understood the issues involved. There have been similar issues raised more recently with girls under 16 having abortions without parental consent.

Policy in statutory interpretation

Judges who argued for the literal rule usually did so on the principle that they should not change the wording of statutes, because to do so would be to usurp the legislative function and that was not their role. If the outcome of a judicial decision was inconvenient, the proper solution was for Parliament to make any alteration it felt necessary.

Judges adopted this approach in *In the Estate of Bravda* (1968), where the Court of Appeal had to deal with a situation under the Wills Act 1837. The Act clearly stated that any beneficiary who signed a will automatically lost the right to benefit under the will. In this case, a man's daughters were the main beneficiaries, and the court felt that it would be right to ensure that where there are two independent witnesses, the mere fact that a beneficiary has signed as a witness should not operate (as it then did) to defeat the intentions of the testator. However, rather than adopt either the golden rule or mischief rule and change the wording of the Act, the court felt that, as a policy issue, the change should be made by Parliament. The Wills Act 1968 was passed to make the necessary changes.

On the other hand, there are examples of decisions in statutory interpretation that are based on policy. In *Re Sigsworth* (1935), for example, the court ruled that a man who had murdered his mother, who had died intestate, should not benefit from his crime. It was contrary to public policy to allow such an undesirable outcome. The golden rule was used and the words of the statute were amended.

In the case of *Royal College of Nursing* v *DHSS* (1981), the majority in the House of Lords was influenced by what it considered to be the policy of the Abortion Act 1967, namely broadening the grounds of lawful abortion and ensuring that it was carried out with proper skill. The two dissenting judges, Lords Wilberforce and Edmund-Davies, argued that the Act should not be rewritten because it dealt with 'a controversial subject involving moral or social judgements on which opinions strongly differ'. In other words, this was a policy issue, which should be left to Parliament.

Professor J. A. G. Griffith, in *The Politics of the Judiciary*, argues that where there is ambiguity in a statute, judges choose the interpretation that best suits their view of what policy should be. The example that best fits this argument is *Bromley London Borough Council* v *Greater London Council* (1983). Griffith claimed that what the House of Lords did in this case was make a choice between two interpretations, based not on what Parliament intended, but primarily on 'the Law Lords' strong preference for the principles of the market economy with a dislike of heavy subsidisation for social purposes'.

Policy in criminal law

Intoxication

In *DPP* v *Majewski* (1977), policy issues were clearly the basis of the decision. The House of Lords refused to allow intoxication as a defence to a basic-intent offence. Lord Steyn said that one of the prime purposes of the criminal law is the protection from unprovoked violence of people who are pursuing their lawful lives; to allow intoxication as a defence would be to leave the citizen unprotected from such violence. Lord Salmon said: 'If there were to be no penal sanction for any injury unlawfully inflicted under the complete mastery of drink or drugs, voluntarily taken, the social consequences would be appalling.'

Similarly, in *R* v *O'Grady* (1987), the Court of Appeal stated that the principle that a person should not be penalised for an honest mistake gave way to the policy consideration that society should be protected from those who do dangerous things as a result of intoxication.

Provocation

In *R* v *Ahluwalia* (1992), where the defendant had clearly not acted in the heat of the moment, it was held that important considerations of public policy would be involved if provocation were redefined so as to blur the distinction between sudden loss of self-control and deliberate retribution. The court was not willing to consider such a change.

Consent to the infliction of violence

It has long been recognised that to take part in sporting activities is to consent to the possible infliction of some degree of injury. In the case of boxing, for example, some injury is almost inevitable.

In *R* v *Wilson* (1996), it was accepted that consent can be given to the infliction of injury within marriage, yet in *Brown and Others* (1993), consenting adults were found guilty. From the judgements of the House of Lords, it is clear that policy was being considered. For example, Lord Templeman expressed the view that 'society was entitled to protect itself against a cult of violence. Pleasure derived from the infliction of pain was an evil thing. Cruelty was uncivilised.'

Policy in tort

The extension of negligence into ever more diverse areas has also led to policy issues being raised, with reference to wider social or economic considerations, rather than to precedent or to legal principles, to justify decisions. This is apparent in the law relating to pure economic loss. In *Spartan Steel and Alloys Ltd* v *Martin and Co. (Contractors) Ltd* (1972), Lord Denning openly based his leading judgement on policy. He said:

> At bottom I think the question of recovering economic loss is one of policy. Whenever the courts draw a line to mark out the bounds of duty, they do it as a matter of policy so as to limit the responsibility of the defendant. Whenever the courts set bounds to the damages recoverable — saying that they are, or are not, too remote — they do it as a matter of policy so as to limit the liability of the defendant.

A similar situation can be observed in the development of the law relating to nervous shock. In *Alcock* v *Chief Constable of South Yorkshire* (1992), the House of Lords, influenced by the floodgates argument, set out the criteria that successful secondary victims have to fulfil. Lord Oliver openly used the word 'policy' in explaining his decision to limit the range of potential victims to whom a duty of care could be owed.

Should judges create law?

Benefits of judicial law making

Flexibility

An advantage of the common law system is that it is able to respond to new situations. Within the limits set by precedent and the rules of statutory interpretation, judges are able to develop the law in ways that reflect changing social and technological circumstances. For example, the law has been adapted to deal with the effect of life-support systems on the exact point of death, as in *R* v *Malcherek and Steel* (1981), and technical developments in the way abortions are carried out, as in *Royal College of Nursing* v *DHSS* (1981).

In contract law, the postal rule has been adapted to deal with instantaneous forms of communication, as in *Entores* v *Miles Far East Corporation* (1955).

It takes many months for an Act of Parliament to be passed. However, the courts may respond immediately to a novel situation. In *McLoughlin* v *O'Brian* (1982), the House of Lords extended the law on nervous shock to cover situations where the secondary victim came upon the 'immediate aftermath'.

More time to focus

The government is intent on pushing through a legislative programme to fulfil its political goals. Furthermore, in contrast to judges, who have only one case before them at any one time, MPs and peers have many conflicting priorities to attend to, and inevitably the non-controversial, politically insignificant reforms to the law are often left for many years.

For example, despite the work of the Law Commission, the law on non-fatal offences and corporate manslaughter remains unreformed.

Similarly, moral issues are often not included in the legislative programme, and the judiciary is consequently left to determine whether development of the law is required.

This was clearly the case with husband rape. It had long been regarded by society as unacceptable, but successive parliaments had not found time for statutory change. The long-awaited decision was finally made in *R* v *R* (1991).

Legal expertise

Judges have a further advantage over Parliament in that they are legal experts and thus better equipped to develop the law. Because they are trained to apply existing principles and relate developments to the existing law, the law is more likely to remain consistent and coherent. However, the development by judges of gross negligence manslaughter, based as it seems to be on civil law principles, has arguably not made the law of involuntary manslaughter either consistent or coherent.

Problems with judicial law making

Constitutional position

While judicial law making may be desirable for a number of reasons, the constitutional position, as we have seen, is that Parliament creates law and judges apply it. There are two reasons for this:

* The formulation of policy is the role of a democratically elected Parliament that will recognise the will of the electorate. The judiciary is unelected.
* The judiciary is arguably not representative of the population. It is drawn from a narrow social group and this raises the possibility, identified by Professor Griffith, that its views will reflect this narrow social background. Women and people from ethnic minorities are under-represented, especially among the senior judiciary. For example, until the appointment of Lady Hale in January 2004, there were no female Law Lords.

Lack of research

When Parliament wishes to introduce a new piece of legislation, there is considerable opportunity for research. Often, legislation is the result of recommendations from law reform bodies, which possess the expertise to research an area thoroughly.

The Law Commission is a permanent law reform body and has achieved considerable success in having recommendations recognised in Acts of Parliament. Examples of such legislation include the **Contract (Rights of Third Parties) Act 1999** and the **Computer Misuse Act 1990**. The Green Paper stage allows for interested parties to be consulted, and the passage of a bill through Parliament involves many debates among people who are able to research the relevant issues.

Judges, however, cannot be so comprehensive in their approach. Their decisions are based on the evidence presented to them by the parties involved in the case. They cannot consider arguments about the general social, economic or moral aspects, even though their decisions, as in *Gillick,* may have implications for society generally.

Judge-made law operates retrospectively

Judge-made law applies to events that took place before its creation. This can be illustrated by *Launchbury* v *Morgans* (1973), in which the House of Lords rejected Lord Denning's concept of the matrimonial car. The decision would have applied to accidents occurring before the judgement, and therefore insurers would have had to pay out in respect of a risk that had not been taken account of when the insurance premium was fixed.

Perhaps a more familiar example is that of *R* v *R* (1991), the effect of which was to turn an act that was lawful at the time it was committed into a serious criminal offence. Nevertheless, the decision was upheld by the European Court of Human Rights. In *SW and CR* v *United Kingdom* (1995), the ECtHR held that the UK had not been in breach of Article 7 of the Convention, which provides that no one should be found guilty of an offence that was not an offence at the time it was committed. The court's reasoning was that judicial law-making was well entrenched in legal tradition and the development of the law in this case had been reasonably foreseeable.

This reasoning of the ECtHR was followed by the Court of Appeal in *R* v *Crooks* (2004). The defendant had forced his wife to have sexual intercourse without her consent in 1970, 21 years before the *R* v *R* case made such behaviour illegal. In upholding the rape conviction, Judge LJ said that the defendant should have foreseen that the marital exemption was about to be removed. He also justified the decision on the basis that the right of the wife to freedom from inhuman or degrading treatment outweighed the defendant's right not to be tried retrospectively.

This problem does not arise with legislation, which operates prospectively. It is usually the case that legislation comes into effect on a fixed date after the Act has received royal assent, in order to allow time for people to prepare for the change in law.

In some countries, including the USA, cases only apply prospectively. This concept has been considered in relation to the English legal system. In a speech in 1987, the then Lord Chancellor, Lord Mackay, discussed the possibility of allowing prospective overruling, whereby the court might uphold the existing precedent in the current case but declare it overruled for the future. The main problem with this idea is that while most litigants are prepared to accept defeat if the judge decides the law is against them, they would find it hard to accept that they had won their case only for future litigants, not for themselves. There would seem little point in going to court at all.

Judge-made law is incremental in nature

Judges can only make law on the facts of the case before them. They cannot lay down a comprehensive code to cover all similar situations. Some areas of law, for example negligence, might be well suited to this case-by-case approach. However, with other areas it is not helpful when small changes are made, such as the introduction of gross negligence manslaughter in *R* v *Prentice* (1994) and *R* v *Adomako* (1995), clarified in *R* v *Misra* (2004), when really the whole area of involuntary manslaughter needs to be properly reformed.

Judge-made law thus develops in an unstructured, random way. It is dependent on cases being brought and then appealed through to a court sufficiently senior to make a new precedent.

Complexity/technical distinctions

One of the arguments often used against precedent as a law-making process is that judges make technical distinctions between the case they are deciding and the precedent, in order to avoid following the precedent. The result of this is that the law becomes complex and confusing, with many minor technical distinctions.

Judicial preference

Judicial views on the constitutional position

There are contrasting views among judges on the extent to which they should be making new law. Lord Justice Oliver argued that to have judges developing new concepts of law would mean the courts abandoning their proper function and assuming the mantle of legislator.

This judicial view prevailed in the case of Debbie Purdy, who has multiple sclerosis and sought clarification from the Director of Public Prosecutions on how decisions to prosecute are reached under s.2 of the Suicide Act 1961. So far, there have been no prosecutions of relatives of people who have travelled abroad to the Dignitas clinic in Switzerland, where doctors can prescribe lethal doses of drugs. However, the law is not clear, and Purdy sought an assurance that her husband will not be prosecuted if he helps her to get there, for example by purchasing a ticket or pushing her wheelchair. Both judges in the High Court rejected her claim. Lord Justice Scott Baker said:

> We cannot leave this case without expressing great sympathy for Ms Purdy, her husband and others in a similar position who wish to know in advance whether they will face prosecution for doing what many would regard as something that the law should permit, namely to help a loved one go abroad to end their suffering when they are unable to do it on their own…This would involve a change in the law. The offence of assisted suicide is very widely drawn to cover all manner of different circumstances; only Parliament can change it.

The decision was upheld by the Court of Appeal in February 2009.

Lord Scarman, by contrast, put forward the view in *McLoughlin* v *O'Brian* (1982) that the court's proper function was to adjudicate according to principle. If principle led to results that were felt to be socially unacceptable, then Parliament could legislate to overrule them. The real risk to the common law would be if it stood still, halted by a conservative judicial approach.

Acceptability of judicial law making

Some judges argue that the role of the judiciary should be determined by the type of law involved. The view of Lord Reid in the 1960s was that judges should not so readily create new law in areas such as property, contract, family and criminal law, where certainty is of vital importance, but that they could have more freedom to do so in the areas of tort and public and administrative law, where judges regard their creative role as legitimate and appropriate.

Recent cases in which the House of Lords has refused to develop the criminal law include *R* v *Jones and Others* (2006) and *R* v *Davis* (2008):

❖ In *Jones*, the defendants were charged with causing criminal damage to property at military bases. They claimed they had done so to prevent the international crime of aggression. The House of Lords acknowledged that there was such an international crime, but said the prevention of crime in the **Criminal Damage Act 1971** referred to domestic crime. International crime only becomes domestic when Parliament makes the required legislation. Consequently, the House of Lords did not allow the defendants' defence on the basis that such a change in the criminal law had to be made by Parliament.

❖ Similarly, in *Davis*, the main witnesses to a murder were frightened to testify against the defendant. The trial judge ordered their identities to be kept secret from both the defendant and the public. The House of Lords overturned the conviction on the basis that the right of the defendant to confront his accusers was fundamental to a fair trial in the adversarial system, and that any change in the law was a matter for Parliament.

Lord Devlin argued that judges should stick to activist law making, by which he meant developing the law in line with the consensus view of society, and avoid dynamic law making, which involves creating an idea outside the consensus and effectively taking sides on controversial issues. However, judges cannot avoid making decisions in controversial cases. These might be cases which are politically sensitive, such as *Bromley London Borough Council* v *GLC* (1983) and *ex parte Pinochet* (2000), or ones which raise profound moral or social issues, for example *Gillick* v *West Norfolk and Wisbech AHA* (1986) and *Airedale NHS Trust* v *Bland* (1993).

Whatever legal theorists argue, the fact remains that in practice judges have to get involved in controversial areas because such cases are brought before the courts. It is difficult to see how, in deciding any of these cases, judges could have avoided both engaging in dynamic law making and offending at least one section of the community.

Personal preference

We have seen that judges adopt contrasting views on their role and it is difficult to escape the conclusion that the view they take is largely a matter of personal preference. Lord Denning, in particular, had a crusading approach to judicial law making and was determined not to be fettered by existing legal rules. He argued that it was the duty of judges to do justice and not to follow unjust precedents or restrictive approaches to statutory interpretation. However, he was just as firmly opposed by senior Law Lords, including Viscount Simmonds, who described the approach of 'filling in the gaps' that he took to statutory interpretation as a 'naked usurpation of the legislative function'.

David Robertson, writing in *Judicial Discretion in the House of Lords* (1998), concluded: 'Law in almost any case that comes before the Lords turns out to be whatever their Lordships feel it ought to be.'

Conclusion

It is evident that in some respects Parliament is more suited than the judiciary to develop the law. However, areas of the law that are largely judge-made seem to work just as well as those made almost exclusively by Parliament. Through the doctrine of precedent and their role in statutory interpretation, judges frequently have to develop the law by clarifying, and in some cases putting right, what is written in an Act of Parliament.

Sample exam question

With reference to the doctrine of precedent and to the rules of statutory interpretation, discuss the extent to which judges are able to develop the law and consider whether judges should be creating legal rules.

Further reading

Blood, P. (2007) 'Exploring legal theory: separation of powers', *A-Level Law Review*, Vol. 3, No. 1, pp. 2–4.

Blood, P. (2008) 'The meaning of "judicial independence"', *A-Level Law Review*, Vol. 3, No. 2, pp. 14–16.

Russell, S. (2009) 'Avoiding precedent: the Practice Statement 1966', *A-Level Law Review*, Vol. 4, No. 2, pp. 6–9.

Turner, C. (2006) 'Precedent', *A-Level Law Review*, Vol. 2, No. 1, pp. 10–12.

Chapter 27

Fault

Fault is the idea that a person is responsible for his or her actions and that in some way he or she has behaved wrongly. It implies that people should be able to contemplate the damage or harm that their actions might cause and that if they continue with those actions they will be to blame for the consequences. Fault forms the basis of most court proceedings, and the extent to which a person is deemed to be at fault usually determines the outcome of those proceedings.

There are various definitions of the word 'fault'. The *Concise Oxford Dictionary* provides many: 'defect, imperfection, blemish, of character...thing wrongly done...responsibility for something wrong...blame'. The *Collins Concise Dictionary* provides similar definitions: 'responsibility for a mistake or misdeed...guilty of error, culpable...blame'. 'Blameworthy' is defined as 'deserving censure' or 'deserving blame'. 'Blame' is defined in similar terms to fault, with reference to responsibility, fault, culpability and responsibility.

While there are various definitions of fault, perhaps the core meaning is 'responsibility'. The definition 'responsibility for something wrong' would appear to be the most useful for the purposes of discussing the role of fault in English law.

Fault in criminal law

Actus reus

To be found guilty of most criminal offences, an *actus reus* and *mens rea* must be present. The *actus reus*, meaning 'prohibited act', is made up of the acts, circumstances and consequences of a specific offence. It comprises the physical elements of the crime.

In order to be found guilty of a criminal offence, the accused must commit the *actus reus* voluntarily. If the accused is not in control of his or her own actions for any reason, then he or she cannot be said to be acting voluntarily or to be at fault. There are criminal defences, including automatism and duress, which the accused may plead in such circumstances, proof of which will result in acquittal. The accused will thus not be held responsible for actions that are not the result of his or her rational will.

Automatism arises when someone suffers total loss of control due to external factors. In *R* v *Bailey* (1983), the accused, a diabetic, was charged under s.18 of the **Offences Against the Person Act 1861** after he hit his ex-girlfriend's new boyfriend on the head with an iron bar. He successfully claimed the defence of automatism. He had been in a hypoglycaemic state brought about by a failure to eat after having a sugary drink.

Mens rea

The need for *mens rea* is perhaps the most obvious evidence that fault is important in criminal law. To be found guilty of a criminal offence, it is necessary to establish a degree of mental awareness on the part of the defendant. *Mens rea* is the mental element of the crime and is usually defined in terms of intention or recklessness. The state of mind required for a conviction varies between offences.

Intention can be either direct, where the purpose of the accused is to bring about the prohibited consequence, or oblique, where the accused recognises the result is a virtual certainty. Recklessness can be defined as unjustified risk-taking. It is now always considered as subjective following the House of Lords judgement in *R* v *G* (2003), which abolished Caldwell recklessness. Subjective recklessness requires the defendant knowingly to have taken a risk.

Murder and voluntary manslaughter

Murder is the most serious homicide offence, and this fact is reflected in the mandatory sentence of life imprisonment issued for it. To convict someone of murder, it must be proved that he or she had the intention to kill or to cause grievous bodily harm.

In practice, it has not been easy to establish what constitutes intention. Where a person acts deliberately, intention is obvious, but in a number of murder cases the defendant has argued that he or she had some other purpose, and the courts have had to decide whether this can amount to intention. The current law is that outlined in *R* v *Nedrick* (1986), as modified in *R* v *Woollin* (1998) and *R* v *Matthews and Alleyne* (2003). If the defendant is aware that death or serious injury is virtually certain to follow and yet continues with his or her actions, this can be treated as evidence that he or she intended the result. Arguably, this is a fair assumption, and it is reasonable to claim that a person who behaves like this is as much at fault as the person who sets out deliberately to kill.

Partial defences to murder are contained in the Homicide Act 1957 and, if proven, allow the court to find the accused guilty of the lesser crime of voluntary manslaughter. These partial defences, notably diminished responsibility and provocation, apply to situations where the accused is considered not to be totally in control of what he or she is doing. The defences thus recognise that such defendants are less at fault than murderers and so should be less liable for the consequences of their actions. The less serious nature of voluntary manslaughter is recognised through the life sentence being discretionary rather than mandatory.

Under s.3 of the Homicide Act 1957, the defence of provocation requires proof that provocative conduct caused the defendant to lose self-control, and that a reasonable person would have reacted in the same way. In *DPP* v *Camplin* (1978), the murder conviction was reduced to voluntary manslaughter on the basis of provocation. The accused was 15 years old. He killed his victim by hitting him over the head with a chapatti pan, after the victim had sexually assaulted him and then taunted him about it.

One concern about this defence is that a person could claim to be provoked by relatively minor things, such as the crying of a baby in *R* v *Doughty* (1986). It could be argued that the gravity of provocation should be relevant in determining the degree of fault shown by the defendant. Although this is partially addressed through the 'reasonable man' test, the Law Commission in 2005 recommended that the law should be reformed to require 'gross' provocation, which would mean that the defendant would have to have a 'justifiable sense of being seriously wronged'. As the law currently stands, it could be claimed that defendants who have a level of fault that justifies a conviction for murder are able to use minor provocation as an excuse for violence.

An important requirement for provocation to succeed as a defence is that there must have been sudden and temporary loss of self-control. The person who acts in the heat of the moment may do things that under circumstances of cool reflection he or she would regret. As Lord Devlin stated in *R* v *Duffy* (1949), the person is 'so subject to passion as to make him for the moment not the master of his mind'. It is easy to see that it could be claimed that someone like this is not as much at fault as the person who kills in cold blood.

One of the results of this rule is that some women have not been able to use provocation as a defence, because their reaction to the provocation was delayed through fear that their violent partner would overpower them. In *Ahluwahlia* (1992), for example, the defendant waited until her husband was asleep before killing him. Some people have argued that such women should not be treated as murderers because their actions were influenced by fear for their own safety. The law has partially acknowledged this by accepting that, in extreme cases, battered-woman syndrome could develop, which might amount to an abnormality of mind under diminished responsibility. It was on this basis, rather than on the basis of provocation, that Ahluwahlia's appeal against her conviction for murder was allowed.

Questions

1 Referring back to Unit 3 material, consider the cases of *Doughty*, *Ahluwahlia*, *Hancock and Shankland* and *Woollin*. How would you assess the level of fault in each case?

2 Decide whether the defendants should be guilty of murder or manslaughter and explain why.

Involuntary manslaughter

Involuntary manslaughter is more difficult to classify in terms of fault. Now that the definition of recklessness is clearly subjective, it is hard to see how the objective test in the definition of 'dangerous' in unlawful and dangerous act manslaughter can be justified. The definition of 'dangerous' is that given in *R v Church* (1966) as 'in the sense that a sober and reasonable person would inevitably recognise that it carried some risk of harm'.

Should someone be considered sufficiently at fault to be guilty of manslaughter if he or she is genuinely unaware of a danger that other people would recognise? Another aspect of this type of manslaughter is that the only *mens rea* required is that of the unlawful act. This lack of correspondence between the *actus reus*, which is death, and the *mens rea*, which might only be recklessness as to whether unlawful force is applied, seems to suggest that the person is not being convicted on the basis of his or her degree of fault.

Gross negligence manslaughter was reintroduced into English law by the House of Lords in *R v Adomako* (1994). The decision was in line with the Court of Appeal decision in *R v Prentice* (1994), but in this type of manslaughter too it is difficult to see a clear and coherent fault element. The *mens rea* for the offence was gross negligence, which is not fully defined; Lord Mackay in *Adomako* was unwilling to provide a detailed definition. However, he quoted Lord Hewart CJ, who in *R v Bateman* (1925) stated that it was 'such disregard for the life and safety of others as to amount to a crime against the state and conduct deserving punishment'. The problem with this definition is that it is too broad and leaves up to the jury the decision as to what amounts to gross negligence in each case. In *R v Misra and Srivastava* (2004), the Court of Appeal held that there must be a risk of death, and that risk of bodily injury or injury to health was not sufficient.

We are thus left with a position where both types of involuntary manslaughter have significant objective elements, which allow people to be convicted when they may

have been unaware of a risk that others would have noticed. The rules seem to be out of step with most other important areas of criminal law and have been criticised by the Law Commission as unsatisfactory.

Non-fatal offences

The operation of fault in non-fatal offences is also inconsistent. It is clear that all the offences require proof of fault for a conviction. However, while some of the offences have a *mens rea* requirement, which equates with the harm caused, others do not.

Assault and battery require intention or subjective recklessness to bring about the prohibited result of the *actus reus*. However, sections 47 and 20 both require intention or recklessness to bring about a result less serious than that specified in the *actus reus*. If charged with a s.47 offence, the accused can be found guilty of causing actual bodily harm, despite only having the intention of, or knowingly taking the risk of, frightening or unlawfully touching the victim. Under s.20, a conviction can be sustained for wounding or causing grievous bodily harm when the accused only intended or took the risk of causing some harm.

It would appear that under sections 47 and 20, the accused is held legally responsible for a level of harm higher than the one he or she is at fault in bringing about. He or she may have voluntarily performed the act that caused the consequences, but not intended or knowingly taken the risk of the consequences being so serious.

Question

Explain in your own words which aspects of the law on involuntary manslaughter and non-fatal offences appear to be inconsistent with the principle that liability should match the degree of fault.

Distinction between legal fault and motive

In criminal law, the legal fault requirement is stipulated in the definition of the offences. However, criminal law takes no account of motive. This is illustrated clearly by the issue of mercy killings. People who perpetrate mercy killings do so out of care for the victim and often with the best possible motive, but they are still technically guilty of murder.

In *R* v *Cox* (1992), the defendant doctor was found guilty of attempted murder. He had injected a terminally ill, elderly patient, who was suffering constant severe pain, with a lethal drug, after the patient asked him to end her suffering. Where possible, the judge may take account of motive when sentencing, and the defendant was given a suspended prison sentence.

Questions

1 Do you think it is completely true that the criminal law takes no account of motive?

2 What are the reasons for considering the mercy killer to be 'at fault' and therefore criminally liable? In your view, should such people face prosecution?

Strict liability

There are many crimes for which there is no fault requirement in terms of *mens rea*. This is a significant departure from the principle that to be guilty of a criminal offence a defendant should be proved to be at fault.

Strict liability offences are generally regulatory, concerned with public safety, and usually made by statute. They cover situations such as minor road traffic offences, food safety laws,

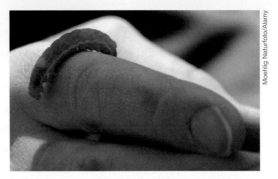

In *Smedleys* v *Breed* (1974), the defendants were convicted under s.2 of the Food and Drugs Act 1955

protection of the environment, and the sale of alcohol and tobacco to underage children.

In *Smedleys* v *Breed* (1974), a caterpillar was found in a tin of peas. The defendants were convicted under s.2 of the **Food and Drugs Act 1955**, despite having taken all reasonable precautions to prevent this sort of contamination occurring. Another example is *Harrow LBC* v *Shah* (1999), in which the defendant, a newsagent, was convicted of selling a lottery ticket to a 13-year-old. The fact that he had advised staff not to sell lottery tickets to under-16s, had put up a notice in the shop to this effect and had told staff to ask for proof of identity were irrelevant.

The courts are reluctant, in the absence of express statutory permission, to impose strict liability for offences that are truly criminal in nature. In such situations, there is a presumption that *mens rea* is required. In *Sweet* v *Parsley* (1970), the defendant owned a house that she rented to students. Unknown to her, they smoked cannabis on the premises. She was charged with being concerned in the management of premises used for the purpose of smoking cannabis. On appeal, her conviction was quashed on the basis that the offence was truly criminal and carried a serious social stigma.

This principle was adopted in the more recent case of *B* v *DPP* (2000). In this case, a 15-year-old boy encouraged a 13-year-old girl (she claimed to be over 14) to have oral sex with him. He was convicted of committing an act of gross indecency on a

child under the age of 14. Both the trial judge and the Court of Appeal agreed that the offence was one of strict liability. However, the House of Lords quashed the conviction on the basis that *mens rea* was required because the offence was truly criminal in nature and carried a serious social stigma. The case of *R* v *Prince* (1874), in which the defendant was convicted of abducting a girl under the age of 16 (she was 13 but claimed to be 18), is outdated and no longer applicable.

While strict liability offences do not require *mens rea*, they do require an *actus reus*. The *actus reus* must be committed voluntarily, so it would appear that even strict liability offences are dependent on proof of fault, albeit to a lesser extent.

Absolute liability

Absolute liability offences require neither *mens rea* nor that the act is carried out voluntarily. They are sometimes referred to as 'state of affairs offences'.

In *Winzar* v *Chief Constable of Kent* (1983), the accused was charged with being found drunk on the highway. He had entered a hospital while drunk and had been asked to leave. When he refused, the police were called. The police forcefully removed him from the hospital to their car, which was parked on the highway. He was convicted, despite having been forced by the police to commit the offence.

Question

Why could it be claimed that there is less of a fault element in absolute liability offences than in strict liability offences?

Mandatory sentences

Mandatory sentences appear to go against the principle that decisions in criminal law should be based on the amount of fault displayed by the defendant. Murder has an automatic life sentence and this has been widely criticised, particularly in the context of 'mercy killing' cases such as *R* v *Cox* (1992). In 1989, a House of Lords select committee recommended that the mandatory life sentence for murder be abolished.

The **Crime (Sentencing) Act 1997**, which first introduced mandatory sentences for offences other than murder, has been challenged under the **Human Rights Act 1998**. It imposed automatic sentences for subsequent offences, such as a second serious sexual or violent assault, or a third drug trafficking offence or domestic burglary. These automatic sentences could only be avoided in 'exceptional' circumstances. In *R* v *Offen* (2001), in order to prevent a possible breach of Articles 3 or 5 of the ECHR, the Court of Appeal interpreted 'exceptional' to mean any case where there was not a danger to the public, thus significantly weakening the scope of the Act to impose automatic sentences for subsequent offences.

The criticism of mandatory sentences is based on the fact that they allow no flexibility and do not allow fault to be taken into account. The decision in *Offen* suggests that the principle should be limited to cases where there is a danger to the public. However, subsequent legislation has retained mandatory sentences. The **Powers of Criminal Courts (Sentencing) Act 2000** sets a minimum of 7 years for a third class-A drug trafficking offence and a minimum of 3 years for a third domestic burglary. Under s.225 of the **Criminal Justice Act 2003**, an automatic life sentence is imposed if a person is convicted of a second serious violent or sexual offence. Section 297 of the 2003 Act requires an automatic 5-year sentence for anyone over 18 convicted of possession of an unlicensed firearm.

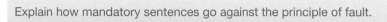

Question

Explain how mandatory sentences go against the principle of fault.

Importance of proving fault in criminal law

Criminal sanctions and procedures

Criminal law is enforced through state procedures and sanctions focused on the defendant. A guilty verdict results in the imposition of a sentence on the defendant. The court has a wide range of sentences at its disposal, some of which directly limit the liberty of the convict, such as electronic tagging, probation and incarceration.

Punishment, however, is only justified if people are at fault. Depriving people of their liberty or imposing other punishments are serious infringements of personal freedom. Furthermore, the liberty of the convicted individual will also be affected by his or her criminal record, which may, for example, prevent access to certain jobs and thus adversely affect opportunities. Opportunities in turn will be affected by the public condemnation of the individual's offence(s). There is still a stigma attached to strict liability offences, and the butcher who unknowingly sells bad meat, for example, will probably find that his trade is adversely affected. Even with minor cases that are currently treated as strict liability, there is a case for arguing that it should be necessary to prove a fault element because the consequences of conviction can be far-reaching.

Moral argument

Offences that are not based on fault can be criticised on the grounds that it is unjust that people should be found guilty of a criminal offence when they have taken

reasonable care and even, as in the case of Mr Shah in *Harrow LBC* v *Shah,* taken specific steps to try to prevent the offence being committed. Also, the claim that it would be harder to enforce the law if it were necessary to prove *mens rea* is morally dubious. It is inconsistent with justice to convict someone who is not guilty in the normal sense of the word just because the penalty is small. For example, the difficulty in proving *mens rea* in rape cases is a weak argument for making rape a strict liability offence.

The need to restrain the power of the state

An important argument in favour of having to prove fault is that decisions on guilt rest with juries or independent magistrates, and anything that reduces their capacity to make decisions inevitably means that more power rests with the prosecutors. In practice, the role of the courts in strict liability cases is limited to sentencing, and because in most cases conviction is a formality, the decision on whether or not to prosecute becomes critical. There are only limited controls over the people who make such decisions.

Strict liability is ineffective

A final argument in favour of fault-based liability is that strict liability may not be as effective as its supporters claim in protecting the public from dangerous activities. It is probable that fear of being caught is the most important deterrent, and just being charged with an offence may bring sufficient unwelcome publicity to deter those in the hospitality industry. Enforcement is often difficult, because the relevant agencies lack the necessary resources, and it could be argued that increasing levels of enforcement would be more effective than making an offence strict liability. Another, more effective, way forward could be to increase the penalties for repeat offenders or for serious threats to public safety.

There is no real evidence that strict liability increases levels of care. This may be partly attributable to the lack of incentive to act reasonably if no account is taken of attempts to prevent the prohibited act occurring. People are also more likely to accept their guilt and punishment if fault has to be proved.

The legal profession, judges and the legislature regard the principle of no liability without proof of fault as important in criminal law.

Arguments in favour of the no-fault principle

Protection of the public

Those in favour of strict liability offences argue that higher standards of care are encouraged. Barbara Wootten has defended strict liability, suggesting that if the objective of the criminal law is to prevent socially damaging activities, it would be absurd to turn a blind eye to those who cause harm because of carelessness, negligence or even by accident. There is also the fact that strict liability offences carry relatively low sentences in recognition of the lower levels of culpability.

The House of Lords, in *Wings Ltd* v *Ellis* (1984), said in respect of the **Trade Descriptions Act 1968** that the Act was not truly criminal even though it imposed criminal liability, because its purpose was not the enforcement of the criminal law but the maintenance of trading standards. It argued that because the purpose of the Act was the protection of the public, the imposition of strict liability could be justified.

Saving of time and expense

There is the further advantage that court time is saved and consequently costs are reduced when there is no need to prove *mens rea*. In the case of *Gammon (Hong Kong) Ltd* v *Attorney General of Hong Kong* (1985), the Privy Council said that if the prosecution had to prove *mens rea* in even the smallest regulatory offence, the administration of justice might quickly come to a complete standstill.

Questions

1 What do you consider to be the most telling argument against strict liability?

2 Why do you think strict liability is so widely used, and what difficulties do you think would occur if it were abolished?

Corporate manslaughter

One of the difficulties caused by the need to prove fault in criminal cases is that corporate fault is much harder to establish than individual fault. One solution to this is to impose no-fault liability in cases that involve companies and organisations. Strict liability offences are often created to try to ensure public safety in areas such as food hygiene and trading standards, and one of their additional benefits is that they make it much easier to prosecute businesses because there is no need to prove *mens rea*.

The law distinguishes between two types of person:
❖ 'natural persons' (human beings)
❖ 'artificial persons', a term covering a range of bodies, including companies

While these bodies have an independent legal status (a legal 'personality'), they cannot have thoughts or intentions like a real person, so they cannot be prosecuted for a crime requiring proof of *mens rea*.

Although one of the benefits of strict liability is that it gets round this problem, it is only acceptable in cases that do not carry the usual stigma associated with criminal liability. Strict liability is not acceptable for crimes that are 'truly criminal'. In particular, it would seem inappropriate in situations of corporate homicide.

Attempts have been made to prosecute organisations for manslaughter. An important example is *R* v *P&O European Ferries* (1990), which involved the sinking of a cross-channel ferry, the *Herald of Free Enterprise*, as it left the Belgian port of Zeebrugge with the bow doors open. It was clear that this was an act of gross negligence, which resulted in the deaths of 187 people, and the company was charged with gross negligence manslaughter. The company argued that the offence of manslaughter could only be committed by a natural person, but it was accepted by the court that in principle a company could be found guilty of manslaughter because the directors and managers can be regarded as the directing mind and will of the company. If they are controlling what the company does, then for legal purposes they become the 'mind' of the company. The prosecution in the *Herald of Free Enterprise* case failed because it could not be proved beyond reasonable doubt that the company's board of directors (its 'controlling mind') was aware of the negligent practices that led to the accident.

Because, on the whole, company directors are sufficiently removed from an organisation's day-to-day activities, they are usually able to deny knowledge of its negligent practices, and as a result all manslaughter prosecutions against large companies have either failed or not been pursued. For example, attempts failed to prosecute Balfour Beatty and Network Rail for manslaughter following the

The prosecution in the *Herald of Free Enterprise* case failed

Hatfield rail crash in October 2000. When sentencing the two organisations in October 2005 for health and safety offences relating to the derailment, Lord Justice Mackay said it was 'the worst example of sustained, industrial negligence in a high-risk industry' he had ever seen.

In the case of small companies, it is easier to establish directors' negligence, and in *R* v *Kite and OLL* (1994), a prosecution for corporate manslaughter was successful. The case involved the deaths of four teenagers on a canoeing trip in Lyme Bay, Dorset. The company in question was run by the sole director, who was responsible directly for all its activities and decisions, and as a result both he and the company were found guilty of manslaughter.

Exam questions are likely to ask you to comment on whether fault-based liability is important, and in that context the issue of corporate homicide is interesting. As we have seen, the law has difficulty because of the need to establish *mens rea*. If, in order to establish corporate liability, a court has to be satisfied that individuals are at fault, *it* might be asked why individuals could not simply be prosecuted. Surely the prospect of a criminal conviction and a probable custodial sentence would be more likely to concentrate the minds of individual managers than the prospect of the company as a whole being fined for corporate manslaughter?

Against this, it can be argued that despite the difficulties, there is value in prosecuting the company. The stigma of a conviction would be hugely damaging to the reputation of large organisations and might help to discourage them from pursuing a policy of profit at the expense of public safety. It would also provide a degree of comfort to the relatives of victims to know that the procedures operated by a company had been identified and condemned, and the organisation as a whole forced to acknowledge blame.

The law has now been changed to address this difficulty in prosecuting large organisations. The **Corporate Manslaughter and Corporate Homicide Act 2007** came into force in April 2008 and introduced a new offence for prosecuting companies and other organisations where there has been a gross failing (throughout the organisation) in the management of health and safety, with fatal consequences. An organisation is guilty of the offence if the way in which its activities are managed or organised causes a death, and this amounts to a gross breach of a relevant duty of care to the deceased. The offence changes the focus of a corporate manslaughter investigation from 'who' at the top was managing a particular activity to 'how' the activity was being managed across the organisation. It therefore avoids the problem of the 'controlling mind'.

The Act also includes an entirely new form of penalty — the publicity order. This allows a court to require a convicted organisation to publicise the fact that it has been convicted of corporate manslaughter, alongside details of the offence, the fine and any remedial action that has been ordered. Publicity orders were not introduced when the rest of the Act was implemented, pending advice from the Sentencing Guidelines Council, but their inclusion is evidence that the government believes that adverse publicity is a powerful deterrent.

In this context, it is interesting to note the controversy surrounding the inquest into the shooting of Jean Charles de Menezes by police officers at Stockwell underground station in July 2005. In December 2008, the jury members returned an open verdict, but the coroner had earlier told them that they could not return a verdict of unlawful killing because the failings that had led to Mr Menezes being mistaken for a suicide bomber were of the whole organisation and not of individual officers. In 2007, the Metropolitan Police was fined £175,000 over the shooting, after it was convicted under the **Health and Safety Act 1974** of 'endangering the public'. More serious charges were not brought against the organisation because it was not possible to establish that specific individuals at a senior level were at fault.

Questions

1 Outline the arguments in favour of prosecuting companies and other organisations for corporate manslaughter.

2 Why have past prosecutions failed?

3 How does the new legislation overcome the difficulties faced in the past?

Fault in the law of tort

Negligence

For a claimant to succeed in an action of negligence, three elements must be proved: duty of care, breach of that duty, and causation. In deciding whether there has been a breach of duty, the courts will apply the standard of the 'reasonable man'. This considers whether the reasonable person would have behaved as the defendant did. If the reasonable person would *not* have behaved in such a way, the defendant can be seen as being at fault.

In *Bolton* v *Stone* (1951), the claimant was hit by a cricket ball, despite standing outside the cricket ground. The court considered the likelihood of the risk of injury to be small, on the basis that balls had flown out of the cricket ground between six and ten times in 30 years. Furthermore, the defendants had already erected a tall fence around the ground. In the circumstances, the court was of the view that the 'reasonable man' would have acted the same way and would not have taken further preventative measures. The defendants were found not to be at fault.

In *Paris* v *Stepney LBC* (1951), however, the court held the defendants to be in breach of duty and at fault. The defendants did not provide a welder, who only had one eye, with safety goggles. The court held the defendants to be in breach of duty because the severity of the potential damage was high and the cost of eliminating the risk, i.e. of providing the goggles, was low. In the circumstances, the 'reasonable man' would have provided the claimant with goggles.

Occupiers' liability

Occupiers' liability is based on the notion of reasonableness. The **Occupiers' Liability Acts 1957 and 1984** make occupiers responsible for the safety of visitors and non-visitors respectively while on their premises. An occupier fulfils the duty owed by taking reasonable precautions.

In *Martin* v *Middlesbrough Corporation* (1965), the council was held liable to the child claimant who slipped in a playground and cut herself on a broken glass bottle. The council did not have adequate arrangements in place for the disposal of such litter. However, in *Sawyer* v *Simonds* (1966), the defendants were not liable when a customer fell and injured himself on broken glass while in their pub. They had made arrangements for the bar to be checked every 20 minutes, and this was considered by the court to be reasonable.

Under s.2(2)(b) of the 1957 Act, people visiting premises in the exercise of their calling are owed a lower duty of care, since they are expected to know what they are doing. There is a shift in responsibility from the occupier to the visitor. In *Roles* v *Nathan* (1963), chimney sweeps had been hired to clean central heating flues. They were warned of danger from fumes but entered the chimney and died. The occupiers were not liable since they were not at fault. The sweeps were acting in the exercise of their calling, so it was their responsibility to know about the dangers.

Most people would argue that an occupier should be less at fault if a trespasser is injured than if the victim is a lawful visitor, and this principle is adopted in legislation. The 1984 Act, which deals with unlawful visitors, imposes a much less onerous duty on the occupier. A duty only arises if the following criteria apply:

❖ the occupier is aware that a danger exists
❖ the occupier is aware that the trespasser is in the vicinity of the danger
❖ the danger is of the kind that in all the circumstances the occupier should guard against

The duty is higher in respect of child trespassers. The Act confirmed the approach taken in the House of Lords in *British Rail* v *Herrington* (1972), in which British Rail was held liable when a boy was injured on a railway line after he gained access through a hole in the fence. It was held that there was a 'common duty of humanity' in such situations, and someone who did not take reasonable steps when he or she knew of the potential dangers would rightly be considered to be at fault.

In a number of recent cases, the courts have decided that the occupiers were not at fault when adults have been injured. For example in *Tomlinson* v *Congleton Borough Council* (2003) the claimant, who was 18, dived into a lake in a public park and suffered a severe spinal injury. The council had placed warning signs and was planning to make the lake inaccessible to the public when the accident occurred.

Contributory negligence

We have already seen that the behaviour of the victim may result in a claim under the Occupiers' Liability Acts being unsuccessful. Even where a claim succeeds, the

law takes into account the fault of the victim when it apportions damages in tort.

Section 1(1) of the **Law Reform (Contributory Negligence) Act 1945** states that where any person suffers damage as the result partly of his or her own fault, the damages recoverable shall be reduced to such an extent as the court thinks just and equitable, having regard to the claimant's share in the responsibility for the damage. In *Froom* v *Butcher* (1975), the claimant's damages were reduced by 25%. He had been involved in a vehicle accident caused by the negligence of the defendant, but was partly responsible for his injuries as he had not been wearing a seat belt.

Questions

1 What is the fault element in negligence and under the Occupiers' Liability Acts?

2 To what extent is the fault of the victims taken into account?

While it can be seen that liability in negligence or occupiers' liability depends upon proof of fault, in other areas of tort this is not the case.

Nuisance

Nuisance involves strict liability, since it does not matter if the defendant took reasonable care to avoid the nuisance. Reasonableness in nuisance concerns the level of interference with the claimant's enjoyment of his or her land, rather than with the unreasonableness of the behaviour. In practice, the law tries to strike a balance. As Lord Wright stated in *Sedleigh-Denfield* v *O'Callaghan* (1940):

> ...a balance has to be maintained between the right of the occupier to do what he likes with his own land and the right of his neighbour not to be interfered with.

Nuisance is not primarily concerned with deciding whether someone is at fault. However, the motive or malice of the defendant may sometimes be relevant. This is illustrated by *Christie* v *Davy* (1893). Whenever the claimant gave music lessons, the defendant deliberately shrieked and banged on the adjoining wall. The claimant succeeded because the defendant had acted maliciously.

Rylands v *Fletcher* (1868)

The rule in *Rylands* v *Fletcher* originally involved strict liability for damage caused by something escaping from the defendant's land. This rule only applied to non-natural or artificial use of land. In this case, the defendants were liable for escape of water into a mine, even though there was no wrongful intent or negligence. The water constituted a non-natural use, due to the non-natural quantity.

Subsequent cases, such as *Rickards* v *Lothian* (1913), attempted to define 'non-natural' in ways that made it hard for claims under *Rylands* v *Fletcher* to succeed. It was recognised that the rule, if strictly applied, would appear to make liable someone who was unaware of the danger that existed on their land. However, the case of *Cambridge Water Company* v *Eastern Counties Leather plc* (1994) introduced a negligence requirement. The House of Lords held that under the rule, defendants would only be liable for damage of a foreseeable type. This effectively introduces a fault element into the rule and makes it unlikely that cases that satisfy all the traditional requirements of the rule, as the *Cambridge Water* case did, will succeed in the future.

Vicarious liability

Under the principle of vicarious liability, liability is imposed for someone else's fault. A key area in which the principle operates is employment. Employers are held vicariously liable for torts committed by their employees in the course of their employment. No liability will be incurred for acts done that are considered to be outside the course of employment or when the employee is considered to be 'on a frolic of his own'. The principle applies in respect of prohibited acts, and acts carried out in a prohibited or unauthorised manner. This is shown by *Rose* v *Plenty* (1976). The claimant, aged 13, was helping the defendant deliver milk, and act forbidden by the defendant's employers. The claimant was injured through the milkman's negligent driving and the employers were held liable. The employee was doing what he was employed to do, i.e. deliver milk, but he was doing it in an unauthorised manner.

It is difficult to see where an employer in a case like *Rose* v *Plenty* is at fault, and vicarious liability is perhaps the most clear example of the principle of fault not consistently applying in tort. However, while it may appear unfair on the employer, the principle of vicarious liability is justified on the basis that the act is done for the employer's benefit, and the victim is more likely to be compensated due to the requirement of compulsory insurance.

Liability for defective products

Until the introduction of the Consumer Protection Act 1987, liability for defective products was dependent upon proof of fault. Claimants had to prove that the manufacturer was in breach of his or her duty of care. The 1987 Act imposed what is, in effect, strict liability on producers for damage caused by defective products.

Moves towards a no-fault-based system for accident victims

In recent years, there has been a move from the *laissez-faire* ideal that dominated in the nineteenth century. The law has increasingly come to focus on the injured victim rather than the blameworthy individual.

Twentieth-century legislation provides a partial no-fault-based system. The welfare state legislation created the Department of Social Security. Victims of accidents at work are now able to claim compensation from the state, without the need to prove negligence. Social security benefits are also available to those who suffer illness or disability.

It must be stressed, however, that these statutory provisions do not affect the general rule that liability in accident cases depends on proof of fault.

Questions

1 To what extent do you think that nuisance is a no-fault tort?

2 Why have the courts been reluctant to allow claims under *Rylands* v *Fletcher*?

3 How would you justify the principle of vicarious liability?

Fault in the law of contract

Contract law provides a comprehensive set of rules to ensure that people entering into contracts have clear procedures to follow. Many of these rules are not, at heart, concerned with fault. This is true, for example, with most of the rules on the formation of contract. However, the basis of contract law is that parties have entered into a legally binding agreement, and that a party that does not perform what was promised is at fault and liable to compensate the other parties.

Breach of contract

Breach of contract occurs where someone fails to fulfil his or her obligations under a contract. The law treats such people as being at fault and requires them to compensate the innocent party for losses suffered as a result.

The rights of the injured party depend on the nature of the term broken. A breach of a condition (important term) gives the right to terminate the agreement and repudiate (cancel) the contract, while a breach of a minor term that does not go to the root of the contract only gives rise to a claim for damages. What this means in practice is that the injured party is prevented from using a minor breach of contract as an excuse for cancelling the whole contract. This would seem to be consistent with the idea that a person's degree of fault should depend on the seriousness of the damage he or she causes.

Frustration

In breach of contract, one party is clearly at fault. If no one is at fault, then under the general principle of no liability without fault, no one should be liable. This is evident in the doctrine of frustration.

Frustration arises when an event occurs over which the parties have no control and which makes performance of the contract impossible. In *Taylor* v *Caldwell* (1863), a hall was hired for staging a concert but burned down before the event. Since the hall was the subject matter of the contract, and had clearly been destroyed, performance of the contract was impossible. However, a contract will not be frustrated if it merely becomes more difficult to perform, as illustrated by *Davis Contractors Ltd* v *Fareham UDC* (1956). In this case, it was unsuccessfully argued that the contract was frustrated due to escalating costs.

The common law position in the event of frustration used to be that gains and losses lay where they fell. This could be unfair, and sometimes resulted in one party bearing all the losses suffered. The situation was improved by the **Law Reform (Frustrated Contracts) Act 1943**, which regulates the financial position between parties when the contract is frustrated and provides for losses to be apportioned more fairly. This would seem reasonable in situations where neither party is at fault.

Misrepresentation

Misrepresentation may be defined as an untrue statement of fact made by one party to the contract to the other, which induces the latter to enter into the contract. A misrepresentation could arise in a number of different ways: a deliberate lie, a statement made carelessly without checking the accuracy, or an entirely innocent statement of facts believed to be true.

The classic definition of fraudulent misrepresentation was outlined by the House of Lords in *Derry* v *Peek* (1889) as a false statement made 'without belief in its truth, or recklessly as to whether it is true or false'. In *Smith* v *Land and House Property* (1884), the landlord of a property being sold described the sitting occupier as a desirable tenant, in the knowledge that the person in question was not good at paying rent. This was fraudulent misrepresentation; the landlord was at fault and was liable in misrepresentation to the purchaser.

Fraudulent misrepresentation is a clear example of fault being relevant in contract law. If someone makes untrue statements either intentionally or recklessly, it is right that the victim should have a number of remedies available. These include rescission, which allows the victim to cancel any contract that is the result of the misrepresentation.

However, the Misrepresentation Act 1967 has made the distinction between a fraudulent misrepresentation and other types of misrepresentation much less significant. Section 2(1) provides that even when the misrepresentation was not made fraudulently, a person may be liable unless he or she proves that he or she had reasonable ground to believe and did believe up to the time the contract was made that the facts represented were true.

This provision reverses the burden of proof. Once a party has proved that there has been a misrepresentation that induced him or her to enter into the contract, the person making the misrepresentation will be liable in damages, unless he or she proves he or she had reasonable grounds to believe and did believe that the facts represented were true. This can result in liability even when the misrepresentation can be claimed to have been made innocently and with an honest belief in its truth. For example, inaccurate information supplied by someone else might have been repeated. Innocent misrepresentation is an exception to the principle of no liability without proof of fault. The maker of the innocent statement is not blameworthy for the statement, yet is still held liable.

Statutory implied terms and exclusion clauses

Statutes such as the Sale of Goods Act 1979 and the Supply of Goods and Services Act 1982 have provided some protection for the purchasers of goods or services, and this has made it more difficult for those seeking to exploit their customers. However, for many years the exclusion or limitation clause provided a means for such people to avoid or limit their liability. Notorious cases such as *Thompson* v *LMS Railway* (1930) allowed people who were clearly at fault to avoid liability, and the proliferation of standard form contracts made it even more difficult to ensure that customers were treated fairly.

The Unfair Contract Terms Act 1977, which dealt comprehensively with such clauses, can therefore be seen as another aspect of contract law where the principle of fault is important. For example, the Act makes void any attempt to exclude liability for injury or death caused by negligence, although those clauses seeking to exclude or limit liability for negligent loss or damage will be valid if reasonable. This distinction suggests that the law regards behaviour leading to death or injury as more blameworthy than loss or damage. The Act also makes a distinction between clauses in consumer contracts and those between businesses. It might be argued that a business is more at fault if it seeks to exploit a consumer rather than another business.

Questions

1 In which areas of contract law is the principle of fault-based liability most apparent?

2 Can the person making an innocent misrepresentation be considered to be at fault?

3 Is the person who exploits a consumer more at fault than the person who exploits another business?

Importance of proving fault in civil law

Those at fault should be accountable

Compensation is regarded as the responsibility of those at fault. Civil law, like criminal law, is based on the notion of individual responsibility. Individuals choose to behave in the way they do and should therefore accept responsibility for the outcomes of their actions. Individuals can choose to be careful so as to minimise the harm they cause. This is the basis of liability in negligence and also the principle on which breach of contract operates. Parties enter into legally binding agreements and they should therefore be expected to honour those agreements or face claims for compensation.

Fault in civil law operates purely to compensate the victim

The principle of fault operates in civil law rather differently to the way it operates in criminal law. There is only a limited concept of punishment in civil law and instead those at fault are simply expected to put right the situation they have created. In breach of contract, this means putting the parties into the position they would have been in if the contract had been carried out properly, and in negligence it means restoring the parties to the position they would have been in if the tort had not occurred.

The fact that fault is only used to identify behaviour that has caused damage or injury means that it does not have the far-reaching consequences that it has in criminal law. Once the injured party has been compensated, the civil law does not impose any further financial restrictions or constraints on the defendant.

A no-fault system would be unfair to those who have taken care

On a number of occasions, it has been suggested that negligence should be replaced by a no-fault system. The Pearson Committee in 1978 recommended such a system, influenced in part by the operation of a no-fault compensation scheme in New Zealand. The Pearson recommendations have not been implemented, and critics

have argued that it is not right that individuals who have made the choice to exercise more care should pay for the harm caused by those who have not. A no-fault system would have to be based on some kind of insurance scheme, to which good businesses as well as bad would have to contribute.

Arguments from contract law

As we saw earlier, rules on breach of contract and fraudulent misrepresentation are clearly designed to protect the innocent party in circumstances where the other party has not acted as it should have done. However, the rules on frustration of contract and innocent misrepresentation impose liabilities on innocent parties. The Law Reform (Frustrated Contracts) Act 1943 operates in a fair and straightforward manner and has resulted in little litigation. The rules on innocent misrepresentation are more contentious, but arguably it is right that a party that volunteers information, on the basis of which the other party acts, should ultimately be responsible for the accuracy of that information.

Insurance costs would rise

While some victims are able to claim compensation without the need to prove fault, there are many who are still required to do so. Road accident victims and victims of medical errors have to satisfy the negligence requirements, despite the defendants being insured. In fact, it may partly be the insurance issue that prevents the extension of the no-fault system. Insurance premiums would inevitably have to rise and might become unaffordable. More people would risk driving without insurance and medical practitioners would be less willing to provide anything other than treatment that they considered totally safe.

Arguments in favour of no-fault compensation

The advantage of the system of no-fault liability for accident victims is that those who are entitled to compensation or social security are more likely to receive it than they would be to receive compensation under the fault-based tort system. It may be fairer for more people to receive compensation, albeit a lesser amount. However, there is the perception of unfairness in all of society having to pay for what often amounts to the acts of blameworthy individuals.

There is no doubt that it is easier for victims to recover compensation if they do not have to prove fault. The Consumer Protection Act 1987, for example, imposes strict liability on producers for damage caused by defective products. However, while it is the producer who directly provides the compensation to the claimant, it could be argued that the burden is indirectly borne by society, because as the risk of liability increases, so too will insurance premiums, and this cost will be passed on to consumers. However, to date the increased cost to consumers seems to be minimal.

Questions

1 Who benefits and who loses from having civil liability based on fault?

2 Suggest why it is unlikely that no-fault liability will be introduced in the near future.

Conclusion

It would seem that the imposition of liability without fault is more acceptable in civil law than in criminal law. The unfairness of leaving an injured victim without compensation increasingly outweighs the unfairness of blameless individuals being required to provide that compensation indirectly through state funds or insurance.

Despite the arguments against the imposition of strict liability in tort, including doubt that it raises safety standards, there are areas in which there is no need to prove fault. These include nuisance, the rule in *Rylands* v *Fletcher* and the principle of vicarious liability.

In criminal law, however, the desire to protect the blameless individual from the outcomes of state procedures and sanctions makes the imposition of liability without fault less acceptable. Strict liability offences can only be created by the legislature in limited circumstances.

Sample exam question

The AQA website (www.aqa.org.uk) provides examples of past exam questions, and candidates are advised to look at these and to practise writing answers to them. The following question is a fairly typical example of the kind likely to be asked.

Referring to either civil or criminal law or to both, discuss the view that liability is and should be based on fault.

Further reading

Price, N. (2007) 'Fault', *A-Level Law Review*, Vol. 2, No. 3, pp. 24–26.

Roberts, H. (2007) 'Fault and corporate manslaughter', *A-Level Law Review*, Vol. 3, No. 1, pp. 12–13.

Chapter 28

Balancing conflicting interests

One of the main functions of the law is to resolve disputes and settle arguments. In order to do this effectively, it has to balance a variety of interests. In almost every situation there are different points of view, different financial interests and different expectations. The law has to arrive at a solution that balances these.

Think about the following situations and identify the interests that might be involved:

* A couple who have been married for 20 years want to divorce.
* An owner of a house wants to build a large extension on the back of his house.
* A person is reported to the police for behaving oddly and making statements about wanting to kill all people who support a particular football club.
* A local authority is thinking of introducing a congestion charge on drivers coming into the town centre.

Essentially, there are two ways in which the law can try to achieve balance: through having institutions to which people can go when they have disputes, and through making laws that attempt to balance interests within a particular area.

Theorists

Karl Marx

Karl Marx (1818–83) believed that law was part of the 'repressive state apparatus' used to ensure the continuing exploitation of the working class (proletariat) by the capitalists (bourgeoisie), i.e. those who own the capital and means of production. For Marx, the law subordinated the interests of the proletariat to those of the bourgeoisie and so did not truly balance conflicting interests. Marx adhered to the conflict model of society, and thus held the view that law did not reconcile conflicting interests in a compromise but rather imposed the interests of one at the expense of the other.

The Marxist approach would therefore conclude that the law is ineffective in achieving balance because it starts from a position of bias. The Marxist would argue that the institutions have been set up by the ruling classes and those who pass the laws; Parliament and the judges have their own economic interests to protect.

Rudolf von Jhering

Rudolf von Jhering (1818–92) believed that the law was a prime method of ordering society. He was a utilitarian and more concerned with social than individual aims. His thinking followed that of Jeremy Bentham (see page 318), whose principle of utility was aimed at maximising human happiness by increasing pleasure and diminishing pain according to the principle of 'the greatest happiness of the greatest number'. Von Jhering saw society as being made up of several competing interests, not all of which could be satisfied. He believed that the interests of the individual would conflict with the interests of society as a whole. The role of the law was to balance interests by reconciling the interests of the individual to society so that they conformed. This was achieved through state-organised coercion, i.e. the law, and through rewards, duty and love.

The von Jhering approach seems to match quite closely what has happened in practice. Many of the issues that we shall examine involve conflicts between society as a whole and the interests of small groups of individuals. Britain is much more democratic than it was at the time of von Jhering's death and, in theory at least, the actions of the state are more strongly influenced by the interests of the majority of people because there is now universal adult suffrage.

Roscoe Pound

Roscoe Pound (1870–1964) divided interests into two main categories: individual and social. He argued that interests could only be properly balanced if placed on the same plane or level. Thus social interests can be weighed against social interests, and individual interests against individual interests. Failure to do this results in a built-in bias in favour of the social interest.

Pound thus developed the ideas of von Jhering. He saw law as being developed according to social needs and only serving those interests that lead to the good of society. He subscribed to the consensus model of society, believing that interests should be balanced in accordance with society's values or 'jural postulates'.

In practice, his view that only interests of the same kind can be balanced does not seem to have been followed. For example, in the classic case of *Miller* v *Jackson*

(1977), involving an application for an injunction against a cricket club by residents whose property adjoined the cricket ground, Lord Denning approached the problem in terms of 'a conflict between the interest of the public at large and the interests of a private individual'. Denning concluded that the public interest outweighed the individual one and refused to grant the injunction, although he did attempt to balance this by awarding damages to compensate for the inconvenience of having cricket balls regularly hit into the garden.

To have followed Pound would have necessitated seeing both interests in the same terms, either as individual interests (one person's desire to play cricket against another person's desire to sit in his/her garden) or as social interests (the value to society of protecting domestic privacy against the value of encouraging recreational activities).

The courts have not generally adopted Pound's approach, and many of the examples in this textbook show the law attempting to balance what are perceived as valuable social interests against the rights of individuals.

Balancing of conflicting interests by Parliament

Legislative process

The balancing of competing interests is to some extent achieved by the process of making an Act of Parliament. The Green Paper invites consultation from various interested parties who may be affected by the proposed legislation. The bill stage requires many debates and votes, involving several political parties reflecting a wide range of views. Before the bill becomes an Act, many compromises and amendments are made, which take into account the different views of those who are both interested and involved in the legislative process.

It is, however, questionable as to whether a true balance of conflicting interests is actually achieved by the legislative process. There are many powerful interest groups and classes within society. These groups influence the views of ministers, Members of Parliament and civil servants. Many politicians are wealthy and influential. They may possess large shareholdings in companies and have directorships or other connections. They may be persuaded more often than they should by groups who are in favour of protecting such interests, despite requirements that these interests should be revealed.

Protective legislation

Parliament sometimes seeks to balance competing interests by passing laws that are advantageous to weaker interest groups and disadvantageous to powerful groups. Examples of such protective legislation can be seen in consumer law:

- The **Consumer Protection Act 1987** imposes strict liability on producers in respect of damage caused by dangerous products.
- The **Sale and Supply of Goods Act 1994** applies conditions to consumer contracts in respect of title, description, quality and sale by sample.
- By virtue of the **Unfair Contract Terms Act 1977**, the use of exclusion and limitation clauses by businesses in consumer contracts is significantly reduced.

However, while the provisions contained in protective legislation clearly aim to strengthen the weaker interest groups, it is questionable how successful such legislation is.

Phil Harris, in *An Introduction to Law*, points out that such legislation is not rigorously enforced by the state. This, he argues, results in the protective legislation aiding the stronger group while *appearing* to aid the weaker one. The perceived protection offered to consumers enables businesses to enjoy a better public image and so further their own interests.

An additional problem with consumer legislation is that it depends on enforcement by the consumer. Harris believes that most consumers are ignorant of the rights given to them by such legislation. For example, a shop may tell a customer who has purchased a faulty product that his or her only hope is to deal with the manufacturer directly, or that he or she is only entitled to a credit note, when this is not the case. He also questions whether the average customer would know that a clause in an agreement excluding liability for implied terms is invalid under the **Unfair Contract Terms Act 1977** (UCTA). Consumers who *are* aware of their rights may bring an action for breach of contract. Most such actions usually need to be brought in the small claims court, for which there is no state-assisted funding for legal representation. The result is often that the protective legislation is not enforced, because even those consumers who are aware of their rights may consider legal action to be more trouble and expense than it is worth.

Balancing of conflicting interests by the courts

Judges are more obviously faced with balancing competing interests in the courts, especially in areas such as nuisance, occupiers' liability, crime and consumer law:

- In nuisance, the claimant's interest in being able to enjoy his or her property must be balanced against the interest of his or her neighbours to do what they like with theirs.
- In occupiers' liability, the interests of the occupier of land have to be balanced against those of people who come onto that land.
- In crime, the interests of the offender have to be balanced against those of society.
- In consumer law, the interests of the consumer have to be balanced against the interests of the business.

Public interests usually outweigh private interests

Pound's theory was that genuine balancing of conflicting interests could only be achieved when the interests were placed in the same category. It is apparent that if the interests in *Miller* v *Jackson* had been placed in the same category, the outcome may have been different (see pages 386–87).

Protection of national security is another social interest that nearly always prevails if balanced against an individual interest. Judges regard the protection of national security as paramount. In *Council of Civil Service Unions* v *Minister for the Civil Service* (1984), the prime minister issued an order under which workers at the intelligence-gathering centre GCHQ were no longer permitted to belong to a trade union. The House of Lords backed the prime minister's order, as it was made in the interest of national security, despite the valid argument of the unions that they had not been consulted. When Tony Blair became prime minister in 1997, he restored the right of workers to belong to a trade union, so the original threat to national security posed by such membership appears doubtful.

Jurors are not part of the permanent state machinery of enforcement. Perhaps, as a result, they are more willing than judges to question claims made by the executive or legislature of threats to national security. In *R* v *Ponting* (1984), a civil servant was charged under the **Official Secrets Act 1911** for leaking information about the sinking of the *Belgrano*, an Argentinian ship, during the Falklands War. Ponting argued that leaking the information was in the public interest because it showed that the British government had not been telling the truth. The judge said that Ponting's argument was no defence. The jury took a different view and acquitted him.

Question

In each of the three cases referred to above, explain:

❖ what the conflicting interests are

❖ the means that are used by the law to balance them

❖ how effectively balance is achieved

Civil liberties

Human Rights Act 1998

This important statute incorporates the European Convention on Human Rights (ECHR) into English law and allows English courts to consider the extent to which UK legislation is compatible with the Convention. The ECHR is designed to protect the civil and political rights of individuals, but it can only be used when alleged violations are committed by the state, and so its impact has been on cases where there is a conflict of interest between a private interest and a public interest.

On the face of it, public interest further outweighs private interest in respect of most positive rights provided by the ECHR and the **Human Rights Act 1998**. Most of these rights are subject to derogation clauses, which are sometimes drafted in broad terms.

An interesting example of this is *R (Begum)* v *Headteacher and Governors of Denbigh High School* (2006). A student, Shabina Begum, claimed that her rights under Article 9 had been violated because the school's uniform policy restricted her right to practise her religion. She wanted to wear the jilbab, a one-piece garment covering her from head to toe, and the school would not allow this. Under Article 9, the right to

In the *Begum* case (2006), the House of Lords decided that Shabina Begum's rights under Article 9 had not been violated

practise a religion is absolute, but the right to manifest a religious belief is qualified and subject to limitations that are 'prescribed by law and are necessary in a democratic society for the protection of the rights and freedoms of others'. This means that the right must be balanced against the rights of others and the good of society as a whole, and also that any restrictions must be proportionate.

The House of Lords in this case concluded that Shabina Begum's rights had not been violated. In the words of Lord Bingham, 'the school had taken immense pains to devise a uniform policy which respected Muslim beliefs but did so in an inclusive and uncompetitive way'. It said that people might reasonably be expected to suffer a little inconvenience in order to manifest their beliefs, and it was influenced by the fact that there was another school a little further away that she could have attended, which allowed the wearing of the jilbab. A fuller account of this case can be found in an article by Margaret Doherty in *A-Level Law Review* (see Further reading on page 401).

Under Article 8 of the ECHR, everyone has the right to respect for his or her private and family life, home and correspondence. However, the Article also expressly provides that this right can be overridden:

...in the interests of national security, public safety or the economic wellbeing of the country, for the prevention of disorder or crime, for the protection of health or morals, or for the protection of the rights and freedoms of others.

Thus it seems that the rights of individuals will not prevail in the event of a conflict with the public interest. In *Mosley* v *News Group Newspapers Ltd* (2008), Max Mosley, the head of the world motor sport's governing body, sued the *News of the World* over an article alleging that he had taken part in a sadomasochistic sex session with five prostitutes, which had a Nazi theme. Mosley's action was brought under Article 8 of the ECHR. Mr Justice Eady in the High Court agreed that his privacy had been breached, finding that while the sex session had taken place, the *News of the World* had no evidence to support its claim that Mosley had taken part in a 'sick Nazi orgy'. The judgement added that Mosley had a 'reasonable expectation of privacy in relation to sexual activities, albeit unconventional, carried on between consenting adults on private property'. However, the judge did acknowledge that the *News of the World* honestly believed there were Nazi elements to the orgies, and declined Mosley's request for punitive damages, limiting his award to £60,000.

This judgement appeared to uphold Mosley's private interests over the public interest, and it provoked an angry response from Paul Dacre, editor of the *Daily Mail*. He argued in a speech at the Society of Editors' annual conference that the judge's 'amoral' judgements, in this and other defamation and libel cases, were 'inexorably and insidiously' imposing a privacy law on the press. He said that public shaming had always been a vital element in defending the parameters of what are considered acceptable standards of social behaviour, and without the freedom to write about scandal, newspaper sales would fall, creating 'worrying implications' for the democratic process. Dacre's view was that the judgement was an attack on freedom of expression.

However, Lord Falconer, the former Lord Chancellor, defended the judgement, saying that it was not necessarily acceptable for public figures to have aspects of their private lives, such as abortions and other medical treatments, reported in the newspapers. He added:

...of course, if I'm acting hypocritically or I'm accountable, or there's something that may affect what I do in my public life which emerges from my private life, then that should be published. But there are things which are private and just as we don't want the state to know everything about us, do we want things that are legitimately private to be made public? I don't think we do.

Article 8 is an attempt to balance, among other things, the right to privacy against the right of the media to investigate and comment on the private lives of public figures, and this judgement has provoked, as we have seen, two quite different views on how effectively that balance has been achieved.

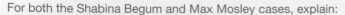

Balancing interests: terrorism

Most rights in the European Convention, even the right to life, are subject to qualification, but some rights, including the right not to be subjected to torture or to inhuman or degrading treatment or punishment (as provided by Article 3) are non-derogable.

Rights under Article 3, and other rights under the ECHR, have been brought into focus as a result of measures taken to combat terrorism. The threat of terrorist attacks by Islamic extremists following the 11 September 2001 attacks on the USA has highlighted the problem of how to achieve a balance between such fundamental rights and the need to protect citizens from the threat of mass murder. The attacks in London on 7 and 21 July 2005 added to the sense of urgency and resulted in measures being proposed that were either challenged under the Human Rights Act or were resisted in Parliament.

Detention without charge and control orders

One of the first responses of the UK government to the threat following 9/11 was to try to deal with foreign nationals who had not committed offences in the UK but who were suspected of being involved with terrorism. Article 3 prevented their deportation to their home countries because all of them claimed that they would be in danger if they were sent back. The government therefore opted for detention without trial, a measure that had previously been used as a response to the terrorist threat in Northern Ireland. However, in *A and Others* v *Secretary of State for the Home Department* (2004), the House of Lords decided that the use of s.21 of the Anti-Terrorism, Crime and Security Act 2001 to detain foreign nationals without charging them was unlawful and an infringement of their human rights. Despite the public interest arguments put forward by the Home Secretary, the Law Lords stressed the importance of preserving private interests and protecting individual freedoms.

The government's response was to introduce control orders. These impose severe restrictions on the individuals' travel and communication with other people and create what amounts to house arrest. Control orders are still being used (at the end of 2008, they remained imposed on 16 people), though again the courts have set limits, for example to the hours someone can be confined indoors. The fact that the

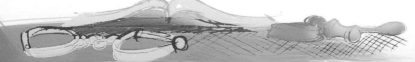

courts have not rejected control orders out of hand demonstrates that they recognise that they are a more proportionate response to the threat and achieve a reasonable balance between the protection of the public and the defence of liberties.

Forty-two days

The arguments over the government's attempt to extend the period suspects can be held by the police without charge is another good example of the difficulty of trying to achieve balance in this area. The government wanted to extend the maximum period a terror suspect can be detained without charge from 28 to 42 days, in order to deal with what it described as 'increasingly complex plots'. The 28-day limit was itself a controversial extension of the period usually allowed and had been introduced in December 2005 after government proposals for a pre-charge terror detention limit of 90 days were rejected by MPs.

The House of Commons passed the 42-day proposal by a majority of just nine votes in June 2008, with 36 Labour backbenchers rebelling. On 13 October 2008, the House of Lords rejected the proposal by a majority of 191 votes, and the government then announced that it would not try to force the measure through.

Much was said about the need to maintain a balance between liberty and security. A number of people with experience in fighting terrorism argued that the extension to 42 days would create an imbalance in favour of security and would threaten traditional liberties. Sir Ken Macdonald, the retiring Director of Public Prosecutions, said in a speech on 20 October: 'We need to take very great care not to fall into a way of life in which freedom's back is broken by the relentless pressure of a security state.' Lord Goldsmith, who was Attorney General when Tony Blair was prime minister, also opposed the plan, saying it risked 'giving away the very freedoms that terrorists are trying to take from us'.

The Conservatives and Liberal Democrats opposed the measure, and a number of Labour peers also voted against it, including former Lord Chancellors Lord Irvine and Lord Falconer. David Davis, the former Conservative shadow Home Secretary, felt so strongly about the proposal that he resigned as an MP and fought a by-election on the issue in July 2008. The other main parties did not put up candidates and he was comfortably re-elected.

Other terrorism issues

A variety of situations have arisen involving terrorist suspects, in which the law has had to balance the rights of suspects with the wider public interest. For example, in April 2008 the High Court decided that rules imposed under United Nations laws to enable the freezing of terror suspects' assets were not lawful because they 'bypassed' Parliament. The five claimants were designated terror suspects in 2007 under two Orders in Council set up to apply UN Security Council resolutions in the UK. Suspected of 'facilitating acts of terrorism', they were denied control of their own property and money.

In his judgement, Mr Justice Collins argued that the Orders in Council were absurd, unfair and a breach of fundamental rights, and were not the proper way to approach asset freezing because they were not subject to the same parliamentary scrutiny as normal legislation. Each order was laid before Parliament the day after it was made, coming into force on the following day. In November 2008, the Court of Appeal agreed the orders were 'oppressive in nature' and were bound to cause problems to anyone served with one. However, it held that with a minor change of wording, the orders would be lawful, rejecting the High Court view that the whole approach was fundamentally flawed. It is likely that the case will go to the House of Lords.

The case is an interesting reminder of the part still played by Orders in Council and raises concerns about whether their use is an appropriate way to balance the interests of the state and those of individuals suspected of terrorism. Mr Justice Collins clearly feels that where significant restrictions are being placed on individuals' rights to control their assets, these should require specific parliamentary approval. It remains to be seen whether the House of Lords takes the same view.

Under the **Human Rights Act 1998**, UK courts have also held up the deportation of suspects to countries where torture might be used against them. At the end of 2008, this was under appeal. A development likely to become an issue in the future is that Britain hopes to create a huge database of e-mail and telephone traffic, collecting addresses and numbers that could be used to track terrorist contacts. This is something opponents fear will be used in so-called 'fishing expeditions' by intelligence services and will be a further erosion of civil liberties.

Question

Choose three examples from the terrorism cases discussed above and explain:

❖ what the conflicting interests are

❖ the means that are used by the law to balance them

❖ how effectively balance is achieved

The ECtHR and balancing conflicting interests

The European Court of Human Rights (ECtHR) remains available as a final court of appeal on issues involving individual rights, when all domestic legal avenues have been exhausted. During 2007, two cases based on Article 8 (the right to private and family life), involving the rights of individuals to have artificial insemination, were heard by the court, and both involved clear issues of balance between conflicting interests.

Dickson v *UK* (2007) concerned a request by a prisoner serving life for murder to be able to artificially inseminate a woman he had married since starting his prison

sentence. The Home Office had refused the request, and this was upheld by the House of Lords.

The ECtHR had to consider whether a fair balance had been struck between the competing public and private interests. On the one hand, when considering the Dicksons' case (the private interest), because Mrs Dickson was already 49, it was accepted that artificial insemination remained the only realistic hope of the couple having a child together. Also, it was not suggested that providing artificial insemination facilities to the Dicksons would have involved any security issues or imposed any significant administrative or financial demands on the state. On the other hand, looking at the situation from the state's perspective (the public interest), it had to be considered whether public confidence in the prison system would be undermined if the effect of a long prison sentence were circumvented by allowing prisoners guilty of certain serious offences (including murder) to conceive children.

In finding in favour of the couple, the court observed that in a democratic society, while it was necessary to maintain public confidence in the penal system, prisoners should not automatically forfeit their rights based on what might offend public opinion. It also concluded that while punishment remained one of the aims of imprisonment, it was equally important to consider the rehabilitative aim of imprisonment, particularly towards the end of a long prison sentence. Presumably this would mean helping the prisoner to make or secure family ties for support on release. The court also considered that the general UK policy of not allowing artificial insemination, save in exceptional circumstances, was a blanket ban and did not give consideration to the competing individual and public interests in each case. In other words, each case should be decided on its merits.

Evans v *UK* (2007) arose out of the request by Ms Evans's former partner to have embryos destroyed that he had fertilised while still in a relationship with her. The couple had become engaged and then Evans was diagnosed with ovarian cancer. She was offered a cycle of IVF treatment before her cancer treatment began, because her fertility would be affected. Eleven of her eggs were removed and fertilised with her partner's sperm, resulting in six embryos that were frozen and placed in storage.

Under the **Human Fertilisation and Embryology Act 1990**, which governed the situation, both parties must consent to the continuation of IVF treatment, otherwise the embryos must be destroyed. Evans challenged her former partner's wishes by asserting her private rights and launching a court case based on Article 8 of the European Convention on Human Rights, the right to private and family life.

Despite sympathising with her, the ECtHR ruled that the right to a family life did not overrule the other person's withdrawal of consent, and it also accepted that embryos do not have an independent right to life. The court had to balance the two competing views and rights. The ex-partner's request, based on public rights and covered by the 1990 Act, was upheld; these public rights, designed to operate in the wider public interest, overruled Evans's private rights.

A fuller discussion of these cases can be found in an article by Nick Price in *A-Level Law Review* (see Further reading).

Question

In both of the cases referred to above, explain:

❖ what the conflicting interests are

❖ the means that are used by the law to balance them

❖ how effectively balance is achieved

Civil courts and access to justice

Interests can only be balanced if there are institutions available to which aggrieved parties have access on an equal basis. The operation of the rule of law, state-assisted funding of legal actions and the independence of the judiciary ensure that, in theory at least, the court and tribunal system is able to achieve balance.

However, the findings of the Woolf Commission provide ample evidence that the civil courts often operate in ways that favour powerful organisations and disadvantage individual claimants. It could be argued that tribunals provide a fairer balance, in that they have fewer formal procedures and encourage claimants to represent themselves. However, the ordinary claimant is likely to be facing an opponent who is represented, such as an employer or a government department, and this puts him or her at a significant disadvantage. Research by Genn and Genn in 1989 found that much of the law in tribunals was complex and technical.

The small-claims procedure is also designed to achieve greater balance between the parties and, as with the tribunal system, the emphasis is on informality. But again, there is evidence that the balance remains in favour of the parties who can afford to use lawyers. The majority of cases are brought by businesses trying to recover bad debts rather than by individual claimants.

Mediation and conciliation services provide an alternative to formal court or tribunal hearings and are increasingly popular as a means of settling disputes. Commercial mediation is common in the business world and encouraged by bodies such as the Confederation of British Industry (CBI). An example is the Centre for Effective Dispute Resolution (CEDR), a professional organisation used by businesses to solve their disputes without going to court. It claims to have an 80% success rate and is much cheaper than going to court. It charges approximately £1,000 for a mediator, compared with more than £100,000 for a complicated court case. However, it could also be argued that informal procedures such as mediation tend to favour the stronger party because it can usually negotiate a compromise on its own terms.

Mediation is also widely used in family disputes. Couples who have children are asked to consider this if they file for divorce. The **Family Law Act 1996** aims to take divorce settlements out of the courts and establish family mediation centres around the country. Here, the importance of preserving relationships for the sake of the children involved would seem to make mediation a more effective way of balancing all the interests involved than having an acrimonious dispute in the courts. However, as with all kinds of mediation, it is only effective if the parties are willing to compromise and reach agreement.

Question

How effective do you think (a) tribunals and (b) mediation are in achieving an effective balance?

Balancing conflicting interests in criminal law

Criminal law is concerned with balancing the interests of the offender with those of society. This can be evidenced both in criminal procedure and in the substantive criminal law.

Criminal procedure

The interest of society is the conviction of the guilty and the acquittal of the innocent. The interest of the defendant is to have an assumption of innocence, to be treated with dignity and to have a fair trial. There is also the interest of the victim to consider. The traditional balance of the law in favour of the defendant may leave victims feeling that their interests are not being effectively represented in the criminal process.

There are many aspects that could be considered here and much specific detail can be drawn from Unit 2. Of particular importance are the **Criminal Procedure and Investigation Act 1996**, which allows for the retrial of someone acquitted by a jury where there is evidence of intimidation of witnesses, and the **Criminal Justice Act 2003**, which gives the Court of Appeal the power to order a retrial where 'new and compelling evidence' comes to light after someone has been found not guilty.

In addition, there is the issue that surrounds the rights of defendants — burden of proof, rules on arrest, rules of evidence, right to silence, effect of not-guilty finding — and how these rules are designed to create balance between the prosecution and the defence. It is important to address the question of whether the balance has now swung too far in favour of the prosecution, and to look at the right to silence and the effect of s.34 of the **Criminal Justice and Public Order Act 1994**, which allow juries or magistrates to draw inferences from a defendant failing to mention, when under caution, facts later relied on in his or her defence. Also of relevance in this respect are sections 36 and 37, which deal with a defendant's failure, when questioned, to account for objects in his or her possession, marks on his or her clothing, or his or her presence at a particular place.

Another example is the issue of whether an accused person should be entitled to bail. The **Bail Act 1976** created a presumption in favour of bail. The courts are obliged to grant bail unless one of the exceptions applies, i.e. unless there are substantial grounds for believing that the accused might commit another offence, interfere with witnesses, fail to fulfil the bail conditions or otherwise obstruct the cause of justice. This Act seeks to ensure the liberty of the accused until the trial. The court has to balance the interest of the public in being protected and the interest of the individual in being presumed innocent until proven guilty. There has been a shift towards the public interest in recent years, with legislation increasingly providing circumstances in which bail may or must be refused.

In each of these areas of criminal law, recent developments have restricted the rights of defendants and placed greater emphasis on the interests of society and the victims of crime.

Substantive criminal law: intoxication

The public interest lies in being protected from those who cause harm when drunk. The individual interest lies in being held less responsible for actions carried out while intoxicated (and thus with limited *mens rea*) than for actions carried out with full awareness.

The availability of the defence of intoxication varies according to circumstances. Where the accused is involuntarily intoxicated, intoxication can be a defence to any crime, provided the accused lacks the necessary *mens rea*. It can be used as a defence to sections 20 and 47 of the **Offences Against the Person Act 1861**. Voluntary intoxication, however, can only be a defence to a crime of specific intent. The reasoning for this is that the courts regard voluntary intoxication as reckless in itself, and recklessness is the level of *mens rea* required for crimes of basic intent.

In *DPP* v *Majewski* (1977), the House of Lords refused to allow intoxication as a defence to a basic intent offence. Lord Steyn said that one of the prime purposes of the criminal law is the protection from unprovoked violence of people who are pursuing their lawful lives; to allow intoxication as a defence would be to leave the citizen unprotected from such violence. The House of Lords firmly resisted the idea that intoxication should become a general defence, because this would be socially undesirable and would not provide a proper balance between the interests of the defendant and the interests of society as a whole. Similarly, in *R* v *O' Grady* (1987), the Court of Appeal said that the principle that a person should not be penalised for an honest mistake gave way to the consideration that society should be protected from those who do dangerous things as a result of intoxication.

Substantive criminal law: strict liability

The concept of strict liability is a departure from the general principle of English law that there should be no liability without fault. In the creation of strict liability crimes, the law may suppress the interests of the individual in the interest of public safety.

The **Rivers (Prevention of Pollution) Act 1951** makes it a criminal offence to pollute rivers, without the need to prove that such pollution is caused intentionally, recklessly or negligently. In *Alphacell* v *Woodward* (1972), the defendants were found guilty of polluting a river, despite the fact that they were not negligent and were unaware of the mechanical breakdown of their equipment, which usually prevented such pollution occurring.

One justification for strict liability in situations like this is that it works to the disadvantage of the more powerful interest and thus helps to achieve balance.

Question

Choose one of the criminal law areas discussed above and comment on how effectively it achieves balance between the public and private interests involved.

Balancing conflicting interests in the law of tort

The law of tort is mainly concerned with balancing two individual interests. However, public interests sometimes arise, as seen earlier when considering *Miller* v *Jackson* (1977). In that case, the public interest was considered when determining whether to award an injunction.

Negligence

The interest of one individual in not being harmed through another's carelessness has to be balanced against the interest of the other individual in not being held liable for unforeseeable and remote consequences.

In the law on psychiatric injury, the law limits liability to secondary victims by applying stringent criteria not applied to primary victims. Primary victims — those directly involved in an accident for example — are clearly likely to have been affected by the defendant's actions. However, the courts apply restrictions on who can claim as a result of seeing or hearing something happen to someone else. To claim as a secondary victim, a person must prove five additional criteria:

1 He or she is a person of ordinary normal fortitude.
2 He or she has close ties of love and affection with those in the accident.
3 He or she is close in time and space.
4 He or she perceived the accident with his or her own unaided senses.
5 It can be shown that psychiatric illness rather than just physical injury was foreseeable.

These criteria were clarified in *Alcock* v *Chief Constable of South Yorkshire* (1992) and *Page* v *Smith* (1995). Victims who cannot satisfy all these criteria are regarded by the law as unforeseeable claimants.

These are difficult decisions to make, and whether a true balance of conflicting interests is achieved is questionable. The trauma of a person identifying a body in a mortuary or seeing an accident on television could be just as great as a qualifying claimant, but the court has to consider the interests of the defendant as well. It is arguably not fair to allow claims from people not directly involved in the accident, unless they are foreseeable claimants.

The rule on remoteness of damage as established in *The Wagon Mound* (1961) requires that the damage must be of a foreseeable type if the defendant is to be held liable for it. In this case, damage by fire was not a type of damage foreseeable as a result of oil being discharged into the sea. If the damage had been fouling by the oil, the claimant may have recovered compensation. Again, the courts struck a balance on the basis of foreseeability.

Nuisance

The law of private nuisance is clearly concerned with balancing one individual's interests against another's and involves the competing interests of neighbours to enjoy their property. It allows for a certain amount of give and take, but maintains that unreasonable interference is unlawful. In deciding whether the level of interference is unreasonable, the courts take into account factors such as locality, sensitivity and malice.

When considering locality, the courts will decide whether a normally acceptable activity is merely being performed in the wrong place. This was the situation in *Laws* v *Florinplace Ltd* (1981), when a shop in a residential area was converted into a sex shop and cinema club. The sensitivity issue arises when someone puts their land to unusual, delicate use. He or she cannot then complain when it is affected by normal activities. However, if a sensitive claimant brings an action against a malicious defendant, as was the case in *Hollywood Silver Fox Farm* v *Emmett* (1936), the interests of the claimant prevail. The claimant bred mink, and mink eat their young when frightened. The defendant objected to the claimant's use of land and therefore

28

fired shots near to the claimant's land. This would not usually constitute a nuisance but the defendant had deliberately set out to cause harm and so was held liable.

Question

Choose three examples from the tort cases discussed above and explain:

❖ what the conflicting interests are

❖ the means that are used by the law to balance them

❖ how effectively balance is achieved

Sample exam question

Consider how well the law achieves a balance between conflicting interests.

Further reading

Doherty, M. (2007) 'Balancing conflicting interests and human rights', *A-Level Law Review*, Vol. 2, No. 2, pp. 10–11.

Price, N. (2008) 'Balancing conflicting interests in the ECtHR', *A-Level Law Review*, Vol. 4, No. 1, pp. 6–8

Index